Nelson GCSE Modular Science

3

Lesley Butcher

Philip Eastwood

Averil Macdonald

Edexcel
Success through qualifications

Published in 2002 by:
Nelson Thornes Ltd
Delta Place
27 Bath Road
CHELTENHAM
GL53 7TH
United Kingdom

02 03 04 05 / 10 9 8 7 6 5 4 3 2 1

A catalogue record for this book is available from the British Library

ISBN 0 7487 6793 2

Illustrations by IFA Design Ltd., Plymouth, Devon.
Page make-up by IFA Design Ltd., Plymouth, Devon.

Printed and bound in Spain by Graficas Estella

Acknowledgements

The authors and publisher would like to thank the following people who supplied photographs.

Advertising Archives: 14.08, 16.32;
AES Education: 14.15;
AIP Emilio Segre Visual Archives:18.07R;
A Macdonald: 18.12;
Avesta: 16.13
Axon Images: 13.75, 14.52, 16.01, 16.02, 16.06, 16.08, 16.30;
Biophoto Associates: 13.60, 14.12;
CERN: 18.06
Corbis: Ted Spiegel 14.58, Bettmann 17.23;
Corel (NT): 13.14, 13.53, page 56, page 61, 14.52, page101L, page105, 15.26, 15.27, 15.33, 16.07, 16.33;
Corus: 16.11;
Digital Vision (NT): 13.14, 13.69, 17.22, 17.24, 18.01, page237L;
Don Green: 18.16;
Dr Abdul-Hamid Sadka: page205R, L;
Elga: 15.38;
Empics: Mike Egerton 13.41;
Fisher: 15.38;
Getty Images: Image Bank, Butch Martin Inc. page153, Harry Sieplinga, HMS Images 17.14;
Hulton Archive: 16.12, Illustrated London News page180R, Keystone 18.07M
Image Library (NT): 13.28R;
Indusphoto: 15.35, page148R;
Jeyes: 13.48;
Louis Psihoyas Matrix: 13.40;
Marlow Foods: 14.16
Martyn Chillmaid: 13.13, 13.71, 14.06, 14.11, 14.13, 14.31, 15.01, 15.02, 15.03, 15.04, 15.05, 15.06, 15.07, 15.13, 15.14, 15.22, 15.23, 15.32L, R, 15.41, 15.42, 15.43, page148L, 16.03, 16.04, 16.17, 16.20, 16.21, 16.23, 16.24, 16.25, 16.26, 17.13, 17.19, 18.05;
Mother Shipton's Well: 15.34
NASA: page237R;
National Health Service: 13.79
National Museums of Scotland: 17.25;
National Portrait Gallery London: 18.07L;
Nick Cobbing: 14.29;
Nobel Foundation: 14.18, 14.20;
Novartis: 13.48;
PANalytical: 18.26;

Photodisc (NT): 13.26, 13.28L, 13.42, 13.45, 13.51, 13.78, page101R,16.34, 17.05T, page215;
Rapid Electronics: 18.24;
Reckitt Benckiser: 13.48;
Roslin Institute: 14.35, 14.41, 14.42;
Russell Kightley Media: page5;
Science Photolibrary: 13.38, 13.72, Dr Gopal Murti 13.25, Astrid & Hans-Frieder
Michler 13.18, 13.44, Manfred Kage 13.19, Philippe Plailly,Eurelios 14.36, Rosenfeld
Images Ltd 14.38, 14.39, Simon Fraser 13.49, 13.70, CNRI 13.01, Dr Tony Brain 13.02, A B Dowsett 13.10, 13.46, 13.54, Claude Nuridsany & Marie Perennou 13.12, 13.34, Dr P Marazzi 13.20, Jeurgen Berger, Max Planck Institute 13.22, Biophoto Associates 13.24, John Greim 13.27, Eye of Science 13.30, 14.33, Sinclair Stammers, WHO, TDR 13.31, Andy Crump, WHO, TDR 13.35, Science Pictures Ltd 13.37, Deep Light Productions 13.50, Hank Morgan 14.02, SCIMAT 14.05, Dr Jeremy Burgess 14.09, Julia Kamlish 14.21, Martin E Rice, Agstock 14.30, Shiela Terry 14.32, Philippe Goutier, Eurelios 14.37, Dr Yorgos Nikas 14.46, david Halsey, Agstock 14.50, Peter Menzel 14.54, Geoff Tompkinson 14.56, Andrew McClenaghan 15.07T, B, Jerry Mason 15.07MT, MB, T H Fotowerbung 16.16, Andrew Syred page185;
Stockbyte (NT): 13.14, 16.31, page180L;
Surrey Space Technology Ltd: 17.26, 17.28;
Topham Picturepoint: 13.15;
UKAEA: 18.19, 18.20;
UNICEF: Nicole Toutounji 13.05;
WHO: Andy Crump, TDR 13.33
Xerox Palo Alto Research Centre (PARC): 17.05B

Cover photos: Lightning, Photodisc 31 (NT); Neon signs, Imagin London (NT); Macae, Frans Lanting/Frank Lane Picture Agency.

Picture research by johnbailey@axonimages.com and Stuart Sweatmore

Preface

Nelson GCSE Modular Science is an extensive and topical series which fully supports the requirements of the Edexcel Science (B) Modular GCSE courses. Books 1, 2 and 3 of the series are designed to deliver the Separate Science Award (B) component.

Book 3 is organised into six modules. Within each module, each sub-topic is individually treated, so that all aspects are covered comprehensively and informatively. The special features included within each sub-topic are…

- Learning Outcomes, outlining the knowledge and understanding you can expect to accumulate by working through each of the topics.
- Key Words, emphasising in bold text the most important scientific terms for you to remember.
- Key Facts, summarizing the essential content of the topic and working as a useful revision aid.
- End of Topic Questions, strengthening your knowledge and understanding, and extending some of the scientific concepts. Where appropriate, answers to these questions can be found in the corresponding Teacher Support File, and at www.modularscience.co.uk

In addition, each module contains…

- Science Today articles – You will find that throughout the book, the content of each Module attempts to place Science in a real-life context. In addition, look out for the individual Science Today articles, which entertainingly explore some of the hottest and most interesting issues in modern science.
- Exam Questions – Answers to these can be found in the corresponding teacher support materials
- A Glossary – Here you will find straightforward definitions for the Key Words highlighted in the main text.

Higher Tier materials are denoted throughout by a coloured panel like this.

Note that further reading, links, answers and activities are provided in the Teacher Support File, and at www.modularscience.co.uk

We hope that this book will give you all the information and support you need to do well in your assessments and examinations at GCSE. We hope too that it will help you develop a fascination for Science that will serve you well, long after your studies are over.

Lesley Butcher
Philip Eastwood
Averil Macdonald

Contents

Although people have seen the effects of microorganisms for thousands of years, no one actually knew they existed until the 17th century. Ancient societies used them to make bread, beer, cheese, yoghurt and wine. They knew that food would taste bad or turn mouldy if it wasn't eaten promptly, so ways were devised to preserve food by drying, pickling or salting, but the link with microscopic organisms was still not made.

Diseases such as plague wiped out whole villages but no one knew why. Simple hygiene measures were not taken, such as doctors washing their hands; no one realised this would have cut down on the transmission of infection. Vast numbers of women and their babies died in childbirth, through lack of knowledge of the devastating power of microorganisms. Antibiotics are a 20th century luxury; before their discovery, an infected wound meant amputation or death.

This module looks at how our knowledge of microorganisms has increased since microscopes have become powerful enough to show their detailed structure. It looks at how this has allowed us to combat disease by prevention as well as cure.

Our relationship with microorganisms has another side to it too. We continue to use microorganisms for food manufacture, as this module will show. But now we exploit their capacity for rapid reproduction to our own advantage by giving them the conditions in which they will grow best. Quite the opposite of what we try to do with those that cause disease!

Even now there are many things that we still do not know about microorganisms. Nationwide outbreaks of foot and mouth disease, headline news about 'mad cow disease' and anxieties about drug-resistant 'super-bugs' are just three examples which make us realise that some microorganisms may always be one step ahead.

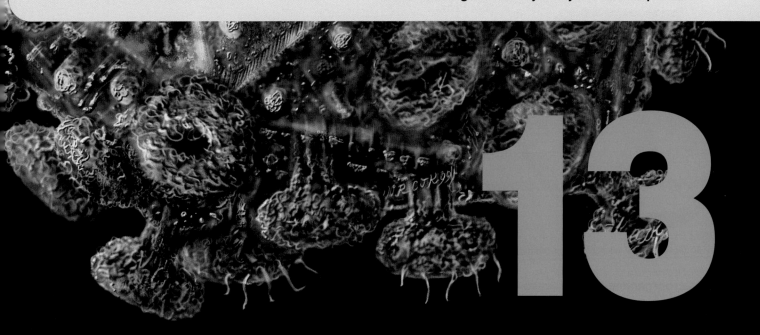

13

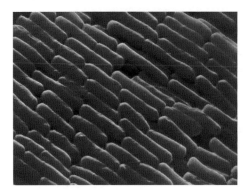

Figure 13.01 Anthrax bacteria.

Our knowledge and understanding of microorganisms has been closely related to the development of microscopes. We call them microorganisms for that very reason – they are organisms that are too small to see without a microscope! A few, such as some of the larger **Protoctista**, are just about visible to the naked eye, but no detail can be seen unless a microscope is used. The internal structure of bacterial cells and the structure of viruses can only be seen using an **electron microscope**.

It is sometimes difficult to appreciate just how small these organisms are, so it is understandable that people living in pre-microscope days had difficulty in believing that microorganisms were there at all.

Type of microorganism	Typical size in μm (micrometres)
Protoctist e.g. protozoa	150 to 200
Single-celled fungus e.g. yeast	20
Bacteria e.g. *Escherichia coli*	1.0
Virus e.g. polio virus	0.02

Table 13.01

The term 'microorganism' is preferable to the word 'germ', which will not be credited in your examinations. However, apart from their small size and the fact that they are usually single-celled, microorganisms do not have common features. We therefore find bacteria (Figure 13.01), viruses, fungi and protoctists collected together under this very broad heading (Table 13.01). In this book, the only protoctist that we meet is the malarial parasite ***Plasmodium***, which belongs to the group of protoctists known as **protozoa** (Figure 13.02). Therefore the term protozoa, rather than protoctists, will be used occasionally both in this book and in your examinations.

Not all microorganisms are harmful; for example, some are very useful in wine, bread and cheese-making. Those that do cause disease are known as **pathogens**. If a pathogen enters the body tissues of another organism and reproduces it has caused an **infection**.

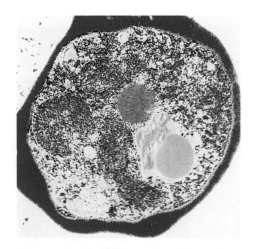

Figure 13.02 A malarial parasite – *Plasmodium*.

When pathogenic microorganisms invade another organism's body and live there, using the organism as a **host**, the microorganism is living as a **parasite**. The microorganism is gaining from the relationship, whereas the host is suffering harm as a result of the parasite being there. These parasitic microorganisms include some bacteria, some fungi and ALL viruses. Viruses have no other way of life apart from living parasitically on or in a host. Pathogens can infect an organism in a number of ways. Its pathway into the host's cells may be through the outer surface, or the pathogen may enter the host first through an opening and then attack from the inside. Pathogens can reach their host to cause infection in many ways (see Figure 13.03).

Safe drinking water

One of the ways in which transmission of disease could be reduced in many parts of the world would be to supply everyone with safe drinking water. For many students reading this book, **diarrhoea** will have been met only as an unpleasant side-effect of a 'tummy bug' that perhaps kept you off school for a few days (Figure 13.04). However, in many parts of the world, diarrhoea causes death, particularly among children.

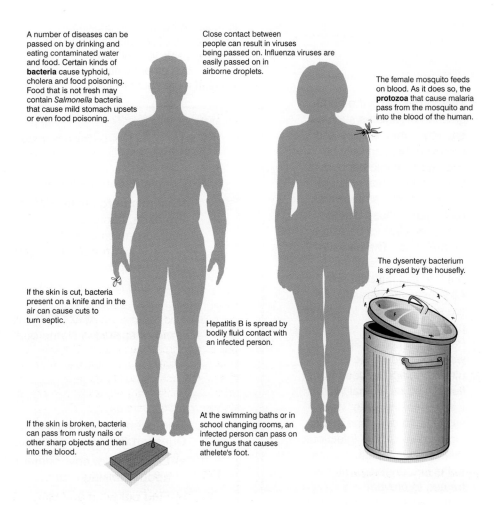

A number of diseases can be passed on by drinking and eating contaminated water and food. Certain kinds of **bacteria** cause typhoid, cholera and food poisoning. Food that is not fresh may contain *Salmonella* bacteria that cause mild stomach upsets or even food poisoning.

Close contact between people can result in viruses being passed on. Influenza viruses are easily passed on in airborne droplets.

The female mosquito feeds on blood. As it does so, the **protozoa** that cause malaria pass from the mosquito and into the blood of the human.

If the skin is cut, bacteria present on a knife and in the air can cause cuts to turn septic.

Hepatitis B is spread by bodily fluid contact with an infected person.

The dysentery bacterium is spread by the housefly.

If the skin is broken, bacteria can pass from rusty nails or other sharp objects and then into the blood.

At the swimming baths or in school changing rooms, an infected person can pass on the fungus that causes athelete's foot.

Figure 13.03 Some of the ways pathogens spread disease.

NOT @ SCHL –
GOT THE RUNS.
CU MNDY.

Figure 13.04 Most students in the UK are unlikely to be away from school very long with diarrhoea – it soon clears up.

Around 5 million people a year die due to diarrhoea resulting from water-borne bacterial infections picked up from contaminated drinking water. **Cholera** is caused by a bacterium transmitted in water; one of the symptoms of cholera is diarrhoea. But the major cause of diarrhoea deaths is from drinking water contaminated with human faeces. The bacterium *Escherichia coli* (*E. coli*) is naturally present in our intestines, but a few strains of the bacterium are pathogenic. It is the **toxins** that these pathogenic *E. coli* produce that lead to the diarrhoea. A lot of water is lost from the body when such 'runny' faeces are produced; valuable salts are also lost in excessive amounts (Figure 13.05).

Figure 13.05 Replacing lost fluid is vital.

Microorganisms and disease in humans 7

In most UK homes, the drinking water from our taps has been stored in a reservoir, away from the risk of contamination by human faeces, and has been filtered and **chlorinated** to make it safe to drink. Sewage is also treated to ensure that any pathogens carried in it do not reach other humans who drink water or bathe near where it is discharged. You will read more about this later in this module.

Key Facts

- Microorganism is the name given to organisms such as bacteria, fungi, viruses and protozoa that can only be seen using a microscope.
- Some microorganisms are useful but others, known as pathogens, cause disease.
- Pathogens live as parasites on their host. The parasite gains from the relationship but the host suffers harm.
- All viruses are parasitic. So are some bacteria, fungi and protozoa.
- Pathogens can be spread by water or food, in the air, by direct contact between bodily fluids, and by animal vectors.
- If safe drinking water were available to everyone in the world, deaths from infectious diseases would fall.
- In the UK, drinking water is treated to prevent contamination by pathogenic strains of *E.coli* found in human faeces.

Questions

1 Copy and complete:

   Most microorganisms cannot be seen without a .... Protozoa, bacteria, ... and .... are all examples of microorganisms. Pathogens cause .... They live as .... on another organism. The parasite gains from the relationship but the .... suffers harm.

2 Copy and complete the table:

Ways that pathogens can spread		
Method of spread	Name of microorganism	Disease it causes
Water		
Air		
etc.		

3 Find out more about each of the diseases you have listed in Question 2. Record your information in a table:

4 a) Look at www.environment-agency.gov.uk to find out more about drinking water.

   b) Find out what oral rehydration therapy is from www.diarrhoea.org

Disease	Symptoms	Other information

Did you know?

Dehydration kills a child every 10 seconds. That's approximately 3.5 million children every year.

Bacteria

biology · chemistry · physics

Where are bacteria found?

Bacteria can be found in the food that we eat, in the water that we drink and in many places inside our body and on its surface. They are found at the top of mountains and at the bottom of the sea; in the air we breathe and in the soil. They are probably the most widely distributed organisms on the earth, yet without the aid of a microscope, we cannot see them (Figure 13.06). Even when they are viewed with a **light microscope**, bacteria will only appear as specks of living matter which differ from one another only by their shape (Figure 13.07).

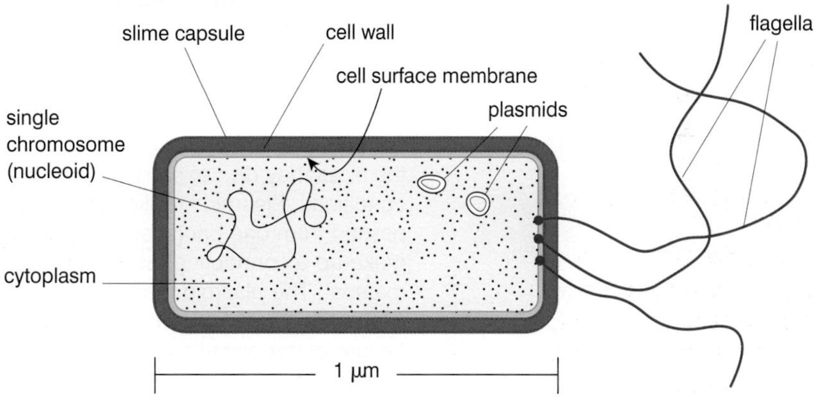

Figure 13.06 A typical bacterial cell.

Structure of a bacterial cell

A typical bacterial cell is smaller than a plant or animal cell, but much larger than a virus. A cell surface membrane surrounds the cytoplasm inside. As well as controlling the materials that can enter and leave the cell, the bacterial cell surface membrane is also the site of respiration, as the bacterium has no **mitochondria**. From here enzymes and toxins can be secreted into the **substrate** or the host cell which the bacterium is living in. Surrounding the cell surface membrane is a much tougher, rigid **cell wall** for protection and to maintain the cell's shape. There may be a **slime layer** on its outer surface. This may vary from a thin, loose soluble covering that can easily wash off, to a much thicker layer known as a **capsule**. This outer coating on the cell wall helps to prevent the bacterial cell from drying out. Its slightly sticky consistency allows bacteria to

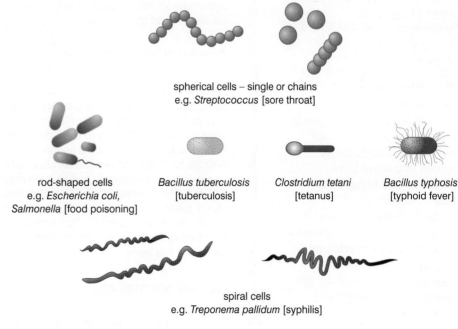

Figure 13.07 Assorted shaped bacteria.

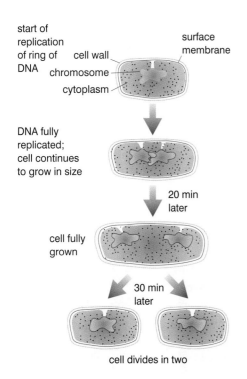

start of replication of ring of DNA

cell wall

surface membrane

chromosome

cytoplasm

DNA fully replicated; cell continues to grow in size

20 min later

cell fully grown

30 min later

cell divides in two

Figure 13.08 Binary fission.

Key Facts

- A typical bacterium consists of a single cell surrounded by a cell surface membrane containing cytoplasm and a single chromosome (nucleoid).
- The cell surface membrane is enclosed in a tougher cell wall which is sometimes coated in a slime layer.
- Plasmids and flagella may also be present.
- Bacteria divide by binary fission and may form spores in unfavourable conditions.
- Spores are resistant to extremes of temperature, pH change and the effects of chemicals.

stick to one another in clumps and also to attach to the surfaces of both living and non-living things. A slime capsule is an advantage to pathogenic bacteria because it makes an attack from the host's white blood cells more difficult, as they cannot bind onto its cell wall. This allows the bacteria to have a head start in invading the host's tissues. Many bacteria have long hair-like structures known as **flagella** (singular: **flagellum**). There may be just one, several or many flagella, depending on the type of bacterium. Flagella allow the bacteria to move and therefore respond to chemical **stimuli** by moving towards favourable ones, or away from unfavourable ones.

Apart from the size difference, bacterial cells differ from the animal and plant cells which you may be familiar with in one major way. The **nucleus** of a bacterial cell does not have a membrane around it. So, whereas you may have drawn a very distinct 'blob' to represent the nucleus in an animal or plant cell, in a bacterial cell this is replaced by a tightly coiled double-stranded loop of DNA, sometimes known as the bacterial chromosome or **nucleoid**. This DNA loop contains about 4000 chromosomes on which the information for day-to-day activities, growth and reproduction is stored.

In addition to this main area of nuclear material, there are often one or more **plasmids** present. Plasmids are circular pieces of DNA made up of typically 10–30 genes, but this number can vary widely; a large plasmid could carry 100 genes. The plasmid genes are not part of the bacterial genome; in other words, the bacterium could survive without them, as they do not carry information that is essential to keep it alive in normal conditions. Plasmids replicate separately to the main nuclear material and can be passed from one bacterial cell to another. The plasmid genes code for the proteins that make up a connecting tube between bacteria that are about to exchange genetic material. The plasmid may also carry genes which enable the bacterium to make use of a wider range of food materials than it otherwise could. Perhaps the most significant feature of the plasmid is that it is the site where **antibiotic resistance** genes may be found. This could make the bacterium resistant to one or several types of **antibiotics**. When bacteria reproduce, this resistance will be passed on when the plasmid itself replicates, separately from the main nuclear material.

Plasmids are now used regularly in the production of **genetically modified organisms** because they can be used to transfer a chosen section of DNA from a **donor cell** into a bacterium. When the bacterium goes on to reproduce many times, the plasmid inside it will also be replicated.

Asexual reproduction

Bacteria reproduce asexually by dividing into two. This is known as **binary fission**. It takes place in a series of steps (Figure 13.09). First, the cell elongates and during this time its DNA replicates. A dividing wall begins to form in the centre. The genetic material splits with one half going to each daughter cell. The dividing wall continues to grow and finally the two daughter cells separate.

A single bacterial cell will first divide into two; each of these cells will divide into two and so on. In ideal conditions, cell division may take place as frequently as once every 20 minutes. This continued doubling of numbers is described as **'exponential growth'**, and allows bacteria to colonise a new substrate, or invade animal or plant tissues very rapidly. Such rapid reproduction cannot continue indefinitely because nutrients may run out or other factors may prevent further growth. You will read more about this in a later section of this book.

Spore formation

Conditions for bacterial growth will never remain ideal. Growth depends on the availability of sufficient water and a suitable food supply. Most bacteria favour a slightly

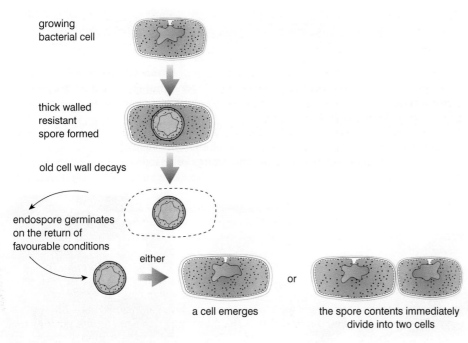

growing
bacterial cell

thick walled
resistant
spore formed

old cell wall decays

endospore germinates
on the return of
favourable conditions

either

a cell emerges

or

the spore contents immediately
divide into two cells

Figure 13.09 Bacterial spore formation.

alkaline pH of about pH 7.4, although a few can tolerate more extreme acidity or alkalinity. Most bacteria favour a temperature within the range 25–45°C although again this can vary. Most bacteria are **aerobic**, requiring oxygen to live, but many of these aerobic bacteria can survive without oxygen if they have to. Some bacteria are always **anaerobic**, so specifically require oxygen to be absent.

When conditions become unfavourable, bacteria may form **spores**, called **endospores**, as a way of surviving (Figure 13.09).

The living contents of the cell become surrounded by a thick coating which protects them from desiccation if water becomes in short supply. These spores can resist extremes of temperature, pH change and the effect of radiation and toxic chemicals. Once favourable conditions return, these **dormant** endospores can germinate into new bacterial cells and start to multiply rapidly. The bacterium responsible for the disease anthrax forms endospores which can remain viable for 50 years (Figure 13.10).

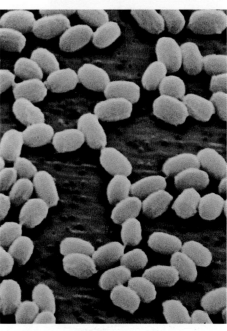

Figure 13.10 Anthrax spores.

Questions

1 Copy and complete:

Bacteria are single-celled organisms which have a cell surface membrane surrounded by a ....
Sometimes there is an outer ....
Inside the cell there is a single .... and often several .... Some bacteria have one or more .... for movement.

2 Draw and label a typical bacterial cell. Add notes to your labels to show the function(s) of each part you have labelled.

3 Explain each of these terms:

a) binary fission

b) exponential growth

c) endospores

Fungi

Learning outcomes

After completing the work in this topic you will be able to:

- recall the structure of fungi, including mycelium of branched hyphae with nuclei, cytoplasm, surface membrane and wall; understand that reproduction is by spore production

- recall the structure of yeast and understand that it reproduces by budding

- recall the word equation for anaerobic respiration in yeast:
  glucose → ethanol + carbon dioxide and energy released

Figure 13.12 Fly agaric – the poisonous fungus that fairies are always shown sitting on!

Figure 13.13 Bread roll and mushroom soup – both made using fungi.

Figure 13.14 Cheese board – blue veined cheeses are produced using fungi.

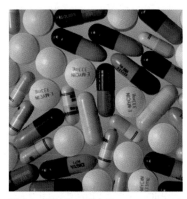

Figure 13.15 Antibiotics – produced by growing fungi in large fermenters.

What is a fungus?

When you eat a bread roll and a bowl of mushroom soup, you are eating fungi. Yeast will have been used as one of the ingredients in the bread roll and mushrooms are used to make the soup (Figures 13.12, 13.13). Perhaps you follow your meal with some cheese – if it is a blue veined cheese, such as Roquefort, it will have been given its blue streaks and characteristic taste by a fungus (Figure 13.14). You may have suffered from athlete's foot. If so, a fungus has been living between your toes. And what about the antibiotics you may have been prescribed by your doctor? Yes, they too were developed from fungi (Figure 13.15).

Fungi can be single celled, such as yeast, or form a thread-like network such as species of *Penicillium* and bread moulds. In these filamentous types, the branching network of threads is known as a **mycelium**.

Structure of a mycelial fungus

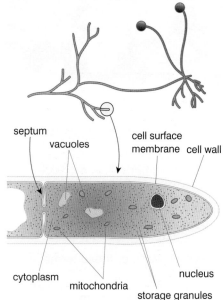

septum

vacuoles

cell surface membrane   cell wall

cytoplasm

mitochondria

storage granules

nucleus

Figure 13.16 The internal structure of a fungal hypha. The one illustrated has a septum.

A mycelium consists of many tiny hollow tubes making a loose, branching network. The individual tubes are called **hyphae** (singular: **hypha**). Around each hypha is a tough cell wall with a more delicate cell surface membrane beneath it. The hyphae are not completely divided up into individual cells. In some mycelia, an extension of the cell wall and cell surface membrane may form a cross wall or **septum** (plural: **septa**) to partially divide up the hyphae into cell-like regions that still remain inter-connected (Figure 13.16). In other types of fungi even these partial divisions do not exist and the whole mycelium remains continuous with no cross walls at all. This allows materials to be moved to different parts of the mycelium more easily than if it were divided up into individual cells. Inside these outer layers is the cytoplasm, which contains many nuclei. In hyphae with cross walls the nuclei are usually distributed as one or two nuclei per 'cell'. Most activity takes place at the tips of the hyphae where the cytoplasm is most dense and it is in these regions that growth of the mycelium will take place. Digestive enzymes will be secreted from the hyphae. These enzymes will break the food material that the fungus is growing on into soluble products that can then be absorbed into the hyphae. These soluble products can then be moved to other parts of the mycelium.

Spore production

A mycelium can start with the germination of just a single spore. You may have seen the network of hyphae spreading over the surface of a piece of food as it 'goes mouldy'. After a few days the surface becomes speckled with black pinheads as some of the hyphae begin to grow upwards and produce a black swelling at their tip. Each black pinhead is a **sporangium** (plural: **sporangia**) and it is in here that spores will be formed (Figure 13.17). When the wall of the sporangium breaks, the powdery spores will be dispersed by air currents. The wall of a spore will protect it until conditions are favourable for it to germinate and form a new mycelium (Figure 13.18).

Yeast

Yeasts differ from the type of fungi described so far. The majority of them consist of separate single cells which can only be seen under the microscope. They live in places where sugar is likely to be found, such as the surface of fruits. A yeast cell consists of a thin outer cell wall with a cell surface membrane and cytoplasm inside. In the cytoplasm there is a vacuole, a nucleus and food storage granules.

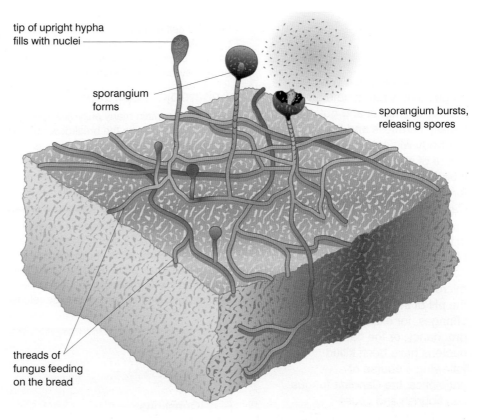

tip of upright hypha fills with nuclei

sporangium forms

sporangium bursts, releasing spores

threads of fungus feeding on the bread

Figure 13.17 Structure of fungal mycelium showing sporangia forming.

Figure 13.18 A mouldy apple.

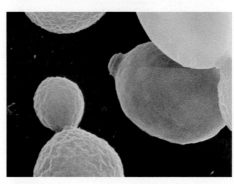

Figure 13.19 Yeast budding.

Key Facts

- Mycelial fungi form a branched network of hyphae which reproduce by spore formation.
- Hyphae consist of nuclei, cytoplasm, cell surface membrane and cell wall.
- Yeast is a unicellular fungus which reproduces by budding.
- When yeast respires anaerobically, ethanol and carbon dioxide are produced; energy is released.

Candida albicans is a yeast-like fungus that is found naturally in the human mouth and gut. It is usually harmless and lives in our body without us being aware of its presence. However if body conditions change, the fungus can cause infection. *Candida* that are normally found in the vagina will be kept in low numbers by the acidic pH (usually pH 4–5) as well as competition from other microorganisms living there. If the pH of the vaginal secretions changes, for example during pregnancy, or the natural bacteria have been killed following a course of antibiotics, the *Candida* fungus can flourish and cause inflammation and itching, together with a discharge, which is known as vaginal thrush. This can be treated with anti-fungal preparations from a doctor or chemist but there is a natural remedy too. Natural yoghurt will reduce the pH of the vagina and also provides a ready supply of natural bacteria to compete with the fungus.

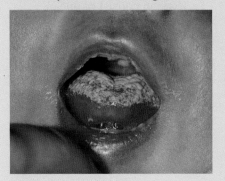

Figure 13.20 Oral thrush.

Yeasts reproduce by budding. An outgrowth from the cell enlarges until it is big enough to break off from the parent cell and live on its own. During rapid reproduction, several buds may be seen (Figure 13.19).

Anaerobic respiration…

Yeast fungi contain many enzymes. One group can be used in the breakdown of sugar. As the sugar is broken down, energy is released which the yeast can use. Alcohol and carbon dioxide are also produced. This can be written as a word equation:

glucose → carbon dioxide + alcohol + energy

This takes place in the absence of oxygen when the yeast has a supply of sugar. It is sometimes known as alcoholic fermentation. This process has been used for many centuries in beer and wine making because of the alcohol that is produced. Yeast is also used in baking because the carbon dioxide released makes dough 'rise'.

In the state of Washington, USA there is a specimen of the fungus *Armillaria ostoyae* that is thought to be somewhere between 500 and 1000 years old. It covers 600 ha (1500 acres) in the foothills of Mount Adams and is the largest living organism in the world. (Source: Guinness Book of World Records 2001)

Questions

Questions

1 Copy and complete:
   Some fungi consist of a branched network of threads, each called a .... Together these form a .... To reproduce asexually, black upright pinheads called .... form. These contain .... Yeasts are single celled fungi. They reproduce by ....

2 energy   ethanol
   glucose   carbon dioxide

   a) Rearrange the words above to form a word equation for anaerobic respiration in yeast.

   b) How would anaerobic respiration of yeast help someone who was:

i) making beer?

ii) making bread?

3 Some fungi can be useful, others are harmful. Complete the table below with some examples from this book. Can you find any others by doing some research?

Useful fungi	
Name of fungus	Use

Harmful fungi	
Name of fungus	Harm caused

4 Visit www.fungalresearchtrust.org to find out more about fungi.

... more at www.modularscience.co.uk

Viruses

Dead or alive?

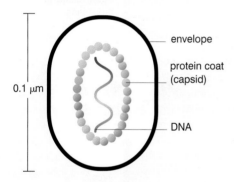

0.1 μm

envelope

protein coat (capsid)

DNA

Fig. 13.21 Structure of a virus.

Viruses are the simplest form of life we know. They can only be seen using an electron microscope and can only reproduce inside living cells. This makes many people question whether they are alive at all – perhaps we should consider them to be the most complex lifeless molecules we know, rather than the very simplest form of life? Unlike other living organisms, viruses do not perform life processes such as respiration or photosynthesis. However, their genetic information contains all the data needed to replicate new viruses and it is encoded in a similar way to that of more complex organisms. So, although viruses do not meet many of the criteria for a living organism that you have met in biology so far, on balance scientists continue to classify them as simple forms of life.

Just the bare necessities…

In simple terms, viruses are a package of genetic material wrapped in a protein shell. Although this seems far too simple to be workable, it is incredibly efficient; viruses are amazingly successful at invading the cells of living organisms, rapidly reproducing and then spreading to other potential hosts. Because a virus can only reproduce within a living cell it does not need its own nucleus, mitochondria or chloroplasts, for example.

Detailed structure…

The outer protein coat of a virus, known as a **capsid**, protects the inner genetic material from damage and helps the virus to break into host cells (Figure 13.21). The genetic material may be RNA rather than the DNA used by other cells; there is often just a single strand. Viruses vary in size, 0.01–0.1 micrometres (μm) is the usual range but RNA viruses are much more fragile than DNA viruses so tend to be at the smaller end of this range; a few viruses are larger.
There is no nucleus or cytoplasm. Sometimes the capsid is enclosed in an 'envelope' which was formed from a piece of the surface membrane of the host cell in which it was made.

Did you know?

Even bacteria cannot escape attack by viruses. Some viruses, known as bacteriophages or 'phages for short, actually live as parasites in bacterial cells.

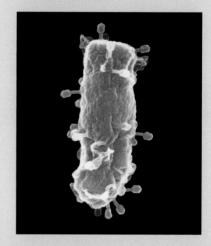

Figure 13.22 Bacteriophages attacking a bacterium.

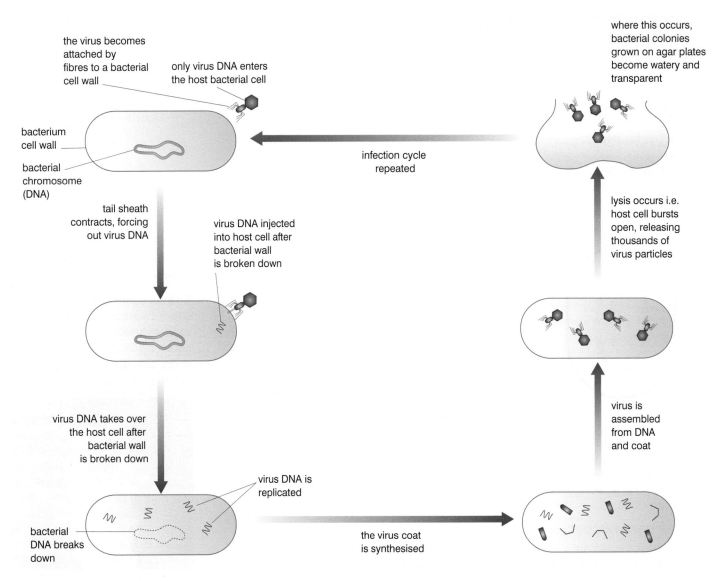

the virus becomes attached by fibres to a bacterial cell wall

only virus DNA enters the host bacterial cell

where this occurs, bacterial colonies grown on agar plates become watery and transparent

bacterium cell wall

bacterial chromosome (DNA)

infection cycle repeated

lysis occurs i.e. host cell bursts open, releasing thousands of virus particles

tail sheath contracts, forcing out virus DNA

virus DNA injected into host cell after bacterial wall is broken down

virus is assembled from DNA and coat

virus DNA takes over the host cell after bacterial wall is broken down

virus DNA is replicated

bacterial DNA breaks down

the virus coat is synthesised

Fig. 13.23 Virus replication: the diagrams show a bacterial cell being attacked by a virus (bacteriophage).

Invasion of the host...

Viruses are obligate parasites – in other words they *have to* live in the cells of another living organism, known as their host. A virus identifies the host cell it needs by the proteins found on its cell surface. This explains why a certain type of virus will infect some organisms and not others. Some viruses may just infect one particular species, others may be able to infect several different species of host; often these species will be closely related types of animal or plant.

Once the virus has attached itself to the outside of a suitable host, it must put its own genetic material into the host cell (Figure 13.23). Usually the protein coat of the virus is left outside the host cell and only the genetic material is injected into the cell.

Within a few hours of entry, the virus has effectively 'taken over' the host cell and thousands of new viruses are being made. The virus has supplied the 'instructions' in the form of the DNA or RNA it put into the cell; the cell has provided the raw materials and 'machinery' to enable the instructions to make new viruses to be carried out. The cell manufactures viral proteins to make the capsids, as well as copies of the viral genetic material to go into them; it even assembles them into new viruses. These new viruses will then break out of the cell, ready to invade more cells of the same host or to spread to a new one.

Cells are often damaged when the new viruses that have been made inside them burst out. The blistering of our skin caused by the chicken pox virus shows where cells have been damaged and killed.

Cold sores are a result of the destructive action of the *Herpes simplex* virus.

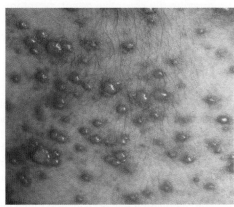

Figure 13.24 Chickenpox blisters.

Key Facts

- Viruses are not cells but are a very simple form of life.
- They can only reproduce in living cells of other plants, animals or bacteria.
- The outer coat of a virus is called a capsid and is made of protein. It may be surrounded by an outer envelope.
- Inside there is a single or double strand of either RNA or DNA.
- There are no other cell structures such as nucleus, cytoplasm, mitochondria or chloroplasts.
- A virus does not carry out many of the usual life processes such as respiration, photosynthesis or excretion.
- To replicate, a virus injects its DNA or RNA into the host cell. The host cell uses this information to make and assemble new viruses.
- New viruses burst out of the host cell in large numbers to infect new cells; often host cells are damaged beyond repair.

Questions

1 Draw a simple diagram of a virus like the one in this book. Beside each label write one or two sentences about the part you have labelled, using the information on these pages.

2 Make a table to compare a virus with a typical animal cell. An example is shown below:

Virus	Animal cell
Does not respire	Respires to release energy

3 Find as many examples as you can of diseases caused by viruses. Include both animal and plant diseases and try to find out some of the symptoms of each disease.

4 Work with a partner to write two speeches for a debate with the title 'Viruses are too simple to be alive'. One of you should write the argument that agrees with this statement. The other person should write the argument that disagrees.

... more at www.modularscience.co.uk

Influenza

What is influenza?

Influenza is one of the oldest and most common human diseases. It affects large numbers of people every year in seasonal outbreaks called **epidemics**. Sometimes these epidemics affect people in many countries; these world-wide epidemics are known as **pandemics** and can be responsible for the death of thousands of people. Pandemics in 1957 and 1968 were together the cause of over 1.5 million deaths world-wide. Influenza is caused by a virus that affects the tissues in the upper part of the respiratory system, although it can also reach the lungs (Figure 13.25). Other types of bacteria and viruses often find it easier to invade these influenza-infected tissues; this is known as **secondary infection**. It is these secondary infections such as pneumonia, caused by other pathogens, which result in the death of young children, the elderly and people who were already in poor health.

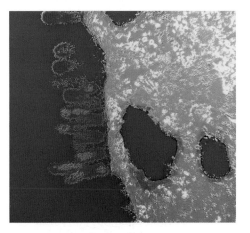

Fig. 13.25 A cell infected with 'flu viruses.

… but isn't influenza just a bad cold?…

Different viruses cause colds and influenza, so they are different diseases. Although they both share some symptoms, such as sore throat, headache and coughing, influenza is a much more serious illness. A cold usually clears up in 3–5 days whereas it can take up to 7 days to recover from influenza even if there are no secondary infections.

Influenza usually starts with the patient's body temperature rising rapidly; it may reach as high as 40°C. This is soon accompanied by headache, sore throat and a blocked nose. The patient's body aches and they feel very tired (Figure 13.26). Although they may have a very high temperature, they can also be shivering.

Coughs and sneezes spread diseases

The influenza virus is usually spread by inhaling the virus in droplets in the air breathed out by an infected person, or when they cough or sneeze. The virus usually spreads from person to person, although animals such as pigs, ducks and poultry can also spread it. Once inside their new host, the viruses invade the epithelial tissues that line the nose and throat and sometimes those in the bronchi. Tissues in the trachea and bronchi are damaged by the viral attack and this is what causes the cough to develop after 3–4 days. Viruses are then coughed out by the patient and are able to infect a new host.

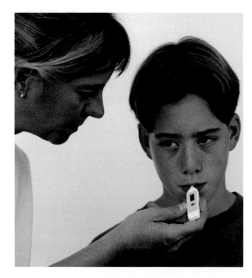

Fig. 13.26. 'Flu causes body temperature to rise rapidly.

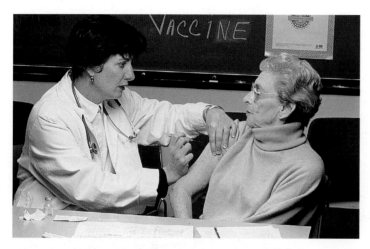

Figure 13.27 A nurse giving elderly woman 'flu vaccination.

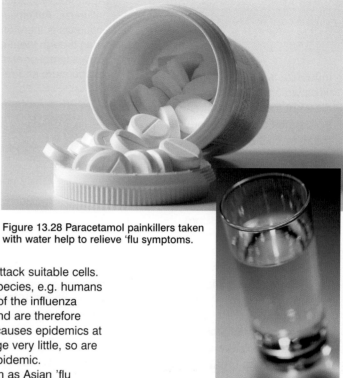

Figure 13.28 Paracetamol painkillers taken with water help to relieve 'flu symptoms.

The structure of the host's cell membranes ensures that the viruses attack suitable cells. This is why particular strains of influenza virus often only affect one species, e.g. humans or a small number of related animals. There are four different strains of the influenza virus, known as A, B, C and D. Viruses of strain A change the most and are therefore usually responsible for annual epidemics. Strain B changes less, so causes epidemics at longer intervals apart, usually every 4–6 years. Strains C and D change very little, so are usually responsible for smaller outbreaks rather than a widespread epidemic.

The influenza A virus which caused the pandemic in 1957, was known as Asian 'flu because its origins have been traced back to China. From there it spread to nearby Hong Kong and from there to most parts of the world. Because Hong Kong was a major centre for world trade, its international sea and airports enabled people to spread the disease world-wide. Today, people travel the world for business and holidays more frequently than ever before; these travellers provide an ideal transport mechanism for viruses. Viruses must have a living host, so they cannot live in luggage or clothing; instead they rely on people who are carrying the infection to transport them to new continents, probably before the symptoms of the infection have shown in the carrier.

Prevention or cure?

A person who has suffered from influenza will become **immune** to that virus and will not suffer further attacks. However, **mutations** of the virus can mean that the body fails to recognise the pathogen next time, and the disease returns. This is why strain A is usually responsible for epidemics; a slight change in the strain A virus will mean that many people world-wide are no longer immune to it.

Doctors often recommend vaccination against influenza for vulnerable people, especially the elderly or those in poor health. For these people, secondary infections in particular could be life threatening. The problem is that **vaccines** can only be developed against individual strains of the virus. This means that organisations such as the World Health Organisation (WHO) have to collect data on new strains of the virus and advise vaccine manufacturers about which strain is likely to cause an epidemic each year. Large quantities of a vaccine to match that particular strain of virus will be made and given to people in the UK in the autumn to prevent them becoming ill over the winter (Figure 13.27). However, the same people will need another vaccination the following autumn against whatever new strain has developed. People who are allergic to eggs cannot be given the vaccination because it is developed using egg products.

Did you know?

The worst ever 'flu epidemic started in 1918, the year the First World War ended. Over 22 million people world-wide became infected with the disease and more people died from 'flu than had been killed during the First World War.

The name influenza comes from the Latin word 'influentia' which means influence. Before people knew that influenza was caused by a virus, it used to be thought that the disease was caused by a bad influence from the heavens.

Apart from vaccination, which is **prevention** of the disease, there is no real **cure** for influenza. Antibiotics do not kill viruses; they only work on bacteria. Treatment of influenza is therefore aimed at reducing the symptoms so that the patient feels better even though the number of viruses in their body is not reduced. For example, paracetamol or aspirin, often in hot lemon drinks, can be taken to lower body temperature and relieve aches and pains (Figure 13.28).

Key Facts

- Influenza is caused by a virus which is found in different forms or 'strains'.
- Epidemics occur regularly; these can affect large numbers of people, often in many different countries.
- Symptoms include high temperature, shivering, headache, tiredness, sore throat, blocked nose and aching body.
- Secondary infections caused by other microorganisms may develop, e.g. pneumonia.
- The virus is transmitted in droplets of moisture when an infected person breathes out, coughs or sneezes.
- Aspirin or paracetamol will make the patient feel better but do not cure the disease.
- Vaccinations are given to people for whom influenza might become life threatening.
- New vaccines have to be developed against new strains of the virus as it changes, so vaccinations have to be given to the same people each year.

Questions

1 Copy and complete:
   Influenza is caused by a .... which is usually spread in .... in the air breathed out by an infected person when they .... or .... Symptoms include a high ...., headache, ... throat and .... nose. Influenza is worse than a cold because it makes your body .... and you feel very ....

2 Explain the difference between these pairs of words:
   a) epidemic and pandemic
   b) prevention and cure
   c) a cold and influenza

3 Explain why increased global travel has had an effect on the spread of disease.

4 Find out what WHO is and what it does.

... more at www.modularscience.co.uk

Learning outcomes

After completing the work in this topic you will be able to:

- distinguish between the terms epidemic and endemic

- describe the causative agents, symptoms, methods of transmission and means of control of malaria

Epidemic or endemic?

A disease is described as **endemic** if the disease or its vector is always found in a particular area.

An **epidemic** is the occurrence of a number of cases of a disease very much in excess of what would normally be expected.

For example, dysentery is said to be an endemic disease in Britain because it is always present, at least at a low level, within the population. Each summer, the number of reported cases increases, usually to epidemic proportions. Cholera, on the other hand, was once endemic in Britain but it is now exceedingly rare. However, in Asia generally, and in India in particular, cholera is endemic and frequently epidemic.

Malaria

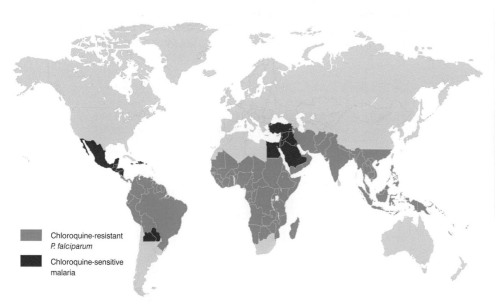

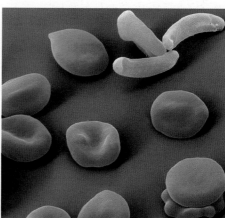

Figure 13.30 Red blood cells with *Plasmodium falciparum* (yellow).

Chloroquine-resistant *P. falciparum*

Chloroquine-sensitive malaria

Figure 13.29 Malaria endemic regions and chloroquine resistance (1997).

Causative agent...

The parasite causing the disease is a microscopic single celled animal (protozoan) belonging to the genus *Plasmodium*. *Plasmodium falciparum* is the commonest parasite species in Africa and the most aggressive. (Figure 13.30)

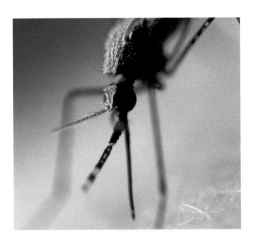

Figure 13.31 *Anopheles* mosquito – the vector of malaria – shown feeding on human blood through the skin.

Transmission…

Female mosquitoes of the genus *Anopheles* are **vectors** of the disease (Figure 13.31). Unlike the males, which feed on nectar, the females are blood suckers. During daylight the females rest in shaded places such as the inside of houses or in the shade of trees or other vegetation. At night they are active, searching for a host from which they can take a meal of blood. They are small insects with long, slender legs so they are able to land on the skin without their presence being felt. The mosquito then pierces the skin with sharp needle-like stylets which penetrate as far as a blood capillary near the surface. Before sucking the blood, the mosquito injects a drop of saliva into the wound. This contains an anticoagulant which prevents the blood clotting in the insect's mouthparts. The mosquito sucks the blood it requires, then withdraws its stylets after feeding. The mosquito's saliva also contains the malarial parasite. As it bites, it introduces hundreds of malarial parasites into its human host. A sleeping person would be unaware of what had happened.

During its time in the human body, the malarial parasite first undergoes changes and multiplies rapidly in the liver without producing any malarial symptoms. The parasites enter their host's red blood cells and multiply further (Figure 13.30). This causes the red blood cell to burst open, releasing the parasites – this will be happening in a large number of red blood cells at the same time. The patient reacts to the poisonous wastes (toxins) that are released with the parasites when the red cells containing them burst (Figure 13.33). Here in the blood the parasite is ready to be taken with the next mosquito bite. In the mosquito it will complete its life cycle and wait in the insect's salivary gland ready to infect a new host.

The illness begins with a high fever and enlargement of the liver and spleen. Several hours later the fever subsides and is followed by chills. Around 2–4 days later the fever/chills cycle repeats. The fevers correspond to the red blood cells bursting (Figure 13.32). This red blood cell damage also explains why the person becomes severely **anaemic**.

Figure 13.33 A Tanzanian child suffering from malaria.

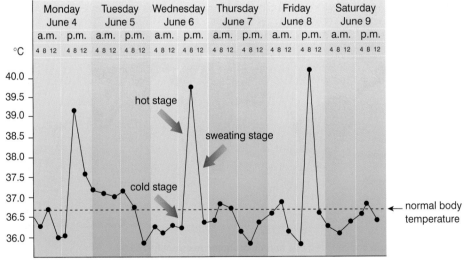

Figure 13.32 Temperature chart for malaria patient.

Each bout of malaria means that the victim is unable to work for about 2 weeks. The more serious forms of malaria can cause damage to the brain and kidneys – death can follow the first fever in as little as 1 day. Chronic malaria, caused by repeated exposure, causes severe and disabling anaemia.

Vector control…

One way of controlling outbreaks of malaria is to attack the vector. Knowledge of the habits and life history of the mosquito is essential if control is to be effective. The mosquito lays its eggs in still water, such as ponds, lakes or swamps, or even in roof gutters, drains and water-filled pots and old cans. The eggs hatch into larvae, which breathe and feed just below the surface of the water, where they cling by surface tension (Figure 13.34).

Control measures…

One way of eliminating the vector is therefore to eliminate wet spots where the larvae live. In some parts of the world, such as China, this policy has been quite effective. In other places, the bodies of water are too extensive and often too remote for drainage to be feasible.

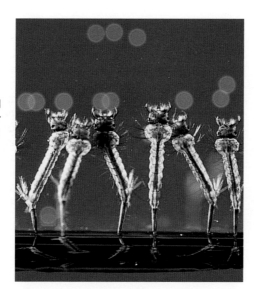

Figure 13.34 Mosquito larvae hanging in water.

Biological control, introducing fish that eat the larvae has been tried, with small-scale success. Pouring oil on the water is a way of suffocating the larvae, but again this is feasible only on a small scale. Oil forms a thin film on the surface of the water, clogging the breathing tube which the larvae use to take in air, so the larvae suffocate. Adding an insecticide to the oil can provide a second line of attack by killing both the larvae and the egg-laying adults that settle on the water. Roof gutters, drains and any other places containing still water should be treated with insecticides. As a prevention measure, old jars, pots and tins should be destroyed or buried so that they will not contain even the smallest amount of water needed for eggs to be laid.

Eventually the pupae develop into adult mosquitoes. Spraying houses with insecticides kills any mosquitoes there, and also leaves a residue that deters others from entering. The insecticide remains effective for weeks or even months and the mosquito only has to land on or walk over the sprayed surface to be affected. To break the life-cycle, spraying for at least 3 years is required. Setbacks occur where the mosquitoes develop resistance to a particular insecticide.

Preventing the spread…

At the same time, a programme of treating human cases of the disease must be set up. It is not always possible to prevent mosquitoes from breeding or to kill all the adults. Therefore, if they can be prevented from reaching malaria patients, who are the only source of parasites, then healthy people could not be infected. To do this effectively, it is essential to work around the habits of the female *Anopheles* mosquito. She feeds on blood before producing eggs and does this almost entirely at night. If both patients and healthy people are protected by mosquito nets or by fly gauze over doors and

Figure 13.35 A mosquito net impregnated with insecticide.

Microorganisms and disease in humans

Key Facts

- A disease is endemic to an area if that disease, or its vector, is always found there.
- An epidemic of a disease occurs when there are a large number of cases of the disease; more than normal.
- Malaria is caused by the single-celled parasite *Plasmodium*.
- The vector of this parasite is the female *Anopheles* mosquito.
- The female mosquito takes blood from humans using sharp mouthparts, usually at night.
- Saliva containing an anticoagulent will be injected into the human while the blood meal is being taken.
- The malarial parasite will enter the blood of an uninfected person with the mosquito's saliva.
- Symptoms of malaria include alternating fever and chills and it can result in severe anaemia. It is often fatal.
- Draining standing water or spraying it with oil will kill the mosquito larvae. Biological control is also used.
- Sleeping under a net, ideally treated with insecticide, will prevent mosquito bites. Repellent creams can also be used.
- Insecticides can be sprayed to kill adult mosquitoes, but insecticide resistance is now common.
- Drugs are available to prevent malaria; they are widely used by people travelling to malarial areas but they are less affordable for people living there.

windows from dawn to dusk, then mosquitoes will not reach them. Often, the mosquito nets are treated with insecticide to kill any mosquitoes that do reach the nets (Figure 13.35). The use of drugs to cure malarial patients, by killing the parasites in their blood and liver cells, means that the patients are no longer a source of the parasites. This approach to control is possible only where hospitals and medical supplies exist. Drugs that will prevent the parasites from ever developing, even in a person bitten by an infected mosquito, have been in use for some time.

Use of such anti-malarial drugs gives a visitor travelling to an area where malaria is endemic almost complete protection, if bitten by a malaria-carrying mosquito. This could, in theory, succeed as a way of protecting the whole population of an area from malaria. However, it depends on the reliability of everyone taking the drug at the right frequency. It is also very expensive and at the moment, mosquito eradication is seen to be giving the most encouraging long-term results.

Questions

1 Copy and complete the sentences by choosing the correct word.

   a) Malaria is caused by the single-celled parasite called *Plasmodium/Anopheles*.

   b) The male/female mosquito is the vector/victim.

   c) Malaria is epidemic/endemic in some parts of the world.

   d) Mosquitoes bite more often during the day/night.

   e) The mosquito's saliva contains a substance which makes the human blood start/stop clotting.

2 Make a list of the ways in which:

   a) mosquito bites can be prevented

   b) mosquito larvae can be killed

   c) adult mosquitoes can be killed

3 Suggest some reasons why malaria is still so common in many parts of the world.

4 Design a leaflet to advise someone travelling abroad how to avoid catching malaria.

5 Visit www.malaria.org to find out more about malaria.

... more at www.modularscience.co.uk

Learning outcome

After completing the work in this topic you will be able to:

* explain the importance to the individual and to the community of personal hygiene measures in preventing disease

Figure 13.36

Every day we handle things that have been touched by other people, such as door handles, handrails, light switches or even the seat you may be sitting on right now! These are all covered with microorganisms that will stick to the skin of our hands, which we use more than any other part of our body. Added to these are the microorganisms that we pick up when stroking our pets, raising or lowering a toilet seat or turning a tap on.

Hand washing

We build up resistance to many of the microorganisms that are spread in these ways but outbreaks of diseases such as dysentery still occur annually, often among school children. Many students will not have a natural immunity because they may not have come into contact with the dysentery bacterium before. Students will become infected if they do not wash their hands after using toilets that have been used by other infected students.

It is important that hands are washed thoroughly, using hot water and soap, after using the toilet, touching the genital or anal areas, or the nostrils, and also before handling food. This is especially important before preparing food for others to eat. Using soap, or a similar detergent, is important because this will dislodge bacteria that are being held on the skin by fats and oils. Using a nailbrush will clean out any bacteria that are trapped under the fingernails (Figure 13.37).

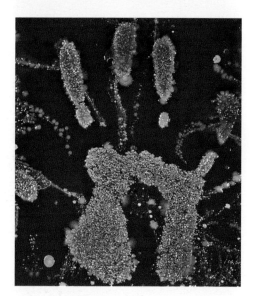

Figure 13.37 Bacterial colonies growing in the print of a human hand.

Microorganisms and disease in humans 25

Toilets

Toilets which are used by many people, such as those in shops or offices, can be a source of pathogens simply because the people who use them will be carrying lots of different microorganisms. Inevitably, drops of urine or specks of faeces will remain in and around the toilet area. These make an ideal place for bacteria to multiply.

During an epidemic of any disease for which diarrhoea is a sign, toilet hygiene is very important in controlling the spread of the disease. This applies to homes as well as public toilets. The whole area must be kept clean using disinfectant or similar products to kill the bacteria and hands must be washed using an anti-bacterial hand wash.

Feet

The fungus which causes athlete's foot is usually caught by people walking barefoot in changing rooms, in communal shower areas or around the sides of the pool at a public swimming pool. Fragments of the fungus drop off the feet of an infected person only to be picked up by someone else walking in the same place. The spaces in between the toes are often damp with sweat, or have been left wet after washing or swimming. This is where the fungus starts to grow. The growth of the fungus itself causes some discomfort or itching but if it is left to grow, the skin will become damaged leaving cracks where other microorganisms can enter causing secondary infections (Figure 13.38).

Special foot powders and fungicidal creams can be used to treat athlete's foot. An infected person should also try to prevent the spread of the fungus by keeping the infected foot covered in changing rooms. Waterproof 'socks' prevent transfer in wet areas and should be worn from the time that the usual socks are taken off until they are put on again, including in the pool or shower. Using the footbath before going into a swimming pool also helps prevent the fungus spreading (Figure 13.39). The area between the toes is difficult to dry quickly but by keeping it as dry as possible, the fungus is less likely to grow. For the same reason, sweaty feet will encourage fungal growth. Regular washing and clean socks help to prevent sweat being left between the toes. It makes them smell better too!

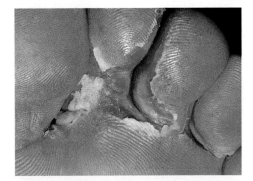

Figure 13.38 Athlete's foot infection.

Figure 13.39 Swimming pool footbaths can help prevent spread of infections.

Washing

Most skin infections are spread by direct or indirect contact with an infected person. This is hard to avoid in crowded areas, but personal hygiene is very important in controlling the spread of an infection and how quickly it clears up. Our whole body surface needs regular washing, ideally by bathing or showering. Anti-perspirants and deodorants are only intended to 'bridge the gap' between washes, by keeping you feeling fresher. They are not a substitute for regular washing (Figure 13.40).

Changing underwear regularly will not only help to control the build up and spread of bacteria but will also make you smell better too! Clean clothing, especially cotton fabrics, absorbs sweat from the skin's surface.

Sports clothes are often made of fabrics specially chosen to do this (Figure 13.42). Sweaty skin provides an ideal place for bacteria to grow, so by removing sweat from the skin you are removing another potential source of infection.

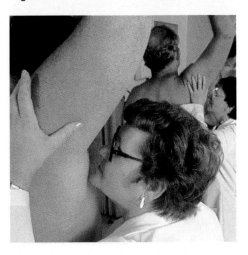

Figure 13.40 How about a career as a deodorant tester?

Nasal mucus

Although we can breathe in through our nose or mouth, breathing through the nose makes sure that the air is warmed and moistened by the mucus in the nasal passages as it enters. But the hairs and mucus in the nose perform another important job – they trap dust and microorganisms as they enter with the inhaled air. Blowing the nose rids the body of these organisms. A strong tissue is ideal because it can then be thrown away,
taking the microorganism-laden mucus with it. It is also important to hold a handkerchief or tissue up to the nose when sneezing. This prevents the people around you being sprayed with moist droplets packed with microorganisms.

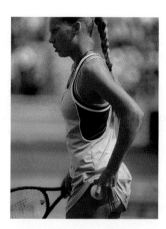

Figure 13.41 Underwear is just as important as the clothes on top.

Key Facts

- Bacteria are carried on unwashed hands, especially after visiting toilets.
- Soap should be used to remove bacteria from hands; disinfectant will kill bacteria in toilets.
- The fungus which causes athlete's foot is spread by coming into contact with it at swimming pools and changing rooms.
- Bathing and showering remove sweat from the skin where bacteria would grow.

Questions

1 Copy and complete the sentences by choosing the correct word each time.
   a) Athlete's foot is caused by a bacterium/fungus.
   b) It grows in between the fingers/toes.
   c) The easiest way to prevent it is to keep the skin dry/moist.
   d) You are most likely to catch it or pass it on at a swimming pool/public toilet.

2 Read through all of section 13.07 and make a table summarising all the personal hygiene points mentioned together with the reason(s) for doing them. One is done for you in the table below.

3 In public toilets there are often signs that say: 'Now wash your hands, please'. Design an A4 poster of your own that tells people to do this, but also tells them how they should wash them and the reason why.

4 A new swimming pool is opening. Make a leaflet about athlete's foot that could be given to people on their first visit. You should include information about how to prevent it and how to avoid giving it to other swimmers.

5 Design a personal hygiene questionnaire to give to your class or year group to complete. By allowing the responses to be anonymous, you may get more honest answers!

What to do?	Why do it?	Example of what type of infection could be prevented
Washing hands after using the toilet	To remove bacteria from the toilet area which are on the hands	Dysentery

Figure 13.42

... more at www.modularscience.co.uk

Did you know?

Feet sweat a lot. The palms of your hands are the only other place in your body that have as many sweat glands per unit area as the soles of your feet. But the difference in smell between these two areas is well known. The sweat itself doesn't smell 'cheesy' but when it is shut inside socks and trainers, bacteria and fungi grow in it. It is their waste that makes the smell. Sweat on the palm of your hands is able to evaporate into the air. Unless you wear rubber gloves!

According to the Guinness Book of Records, athlete's foot is the most common skin infection in humans, affecting up to 70% of the population at least once in their lifetime.

Learning outcome

After completing the work in this topic you will be able to:

- explain the treatment of sewage by the 'activated sludge' method, including the part played by the respiration of aerobic bacteria and of anaerobic bacteria, producing methane; label a diagram showing this sewage treatment process

What is sewage?

Sewage is the name given to the waste from a community of people that is carried in water (Figure 13.43). There are three types of waste involved.

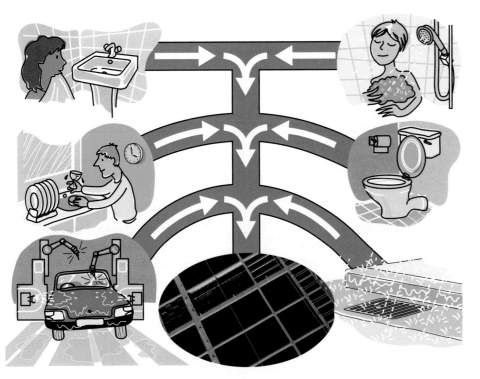

Figure 13.43 Sewage is made up of waste from a variety of sources.

1 Domestic waste

Sewage from our homes is made up of everything we wash down the plug hole of sinks or basins, or flush down the toilet. This will be a mixture of human urine and faeces, toilet tissue, dirty bath water, shampoos, shower gels or even yesterday's lumpy gravy or custard. Added to this will be the waste water and detergent from appliances such as washing machines or dishwashers.

2 Industrial waste

Water-borne waste from industry such as cellulose from paper mills or heavy metals such as lead, zinc or mercury is also a component of sewage. Animal waste such as blood from slaughter-houses may be present in sewage, as well as everything you put down the sink in your school laboratories.

3 Surface water

This is mainly rainwater from pavements, roads and roofs, which has entered the outside drains around your home or in the street. Although these drains have a metal grille to help prevent large items of rubbish such as drinks cans or take-away cartons from entering, inevitably small items such as sweet wrappers, leaves and gravel or grit will be carried with the rainwater down the drain and into an underground pipe. It is here in the sewers that the three categories of sewage will mix and travel on to a sewage treatment plant or sewage works.

Is sewage treatment necessary?

If sewage enters a river untreated, not only is it a health hazard but the aerobic microorganisms, mainly bacteria, will break down any organic material in it to carbon dioxide and water. To do this they require oxygen, which they obtain from the dissolved oxygen in the water. This reduces the amount of oxygen for larger animals, such as fish.

Therefore, if large quantities of raw (i.e. untreated) sewage were allowed to enter rivers, no fish would survive.

Sewage contains microorganisms, most of which have come from the human waste in it. Among these microorganisms there will be pathogens, for example bacteria from the intestines of people with dysentery, typhoid fever or cholera. Viruses that cause poliomyelitis (polio) and infectious hepatitis are also spread in water.

So, by treating sewage, the aim is to:

1 Reduce the organic material so that when the treated sewage is discharged into a river it will not encourage large numbers of aerobic bacteria to use up the river's dissolved oxygen.

2 Prevent outbreaks of disease by destroying, or making harmless, any pathogens in the sewage.

This is done using a combination of physical, chemical and microbiological processes.

Stages in sewage treatment

Sewage can be treated in many different ways, depending on the quantity, its contents, where it will be discharged after treatment, the possible effects on the environment and also the cost. Modern sewage treatment works generally divide the treatment process into three main stages (Figure 13.44):

1 Primary
2 Secondary
3 Tertiary

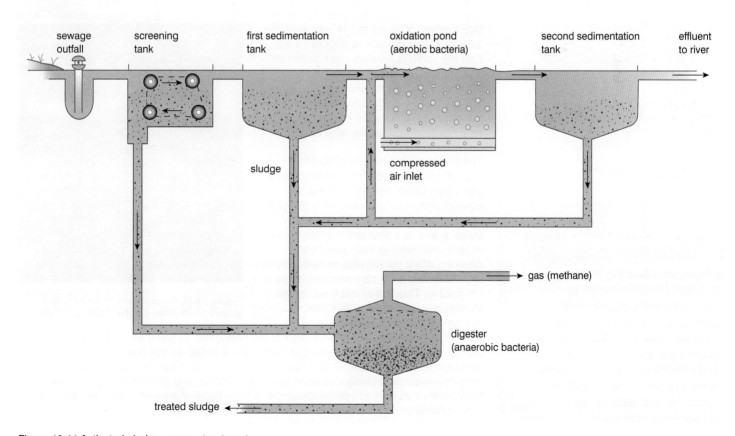

Figure 13.44 Activated sludge sewage treatment.

1 Primary treatment

As sewage enters the treatment works, it passes through fixed screens made of parallel metal bars. These trap any large objects such as rags or sticks, which may have been carried in with the sewage. These objects could block pipes later on in the treatment process. Grit must also be removed at this stage to prevent excessive wear and tear on the pumping mechanisms.

After this initial screening, sewage enters the first sedimentation tank. Here the solid waste is allowed to settle to the bottom of the tank with the liquid waste above it. The settled solids, known as **sludge**, and the liquid **effluent**, are then treated separately.

2 Secondary treatment

This stage of treatment relies on the activity of microorganisms. The sludge from the sedimentation tank is transferred to another large tank for digestion. This large, closed tank is almost filled with sludge, so little air is present. Bacteria feed on the sludge, which is largely organic material, breaking it down to release carbon dioxide and methane gas. As there is little or no air in the digestion tank, these bacteria must be anaerobic i.e. they must be able to respire without oxygen (Figure 13.45).

The methane, sometimes known as biogas, can be used to produce electricity for the sewage works and heat to keep the digestion tank warm. The digestion process is speeded up by constant stirring of the sludge and maintaining it at a temperature of 50–55°C. The digested sludge may then be dumped at sea, spread on farmland, buried in landfill sites, burnt in large incineration plants, or dried and sold to the public as compost.

The liquid effluent still contains plenty of organic matter, which must be broken down before it leaves the sewage works. One method of doing this is known as the activated sludge process (Figure 13.46). First the liquid is aerated in an oxidation pond where it is constantly stirred and vigorously aerated by allowing compressed air to bubble through it. This maintains a high oxygen level in the liquid for a range of aerobic bacteria and protozoa to live.

These aerobic bacteria feed on the organic matter, producing carbon dioxide and water. Other aerobic bacteria will convert ammonia to nitrate. After about 16 hours of aeration, most of the treated liquid is sent to a final sedimentation tank. In here, the bacteria that have been breaking down the organic material, plus any remaining solid particles, can settle to the bottom. This leaves the liquid above looking cleaner. Some of this settled sludge will be returned to the aeration tanks to provide bacteria for digestion of the next batch of liquid effluent. The remaining sludge will be sent to join the sludge from the anaerobic sludge digestion.

Although the liquid effluent that remains is now relatively clean in appearance, it still contains dissolved substances such as excess nitrates and phosphates, pesticides and heavy metals as well as some pathogens. A third stage of treatment may be required to reduce these to safer levels.

Figure 13.45 Biological anaerobic treatment of sewage. Methane gas bubbles are produced by the bacteria breaking down the sewage.

Figure 13.46 Aeration tank in an activated sludge plant. Here aerobic bacteria are at work.

Did you know?

A European Bathing Waters Directive is now in force. In 100 ml samples of sea water taken at a holiday resort, there must be fewer than 2000 live microorganisms. This means that effluent from sewage works in the area must be treated to reach this standard at the tertiary treatment stage.

3 Tertiary treatment

Liquid from the final sedimentation tank may be disinfected with chlorine or with ozone to kill pathogenic bacteria. However this is only done if the liquid is required for immediate re-use as clean water. Chlorine is toxic to fish so chlorine-treated effluent could not then be discharged into rivers. However effluent from sewage works near holiday resorts must be treated to reduce the number of pathogenic bacteria discharged into areas of the sea near beaches used for swimming (see 'Did you know?').

The effluent may also be treated chemically or by using ion exchange to remove other dissolved materials such as excess nitrates, phosphates, pesticides or heavy metals. However laws requiring factories to regulate the discharge of heavy metals themselves have done a lot to reduce the amount of metallic ions in the effluent, as fewer will reach the sewage works.

Key Facts

- Sewage consists of domestic waste, industrial waste and surface water.
- Raw sewage must be treated before discharge into rivers by reducing the organic material and pathogens in it.
- In primary treatment, large objects and grit are removed.
- Liquid waste is called effluent; solid waste is called sludge.
- Secondary treatment consists of an anaerobic breakdown of sludge, producing methane, and an aerobic breakdown of the effluent.
- Tertiary treatment may be needed to further reduce numbers of pathogens, excess nitrates, phosphates, pesticides or heavy metals.

Questions

1 Draw and complete a table like the one shown below.

Stages in sewage treatment

What is done to the sewage?	How/where is it done?	Why is it done?
Screening		
Grit settlement		

2 Suggest how each of the following causes concern at a sewage treatment works.

   a) Several days of heavy rain and gales.

   b) A new factory opening nearby which makes disinfectants.

   c) A statement from a local hospital reporting that a patient on holiday in the area has polio.

   d) More households using a dishwasher instead of washing up in the sink.

3 In aerobic digestion tanks, the sludge is stirred and heated to 50–55°C. Suggest why this is done.

4 Keep a record for a week of how many times the toilets, sinks, baths, basins etc. in your home are used to send waste to the sewage works. You could try to list the contents each time.

5 Visit www.environment-agency.gov.uk to find out more about water treatment.

... more at www.modularscience.co.uk

Growing microorganisms in the laboratory

Many microorganisms can be grown in a laboratory culture if they are given a watery solution containing essential nutrients. There must also be oxygen available if they are aerobic, a suitable temperature and an optimum pH. They will need space to grow and reproduce without competition from other organisms. This is why the equipment and the culture medium used must be sterile; microorganisms, other than the ones being grown, would compete for space, nutrients and oxygen. Viruses and other microorganisms that are obligate parasites cannot be grown in a laboratory culture; they must have the correct host to grow on.

In favourable conditions, the number of single-celled microorganisms in the culture will double at regular intervals. This is because each parent cell will produce two daughter cells, which both produce two daughter cells of their own. The time required for the number of cells to double is known as the mean doubling time. Calculating the mean doubling time i.e. the time taken for the population to double, can be used to compare the growth rates of different populations or of the same population at different stages if its growth rate changes.

Limiting factors

There are a number of factors that will influence the growth of cells in a laboratory culture. They are:

- availability of nutrients
- temperature
- pH
- oxygen
- build-up of toxic material

A population of microorganisms will increase until one or more of these factors becomes a **limiting factor**. This limiting factor will slow down the rate of growth. For example, when the culture solution is freshly made it will contain all the essential nutrients needed by the microorganisms to grow unchecked. When one of the nutrients is almost used up, this will limit the growth of the population. If more of the limiting nutrient is added, growth will accelerate again until another factor becomes limiting. Alternatively, if more of the essential nutrient is not added, the population will stop increasing and will start to decrease, because new cells cannot be made.

Cell growth and doubling, even with an unlimited supply of nutrients, does not continue indefinitely. If the growth of the population is not limited by the exhaustion of one or more essential nutrients, it is often limited by the build up of toxic waste from the cells' metabolism as their numbers increase. Therefore a more realistic picture of the pattern of change in cell numbers is shown on the graph in Figure 13.48.

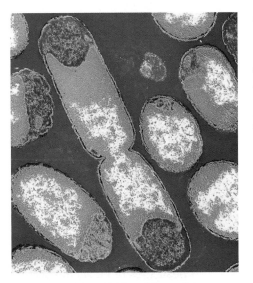

Figure 13.47 *Escherichia coli* bacterium dividing.

Time/ min	No. of divisions	No. of cells present
0	0	1
20	1	2
40	2	4
60	3	8
80	4	16
100	5	32
120	6	64
140	7	128
160	8	256
180	9	512
200	10	1024

Interpreting a growth curve

Growth curves for a single population of bacteria or yeast growing in a laboratory culture usually show a similar population growth pattern. This is most easily seen when plotted as a graph; it is often S-shaped.

The growth curve can be divided into four main stages, often known as **phases**.

1 Lag phase

At this stage there is little or no increase in cell numbers even though the cells are active. The bacteria are adjusting to their new conditions and the correct **enzymes** to break down the substrate are being made. The length of this stage depends on whether the bacteria were growing in similar nutrients before being put into the culture being studied. If they were, the adjustment period will be shorter than if they were not.

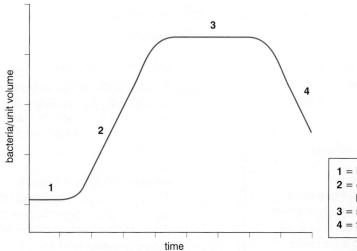

1 = lag phase
2 = exponential or
    log phase
3 = stationary phase
4 = final or death phase

Figure 13.48 Growth curve of bacterial population.

2 Log or exponential phase

This is a period of rapid growth during which the population increases by doubling and redoubling. Food is in plentiful supply and the conditions for growth are ideal. The microorganisms feed, grow and multiply at a rate that is as fast as their genetic make-up will allow. Two cells divide to become four, the four will become eight and so on. This is described as exponential or logarithmic growth and is shown on the curve by the steepest gradient.

3 Stationary phase

After a period of exponential growth, the habitat becomes overcrowded with many organisms, each needing a supply of food. Competition for food leaves some cells without enough for growth and reproduction. Waste products may build up to toxic levels or alter the pH. One of these factors becomes a limiting factor. To conserve energy, many cells stop dividing and the growth curve starts to flatten out. The curve does not flatten immediately because although the number of new cells being produced decreases, it will remain higher than the number that are dying at first. However, when more cells stop multiplying, population growth falls to zero, i.e. the curve flattens, when the number of cells being produced exactly balances the number of cells that are dying.

4 Death phase

Build-up of toxic wastes or lack of food or oxygen has now produced conditions that are unfavourable for maintaining life. This limiting factor gradually has its effect, and fewer and fewer cells are produced, more and more die and the population starts to decline. Since large numbers of cells are dying and are not being replaced, the population numbers fall rapidly. The steep drop in the curve shows this.

Did you know?

Examiner's tip
When you are asked to describe the shape of a curve or to explain what is happening at each stage, try to organise your answer. You must describe each section of the curve and/or explain what is happening at that particular stage. If the curve is steep and then it levels out, say something about each section in turn. This type of question is often worth several marks. Even very able candidates do not always obtain full marks. It is not enough just to give a mathematical name to the relationship. If you are asked for a description or an explanation, make sure you give one.

Key Facts

- Microorganisms such as bacteria and yeast can be grown in a laboratory culture to study their population numbers.
- Viruses or other obligate parasites cannot be grown in a laboratory culture.
- Nutrient supply, temperature, pH, and available oxygen affect growth. An unfavourable level of any one of them can slow down or stop growth. This is known as a limiting factor.
- There are four phases to a growth curve. In the lag phase, cells are getting used to where they are. In the exponential phase, cells are growing and dividing very rapidly. In the stationary phase the rate of cell increase balances the rate of cell death. In the death phase, more cells die than are produced.

Questions

1   Copy and complete.

A population of bacteria can reproduce very rapidly if the right conditions are available. To grow well, it must have the correct ....,

................, ..., and enough oxygen, if required. Toxic .... building up will also affect growth. Any of these factors which slows or stops growth can be described as a ....

....

2   a) Make a table to show what happens in the four phases of a typical bacterial or fungal growth curve.

Phase	What is happening?
Lag	
Log or exponential	
Stationary	
Death	

b) Now draw a sketch graph to show the shape of the growth curve. Mark these stages on it.

3   Look at the data in the table on page 32 showing increase in bacterial cell numbers.

a) If doubling continued at this rate, how many cells would be present after 4 hours from the start?

b) Why won't these bacteria continue to multiply for ever at this rate?

4   The data below show the growth of a population of yeast.

Hours after incubation	Number of cells counted per unit area
0	10
2	30
4	75
6	180
8	340
10	520
12	600
14	635
16	650
18	660
20	665

a) Plot the data on graph paper.

b) Describe the shape of the curve and explain what is happening in the yeast culture to produce this shape. Remember to organise your description into sections – see 'Did you know?' – examiner's tip.

... more at www.modularscience.co.uk

Learning outcomes

After completing the work in this topic you will be able to:

- understand that sterilisation can be achieved by the use of heat, chemicals (including chlorine) and irradiation

- understand the danger of consuming irradiated food in which microorganisms have been killed but which may still contain their toxins

- distinguish between antiseptics and disinfectants and explain their different characteristics and applications

- explain the 'flash' process for milk pasteurisation; interpret data from experiments to investigate the effectiveness of pasteurisation

Killing microorganisms

For as long as we have been aware of decay, even before microorganisms were known to be the cause, humans have taken steps to control it. Some of the reasons that we need to control the growth of microorganisms are listed below:

- to prevent the spread of food-borne disease
- to provide clean, safe drinking water
- to prevent the spread of disease
- to prevent infection during surgery or childbirth
- to prevent contamination in laboratories

Now that we have found ways to control the growth of microorganisms in these situations, our life expectancy has increased and fewer women and their babies die during childbirth. The population in general is able to lead a relatively disease-free life in comparison with those living even just a century ago.

The methods of control used today are largely divided into methods used on living tissue and those used on non-living items such as surgical instruments, work surfaces and toilets.

Figure 13.49 Commercial antiseptics and disinfectants.

Disinfectants

Disinfectants are used to kill microorganisms on or in non-living objects. They are highly toxic. Commercial disinfectants are usually a mixture of chemicals marketed for a particular range of situations. For example in the home, baby equipment might be disinfected with Milton fluid but a greenhouse would be disinfected with a more suitable disinfectant such as Jeyes fluid. Disinfectants work best in warm solution because heat increases the kinetic energy of the disinfectant molecules. This results in them moving more quickly and they are therefore more likely to collide with their target microorganisms in a shorter time. Disinfectants will reduce the number of microorganisms on a surface or in a container, but they may not all be killed, and spores are also likely to survive. If low concentrations of disinfectant are used, there may not be enough disinfectant molecules to kill large numbers of microorganisms. This is why it is important to follow the dilution and usage instructions on the disinfectant bottle. Although using too little may not be effective enough, using too much or too high a concentration of disinfectant can also cause problems. Many disinfectants are highly toxic so the lower the concentrations used, the less risk to people using them. Using more disinfectant than is needed to do the job effectively is also more expensive and can lead to disinfectant entering the environment in harmful quantities.

Figure 13.50 A boot being disinfected to prevent spread of infection.

Microorganisms and disease in humans   35

Figure 13.51 A medical technician preparing surgical instruments to be autoclaved.

Antiseptics

Antiseptics are not as toxic as disinfectants and are used on living tissue, such as on the skin to prevent infections of wounds. They have a milder action than disinfectants so often prevent the growth of microorganisms rather than killing them all. You may have used antiseptic cream yourself, such as Germolene or Savlon, on a cut or graze. In hospitals, antiseptics such as iodine, and alcohols such as ethanol, are used in operating theatres.

Sterilisation

As with disinfection, sterilisation can only be used to destroy microorganisms on or in non-living materials because it damages all living tissue. Sterilisation can be carried out in one of three ways, using:
- heat
- radiation
- chemicals such as alcohol or chlorine compounds

Heat sterilisation is used when there is a need to completely eradicate all microorganisms, including bacteria and fungi, their spores and any viruses present. It is difficult to destroy pathogenic bacteria which have formed spores, so using boiling water at 100°C is insufficient. An autoclave is used which can provide effective heat sterilisation after 30 minutes at 116°C or after 2 minutes at 132°C (Figure 13.51).
Many objects that need to be sterilised are unsuitable for such high temperature treatment. Instead chemical methods, or irradiation using gamma radiation, will be used. Irradiation will kill microorganisms in food, making the food appear fresh and safe. However, some microorganisms produce toxins that will not be destroyed by gamma radiation. Although this is a rare occurrence it is one of the disadvantages of using irradiation for food preservation.
One use of chemical sterilisation is in the treatment of drinking water by chlorination. Sodium hypochlorite is used to release chlorine in enough concentration to kill all pathogenic bacteria without affecting the taste of the water. You may have used or seen sterilising solutions for cleaning contact lenses to reduce the risk of eye infections.

Preserving milk

Heat sterilisation can be used to kill microorganisms in milk, but sterilised milk has a characteristic flavour which many people do not like. Instead, in the UK, about 93% of milk is pasteurised (Figure 13.52). This is much more popular than sterilised milk because pasteurisation does not noticeably affect either the flavour or the nutritional value of the milk. Although sterilised milk will keep for several months without refrigeration, pasteurised milk must be kept in a refrigerator between 1°C and 4°C. Here, it will keep for several days. The most common method of pasteurising milk is known as **flash pasteurisation**.

Figure 13.52 Most of the milk we drink will have been pasteurised.

Milk is heated by passing it through pipes or between plates surrounded by hot water. The heating is carefully controlled to ensure that the milk is held at 71.7°C for 15 seconds. It is then cooled rapidly to 3°C. The heating process kills many pathogenic organisms and **spoilage organisms**, while the rapid cooling prevents organisms which survive the heat treatment from dividing rapidly.

Questions

1   Complete the sentences:

   Flash pasteurisation is used to make .... keep fresh longer. The milk is heated to ....°C for .... seconds, then cooled rapidly to .... The heating process kills .... and .... organisms. The rapid cooling prevents any surviving microorganisms from .... rapidly. Pasteurised milk must be stored in a .... at a temperature that is between .... and ....°C. Here it will keep for .... days.

2   Make a table like the one below to show different ways of killing microorganisms.

3   The graph (Figure 13.53) shows different ways of treating raw milk to make it safe for drinking and also to improve its keeping qualities.

   a) What is the highest temperature each milk sample reached and how long was it at this temperature for?

   b) Which line represents milk with fewest bacteria at the end of treatment?

   c) Which line most closely represents milk being pasteurised?

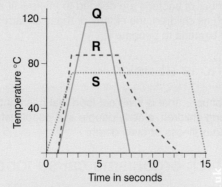

Figure 13.53

Name of method	How it is used	Example of what this method is used for
Disinfectant	To kill microorganisms on or in non-living objects	

... more at www.modularscience.co.uk

- Disinfectants are used to reduce the number of microorganisms and their spores. Not all will be killed but adjusting the concentration gives more control.
- Disinfectants can only be used on non-living things; they are too toxic for use on living tissue.
- The lowest concentration of an appropriate disinfectant should be used to reduce cost, health risks and environmental damage.
- Antiseptics kill or reduce the growth of microorganisms and can be used externally on living tissue, e.g. skin.
- Sterilisation kills all microorganisms and their spores but cannot be used on living tissue as this too would be damaged.
- There are three main ways of sterilising: heat, gamma radiation or chemicals.
- Heat sterilisation needs temperatures over 100°C.
- Gamma radiation is useful for food sterilisation as it does not require high temperature or chemicals. Bacterial toxins may not be destroyed by this method.
- Chemical sterilisation requires the use of chemicals such as chlorine or alcohol. It is most familiar for its use in drinking water and swimming pools.
- Pasteurisation is commonly used to extend the life of milk.

Food poisoning

What is food poisoning?

Food poisoning is caused by pathogenic microorganisms entering our body in contaminated food. Ingesting the harmful chemicals called toxins, which pathogens release into the food, can also cause it. Common symptoms are vomiting and diarrhoea, often with headache and abdominal pain. These symptoms occur either when the microorganisms multiply beyond a certain level in our gut, or as a response to toxins that the pathogen has produced. The number of bacteria present, or the level of toxin needed to produce the symptoms will vary from person to person. Usually, a large number of bacteria are needed to make a fit and healthy adult ill, but vulnerable groups such as children, the elderly or those already in poor health, may only need to ingest a few bacteria to become ill.

Who is at risk?

All of us … that is if we eat food that has not been safely prepared or stored. However, young children, elderly people and people who are already ill are particularly at risk of serious illness or even death.

Which organisms cause food poisoning?

Viruses, fungi and bacteria can all potentially be the causes of food poisoning. *Escherichia coli*, often abbreviated to *E. coli*, is a bacterium found in the gut. It may be present as a result of contamination by faeces, for example, when hands have not been washed before preparing food. Twenty deaths and 200 other cases of illness were caused by a dangerous strain of this normally harmless bacterium in an outbreak in Lanarkshire, Scotland in 1996. As few as 20 bacterial cells may have been ingested in meat eaten by the infected people but this resulted in severe symptoms.
Species of **Salmonella** bacteria are also a common cause of food poisoning. *Salmonella* bacteria are mainly found in the intestines of animals such as cattle, fish and poultry, with chickens being the most common source of human infection.

A closer look at *Salmonella* sources

Many modern methods of animal rearing involve the housing of large numbers of animals in a relatively small area. This is known as **intensive rearing**. These conditions are ideal for the *Salmonella* bacteria to pass from one animal to another. Intensive rearing methods are particularly common in chicken farming, for birds being reared for meat (broilers) and for hens reared for egg production.

When chickens are reared for their meat, the aim is to produce a large group of birds which have all reached a target body mass in a certain time. Their housing will be disinfected as each batch of birds leave for slaughter, but during the time that a particular batch of chickens are being fattened there is a high risk of transferring the *Salmonella* bacteria between birds in infected droppings. It is also inevitable that some of the bacteria will also remain in the chicken carcass after the bird is slaughtered. These bacteria may have been on the skin or in the gut of the infected birds and this is the danger point.

Figure 13.54 Raw eggs pose a risk to vulnerable people.

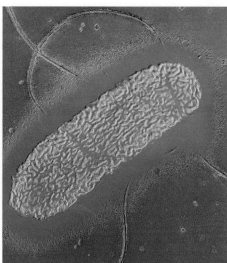

Figure 13.55 *Salmonella* bacterium – a cause of food poisoning.

These *Salmonella* bacteria will survive even while the carcass is in cold storage, ready to infect the human who may consume them.

Hens being reared for egg production may lay eggs infected with *Salmonella* (Figure 13.54). These eggs may have become contaminated in the oviduct or by faeces in the area where they were laid.

How do *Salmonella* bacteria go on to reproduce?

Bacteria can reproduce very quickly in favourable conditions i.e. moisture, warmth and a supply of nutrients. If meat or eggs are stored at too high a temperature, at any stage between production and consumption, the *Salmonella* may have had time to multiply (Figure 13.55). When we eat the contaminated food, the *Salmonella* continue to reproduce in the cells lining our gut. This causes damage to these cells and the bacteria also release toxins, which cause further cell damage and tissue inflammation. This will disrupt enzyme production and also hinder the absorption of digested food and water.

Avoiding food poisoning by *Salmonella*

Salmonella bacteria are destroyed at temperatures above 56°C although heating to above 60°C is recommended. So normal, thorough cooking will kill them (Figure 13.56). As well as ensuring that food is thoroughly cooked, care must be taken with personal hygiene and kitchen hygiene. Personal hygiene is covered in detail in another section of this book, but the most important aspect of it is the thorough washing of hands before touching food. This is especially important if the food is being prepared for others, e.g. in a restaurant, and if a mixture of raw and cooked foods are being handled. Hands that have touched raw food should be re-washed before handling cooked food, to avoid transfer of bacteria.

Kitchen hygiene is very important in controlling the spread of a variety of food-borne disease, but the following precautions are particularly relevant to the avoidance of *Salmonella* infection.

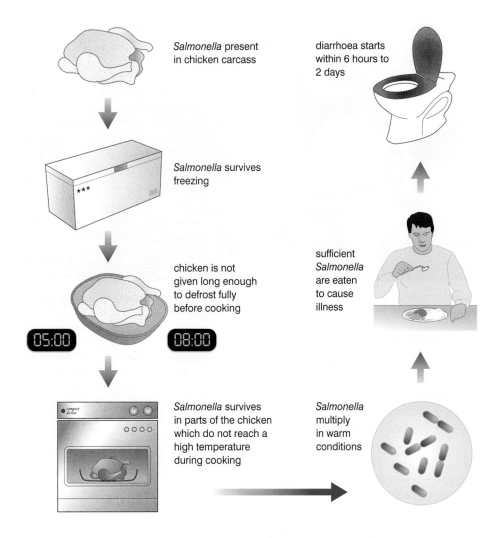

Salmonella present in chicken carcass

Salmonella survives freezing

chicken is not given long enough to defrost fully before cooking

05:00   08:00

Salmonella survives in parts of the chicken which do not reach a high temperature during cooking

Salmonella multiply in warm conditions

sufficient Salmonella are eaten to cause illness

diarrhoea starts within 6 hours to 2 days

Figure 13.56 How food poisoning can occur.

Raw chicken

- Fresh or ready cooked chicken should be stored in a refrigerator.
- Fresh chicken should be cooked within 2 days of purchase.
- Raw chicken must be kept separate from other cooked meats, and its juices must not be allowed to drip onto other foods.
- Use separate knives and cutting boards for raw and cooked foods.
- Frozen chickens must be thoroughly defrosted before cooking, following the guidance on the packaging. This is best done in a refrigerator so that the parts that have already defrosted stay cool. However this will take longer than defrosting in the open kitchen and enough time must be allowed to ensure that the chicken is ice free right through to the centre. In an open kitchen, the thawing carcass must be covered to prevent contamination by dust, air-borne bacteria or flies.
- Check that no ice remains before starting to cook. Many people make the mistake of thinking that it will finish thawing in the oven. This is one of the most common errors, especially with large birds, such as turkeys at Christmas. When the calculated cooking time has passed, the outside will be cooked but the frozen inside will only just have thawed, so will still be raw and any Salmonella will still be alive.
- It is better to put stuffing under the skin at the neck end, rather than in the body cavity. The body is the bulkiest part of the bird, so filling the body cavity with stuffing may prevent the meat at the centre of the bird being thoroughly cooked. If stuffing is to be cooked inside the bird, the total cooking time must be increased.

Cooked chicken

Once cooked, a whole chicken should not be left to cool for more than 1 hour before refrigerating. Chicken joints will be cool enough to refrigerate sooner than this. Ideally, the meat should be covered and cooled as quickly as possible and then refrigerated. It must not be left lying about in a warm kitchen.

Do not reheat chicken, or any other food, more than once. Food that is reheated must be piping hot all the way through. This includes 'ready meals' which have been cooked in a factory then sold to you from a supermarket refrigerator. When these are taken home to 'cook', they are often actually being reheated.

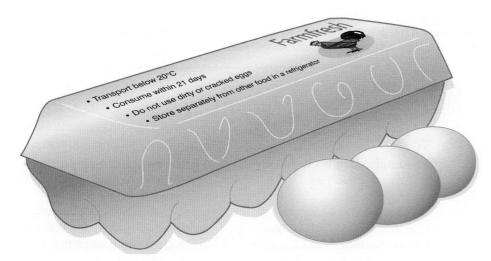

Figure 13.57 Storage instructions can usually be found on egg boxes.

Other dairy products

Avoid unpasteurised milk and raw eggs. Some home-made egg dishes, such as mayonnaise and mousses, contain raw egg although it is now possible to buy pasteurised egg to use as a substitute for fresh raw eggs.

Observe the 'sell by' and 'use by' dates on food. It is easy to see if food is contaminated by mould, but by the time the food looks 'mouldy' it may already contain dangerously high numbers of unseen bacteria.

Figure 13.58 An egg with the Lion Quality mark and date stamp.

Improvements in animal rearing

In 1993 the Government's Advisory Committee on the Microbiological Safety of Food recommended a number of changes to egg production, distribution, handling and storage to try to reduce their risk to human health.

The Lion Quality mark is now put onto about 74% of UK eggs. It appears on the egg and on the packaging to show that the eggs have passed strict safety standards. For example, they have come from hens that have been vaccinated against *Salmonella*. There is also a 'best before' date stamped on the shell.

A European Union Directive now also sets standards for the amount of space in the cages of laying birds. Laying cages have now become one of the most common methods of keeping caged birds for egg production. They give a high degree of control over feeding and hygiene. Cages have sloping mesh floors so that eggs roll away from the birds to await collection. Droppings will pass through the mesh to keep the cage more hygienic, and food is given in a trough fitted to the front of the cage. These measures help to prevent the spread of infection between hens and contamination of the eggs.

Did you know?

People who have been infected with *Salmonella* may carry the bacteria for up to 2 months. This is why it is so important to wash hands before handling food. Rats, mice and cockroaches are pests in kitchens because they too can spread *Salmonella* to humans, as can domestic pets.

Mary Mallon, a cook working in New York USA in the 1900s, was a notorious carrier of *Salmonella*. She was infected with the microorganism but showed no symptoms herself. Mary was responsible for starting at least 20 outbreaks of typhoid by passing the bacterium on to the people she prepared food for. She became known as 'Typhoid Mary'.

Figure 13.59 'Typhoid Mary'.

Key Facts

- Food poisoning is caused by a number of different pathogenic microorganisms. These include *Escherichia coli* and species of *Salmonella*.
- Symptoms such as diarrhoea and vomiting may be caused by the large number of bacteria present or the toxins that the bacteria produce.
- Children, the elderly and people in poor health, are more vulnerable to *Salmonella* poisoning than healthy adults.
- *Salmonella* is especially common in eggs, poultry and meat and unpasteurised milk.
- Intensive rearing of livestock results in overcrowded conditions where bacteria can easily pass from one animal to another or from bird to egg.
- Thorough cooking kills *Salmonella* but poor personal or kitchen hygiene is often to blame for an outbreak.
- Raw and cooked foods should be kept apart during both preparation and storage with separate utensils being used for each.
- Hands should be thoroughly washed especially between handling raw and cooked foods and when preparing food for others.
- Cooked food should be chilled quickly and stored in a refrigerator.
- Food must be reheated thoroughly; this should only be done once.
- Frozen food, especially poultry, should be completely thawed before cooking.

Many customers prefer to buy free-range eggs which have come from birds that have been allowed much more freedom. At least one supermarket chain will now only stock free-range eggs as a result of customer demand.

Questions

1 Copy and complete:
Food poisoning is caused by .... such as .... and species of .... Meat, ..., ... and unpasteurised .... are common foods in which *Salmonella* bacteria may be found.

2 List the improvements that must be made in the shop shown in Figure 13.60 before the food sold in it would be safe to eat.

3 In England and Wales, over 40 000 cases of food poisoning are reported every year.

   a) How many cases per day does this average out at?

   b) The distribution of cases is not evenly spread throughout the year. Suggest reasons for this.

   c) The number of *Salmonella* infections remain high year after year. Some people say that this is because of the modern, busy life-style. Suggest some ways that a busy life-style could increase a person's chances of contracting food poisoning.

4 Design a leaflet which could be given to people at supermarkets when they bought a large, frozen turkey. Include information about how to cook and store the bird which would help them to avoid food poisoning.

5 Visit the Food Standards Agency website at www.food.gov.uk to find out more about safer eating.

Figure 13.60 An unhygienic shop.

... more at www.modularscience.co.uk

We are always under attack by pathogenic organisms, but this does not always lead to an infection. Our bodies are adapted to prevent the entry of microorganisms. Our skin prevents many of the pathogens that land on our skin surface from entering the tissues below. It is only when our skin is damaged by a cut or graze, or when the piercing mouthparts of an insect penetrate its barrier, that pathogens gain entry through it. Even then they have to act quickly before a blood clot blocks the wound. Microorganisms are trapped if they try to enter the respiratory system, tears prevent entry via the eyes and strong acid in the stomach provides another line of defence.

But although we have everything to gain by not allowing these pathogens into our bodies, they have everything to lose. We can provide lodgings and a meal ticket; it is in the parasite's interest to find a way in and sometimes our first lines of defence are penetrated.

White blood cells

Any pathogens, which succeed in entering our body, will multiply quickly and we may begin to show or feel the symptoms of the disease they cause. White blood cells allow us to destroy these invading microorganisms (Figure 13.61), sometimes before they are in sufficient numbers for symptoms to develop. However, if large numbers of pathogens enter all at once, for example in contaminated food or water, the white blood cells cannot destroy them all and disease symptoms develop. Many infections clear up without medical treatment as a result of the action of white blood cells.

There are a number of different types of white blood cell. All are produced in the bone marrow but have developed in different ways in order to specialise in slightly different defence roles. They all have the ability to distinguish between substances they meet daily that are part of the body and foreign substances, or **antigens**, that have entered the body.

Phagocytes

The word phagocyte literally means 'cell-eater'. Phagocytes destroy pathogens by surrounding the pathogen and 'eating' it. Put more scientifically, the phagocyte surrounds the pathogen by extending its cell around it and forming a food vacuole which then allows the pathogen to be taken into the phagocyte to be digested chemically. This process is called **phagocytosis** (Figure 13.62).

Phagocytes can locate pathogens such as bacteria by responding to the chemical substances that the bacteria release into the surroundings. The phagocytes move towards the invading bacteria; this behaviour in response to a chemical is known as **chemotaxis**. Other white cells may have already coated the invading bacteria in particular proteins to assist the phagocytes in detecting them. Phagocytes can move out

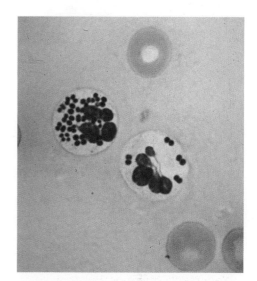

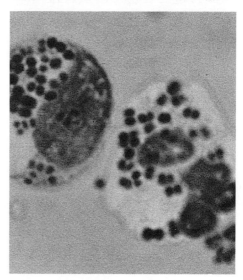

Figure 13.61 White blood cells ingesting bacteria.

Microorganisms and disease in humans 43

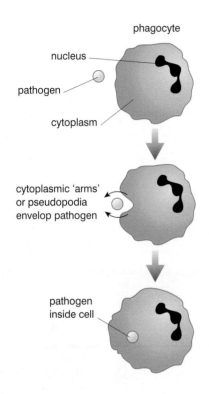

Figure 13.62 Phagocytosis.

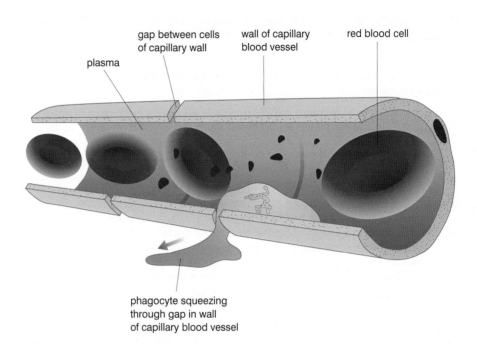

Figure 13.63 A phagocyte escaping from a capillary.

of the blood and into the tissues to pursue pathogens (Figure 13.63). They do this by squeezing in between the cells making up the walls of the blood capillaries. Phagocytes are not always successful in destroying pathogens. The cell wall of the bacterium may have a capsule around it. This may withstand the enzymes which the phagocyte tries to destroy it with.

Lymphocytes

Lymphocytes are another type of white blood cell which start as stem cells in the bone marrow, and remain there to mature. When mature, those that are known as B-lymphocytes may move from the bone marrow to the lymph glands (lymph nodes). Here they patrol the body, moving between the blood and lymph, searching for any foreign particles that might indicate a pathogen is present. They respond to a foreign particle such as a bacterium by swelling and then dividing many times to form a clone of larger, plasma cells. These have a life span of only a few days. These plasma cells secrete large quantities of proteins called antibodies into the blood plasma.

Antibodies

All vertebrates, including humans, produce antibodies to attack viruses, bacteria or foreign proteins. Antibodies are proteins which are extremely specific. In other words each antibody binds to and attacks only one particular antigen. In our body, each one of us possesses millions of different B-lymphocytes, each one genetically programmed to produce just one type of antibody which it displays on its outer membrane. This forms a receptor site for one particular antigen. When an antigen enters the body it eventually meets a B-lymphocyte displaying a matching antibody and they bind together. It is this binding that activates the B-lymphocyte, causing it to produce the plasma cells which secrete more antibodies of the same type that first 'locked on' to the antigen. Antibodies help to destroy pathogens in a number of ways:

- they may link many antigens together. This will enable the phagocytes to 'eat' them more easily
- they may cause lysis of the pathogen i.e. kill it by breaking its cell membrane
- they may neutralise toxic chemicals released by the pathogen

When a B-lymphocyte recognises an antigen that matches the specific antibody it can produce, it will swell and divide rapidly to produce the clone of antibody secreting plasma cells mentioned earlier (Figure 13.65). However, although MOST of the activated B-lymphocytes produce plasma cells when they divide, some form clones of smaller, but longer-living **memory cells**.

All the lymphocytes and plasma cells involved in this first response to a new pathogen, known as the **primary immune response**, will die within a few days of destroying the pathogen. This means that if this same pathogen invades the body again, they will no longer be present to destroy it. However, the memory cells can respond very quickly to a second attack. Within 3 days of the repeat invasion, the memory cells can multiply rapidly and produce the exact antibodies to combat this particular pathogen. This is known as the **secondary immune response**.

The secondary immune response, using the memory cells retained from the original infection, is much faster than the response to a new attack from a different pathogen, which would take 7–10 days (Figure 13.66). Unfortunately, even this fast-track secondary immune response may still not be quick enough to avoid symptoms of the disease but it will result in more memory cells. A third attack of the same pathogen is unlikely to result in any symptoms because so many memory cells, specific to that particular antigen, will be ready to be mobilised for antibody production. The person has now become immune to the disease.

Figure 13.64 An exact match between antibody and antigen must be made.

Did you know?

Each plasma cell is capable of secreting more than 10 million copies of a particular type of antibody molecule per hour. That averages out at more than 2500 per second!

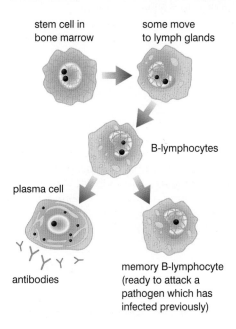

stem cell in bone marrow

some move to lymph glands

B-lymphocytes

plasma cell

antibodies

memory B-lymphocyte (ready to attack a pathogen which has infected previously)

Figure 13.65 Formation of plasma cells and memory cells.

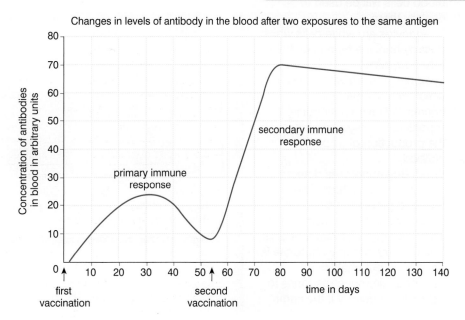

Changes in levels of antibody in the blood after two exposures to the same antigen

primary immune response

secondary immune response

Concentration of antibodies in blood in arbitrary units

time in days

first vaccination

second vaccination

Figure 13.66 Primary and secondary immune responses.

Did you know?

Key Facts

- If microorganisms get past the body's natural barriers, white blood cells will be used to destroy them.
- Phagocytes are white cells which destroy bacteria by eating them (phagocytosis).
- Lymphocytes are white cells which destroy bacteria chemically using antibodies.
- A particular antigen will trigger the production of a specific antibody.
- When B-lymphocytes detect their corresponding antigen, they divide to produce a clone of antibody secreting plasma cells. They also produce memory cells.
- The primary immune response is short-lived but enables a secondary immune response to occur more quickly if the same pathogen is re-encountered.

Questions

1 Copy and complete:
Phagocytes and lymphocytes are both types of …………… …………… cell. Phagocytes destroy bacteria by …………… them. The scientific name for this process is …………….. . Lymphocytes destroy bacteria and other antigens by producing proteins called …………… . Each will attack only one particular …………… .

2 Explain using your own words, where possible, what each of these words or phrases mean. They can all be found in Section 13.12.

a) phagocytosis

b) chemotaxis

c) antibodies are extremely specific

3 The graph in Figure 13.67 shows the pattern of vaccinations usually given to children to prevent polio. Giving a vaccination produces a similar response to coming into contact with a mild infection of the disease itself.

Using the information in the higher tier section of the text, explain what is happening just before and after each dose is given.

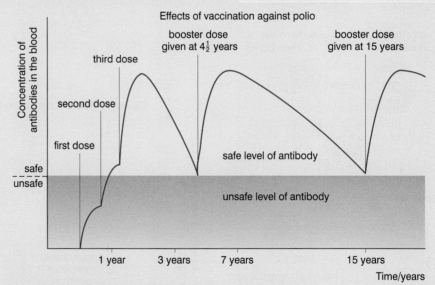

Figure 13.67 Graph showing effects of vaccination against polio. (NB. horizontal axis not to scale)

Learning outcomes

After completing the work in this topic you will be able to:

- describe the production of monoclonal antibodies (technical details of the processes are not required)
- understand the principles behind the use of monoclonal antibodies

All vertebrates, including humans, produce antibodies. These are produced by the white blood cells known as lymphocytes, which you can read about in an earlier section of this book. Antibodies are used by the body to destroy, or make ready for destruction, any foreign substance that enters the body. This may be a virus, a bacterium or a foreign protein. These are collectively known as antigens.

Antibodies have two very useful characteristics:

1 They are extremely specific; each antibody binds to and attacks one particular antigen.
2 Once activated by meeting a particular antigen, they can be produced quickly if the same antigen is met a second or third time.

The second characteristic has been exploited for many years in the production and use of vaccination to prevent disease. However, many new ways of making use of the first characteristic, their specificity, are now being researched.

The big drawback of using antibodies has always been producing them in large quantities, in a pure form, in laboratories. The conventional method had been to inject a laboratory animal with a particular antigen and then, after the antibodies specific to that antigen had formed, collect the antibodies from the animal's blood. Only very small amounts of usable antibody could be produced. A large-scale method was needed to improve both quantity and purity.

The breakthrough

In 1975, Kohler, Milstein and Jerne discovered a method of producing cells that could secrete a single kind of pure antibody corresponding to any chosen antigen … AND it could be manufactured in a laboratory culture in large quantities. This is when the future of antibody technology began.

The players

Kohler and Milstein used two different types of cell. Firstly, conventional lymphocytes, which could produce antibodies but were unable to survive long in laboratory culture (Figure 13.68). This meant that they could not be grown on a large industrial scale. The second cell type used were cells taken from cancerous tumours which could grow very rapidly in the laboratory but were not capable of producing antibodies.

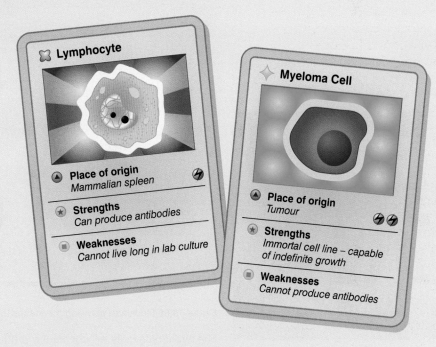

Lymphocyte

⬆ **Place of origin**
Mammalian spleen

★ **Strengths**
Can produce antibodies

■ **Weaknesses**
Cannot live long in lab culture

Myeloma Cell

⬆ **Place of origin**
Tumour

★ **Strengths**
Immortal cell line – capable of indefinite growth

■ **Weaknesses**
Cannot produce antibodies

Figure 13.68 The strengths and weaknesses of each cell type were assessed.

Figure 13.70 Technician using a micropipette.

The team

The scientists now had cells that produce antibodies naturally and cells which could grow continually in culture. By **fusing** them together to form a **hybrid**, they would have 'immortal' cells which could produce the desired antibody. The hybrid cells produced as a result of this cell fusion are called hybridoma cells (Figures 13.69–71).

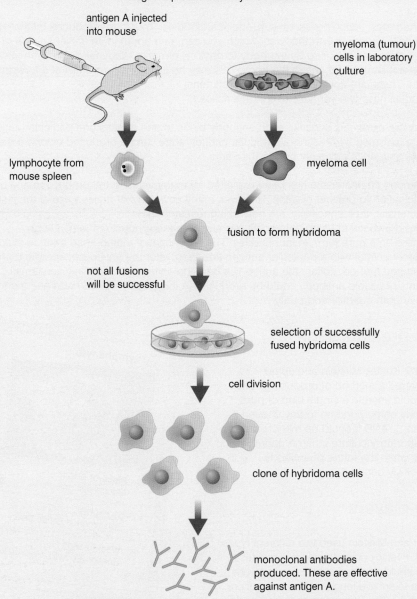

Figure 13.69 Flowchart showing the stages in monoclonal antibody production.

The hybridoma cells will continually produce antibodies. As these antibodies are now being produced by a **clone** of identical hybridoma cells, they are known as **monoclonal antibodies**.

Figure 13.71 Technician taking cells from liquid nitrogen store.

The result

Scientists now had a way of producing a particular antibody in a laboratory, in large quantities. The monoclonal antibodies were pure and would be specific to whatever antigen was first used to produce the lymphocyte component of the hybridoma.

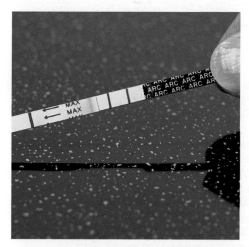

Figure 13.72 A pregnancy test kit showing a positive result.

Potential for the future

The potential of monoclonal antibodies soon became apparent. Not only was there a ready supply of a particular antibody to protect against disease, but the monoclonal antibodies could be used to 'seek out' and bind to the corresponding antigen in the body or in laboratory research and testing.

Here are just some examples of how monoclonal antibodies could be used:

• In cancer treatment: joining a radioactive isotope to the antibody would enable the radioactivity to be 'delivered' by the monoclonal antibody to particular cancerous cells in the body, to destroy them.

• In diagnosing illness: the monoclonal antibody could be coupled to a fluorescent molecule. This could then be used to identify a particular target.

• To detect the presence of drugs, viruses and bacterial products or other antigens in the blood.

• Testing for the presence or absence of **hormones** in the blood, e.g. for pregnancy testing (Figure 13.72).

Questions

1 Copy and complete:

Hybridoma cells are formed by fusing .... with .... cells. These hybridoma cells will continuously produce .... against specific .... These antibodies are known as .... antibodies.

2 Hybridoma cells combine the advantages of lymphocytes and myeloma cells.

a) What are the advantages?

b) Why would each of these cells be unable to be cultured for antibody production on their own?

3 The clone of hybridoma cells all produce identical antibodies. If a different type of antibody is needed, which stage in the procedure would have to be changed and how?

... more at www.modularscience.co.uk

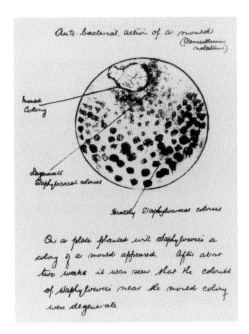

Figure 13.73 Fleming's original notes and drawing.

Mention antibiotics to a scientist and the name Alexander Fleming immediately springs to mind. Firstly because his work led to the discovery of the first antibiotic, penicillin and probably secondly because there is a story of good luck that accompanies the discovery. Fleming had left a culture plate, on which he was growing *Staphylococcus* bacteria, lying about in his laboratory for 2 weeks while he was on holiday. When he returned, he noticed that the plate had become contaminated with mould, probably from a stray spore that had entered when he inoculated the plate with bacteria. The *Staphylococcus* bacteria grew all over the culture plate except in the area surrounding the mould. Fleming concluded that the mould must have been producing some sort of diffusible substance, which killed or inhibited the growth of bacteria.

Fleming examined a sample of the mould and found that it was a strain of the fungus *Penicillium*. (The specific mould, which had grown on the plate, was later found to be *Penicillium notatum*) Fleming therefore named the anti-bacterial substance that it produced 'penicillin' (Figure 13.73).

The scientists Florey and Chain went on to purify penicillin into a usable form and the rest, as they say, is history. Since then, antibiotics have been used to treat many infectious bacterial diseases. Antibiotics are now routinely extracted from a wide range of microorganisms grown in culture on an industrial scale in fermenters. *Penicillium chrysogenum* is now used for commercial production of penicillin rather than Fleming's *P. notatum* and strains have been selected for their ability to produce high yields of antibiotic.

Commercial production of penicillin

The industrial fermenters used to produce the antibiotic penicillin are usually made of stainless steel (Figure 13.74). This can be sterilised by passing high pressure steam through all of the equipment. Each fermenter can hold 100 000– 200 000 litres of nutrient solution that has been inoculated with a starter culture of an antibiotic-secreting fungus, such as *P. chrysogenum*. The nutrient that provides the growth medium for the fungus will also have been sterilised to prevent contamination of the culture by other microorganisms. It will contain a source of carbon such as a mixture of lactose and glucose and a source of nitrogen.

The pH is controlled and adjusted from time to time because ammonia will be produced by the fungus as it grows. The temperature is first set to give the maximum growth rate and then altered to favour penicillin synthesis. A cooling jacket surrounds the fermenter. Cold water is passed through this to remove excess heat produced as a result of the metabolic activities of the growing microorganisms; as their numbers increase the temperature would increase to a point at which enzymes would start to be denatured and this would kill the microorganisms. Sterile air, as a stream of fine bubbles, is pumped into the fermenter under high pressure to keep the oxygen level high. Otherwise this might become a limiting factor to the fungal growth (Figure 13.74). Penicillin will not be produced until the fungal colony is well established and starting to become dense and crowded; this is why it is cultured in batches. In each batch all of the mycelium can reach peak growth at the same time, which is when maximum penicillin can be harvested (Figure 13.75). The antibiotic is excreted into the culture solution so it has to be removed. First this is done by filtration, which separates the fungal material from the culture medium. The penicillin is then extracted using an organic solvent and finally crystallised.

Penicillin G produced in this way is usually modified chemically to produce a range of different semi-synthetic penicillins which can each be used to treat different bacterial infections (Figure 13.76). Some will be more effective on certain bacteria than others.

How antibiotics work

There are about 50 antibiotics in common use, out of at least 4000 that have been isolated. Many of those isolated cannot be used because they are toxic to mammalian cells as well as bacteria. **Broad-spectrum antibiotics**, such as penicillin, act on a wide range of bacteria; **narrow-spectrum antibiotics** are more specific, but are useful because they can be used to target a limited range of bacteria, sometimes only one species.

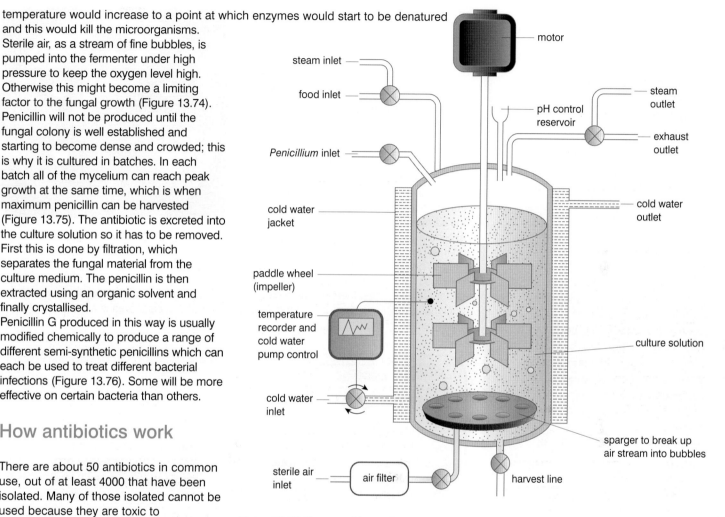

Figure 13.74 Diagram of fermenter.

Many antibiotics are bactericidal, i.e. they destroy bacteria; other antibiotics will prevent their growth. This is done in one of two main ways. Some inhibit protein synthesis in the bacteria. Others, such as penicillin, prevent the bacteria from making strong cell walls. The weakened bacterial cell literally bursts open when it takes up water from its surroundings, because the soft wall cannot withstand the pressure. As human cells do not have cell walls, they remain unaffected by the penicillin.

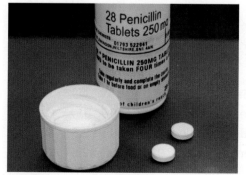

Figure 13.76 Antibiotic tablets.

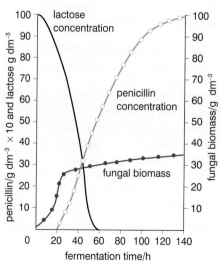

Figure 13.75 Graph of penicillin production.

Microorganisms and disease in humans

Some people are hyper-sensitive to Penicillin G. The allergic symptoms include a skin rash and nausea.

Broad-spectrum antibiotics taken by mouth may kill useful bacteria in our bodies as well as the pathogen that is being targeted. Such useful microorganisms include those which synthesise vitamins in our body, such as vitamin B12 and vitamin K. Prolonged use of broad-spectrum antibiotics can also alter the balance of microorganisms in the body by removing bacteria which might otherwise compete with fungi such as the *Candida* fungus which causes thrush. An attack of thrush is often associated with a long course of broad-spectrum antibiotics (see section 13.03).

Key Facts

- Antibiotics can kill or prevent the growth of bacteria, but not viruses.
- Penicillins are a type of antibiotic produced from the mould fungus *Penicillium*.
- Penicillins prevent bacterial cell wall manufacture.
- Penicillins can be produced by growing fungi in huge fermenters.

The effectiveness of antibiotics

The effectiveness of different antibiotics on a specific pathogen can be compared using a disc diffusion test. Discs impregnated with different antibiotics or varying concentrations of the same antibiotic are placed onto an agar plate containing a pure culture of the pathogenic bacterium (Figure 13.77).

The plate is then incubated together with a control plate. The control plate will have the same antibiotic discs as the experimental plate, but the bacterial culture on it will be one whose sensitivity to the drug(s) being tested is known in advance.

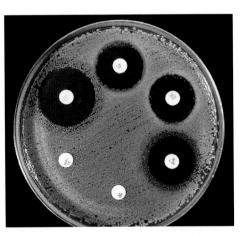

Figure 13.77 Petri dish showing antibiotic sensitivity test.

Antibiotic will diffuse from the discs into the agar and may prevent growth of the organism under test. If it does, there will be a clear area around one or more of the discs where bacterial growth has been prevented. The diameter of this clear area is a measure of the effectiveness of the drug(s).

Questions

1. Copy the diagram of a fermenter (Fig. 13.74) Next to each label, add the function of that part.

2. Suggest reasons why:
   a) the fermenter is sterilised with steam rather than disinfectant
   b) the fermenter is made of stainless steel
   c) the contents of the fermenter are stirred

3. The data in Figure 13.78 show the effectiveness of 4 different antibiotics (lettered A to D) on three different species of Staphylococcus bacteria. What conclusions can be drawn from the data? Figure 13.78

4. Find out more about antibiotics by visiting www.antibiotics-info.org/

5. Read the section on the effectiveness of antibiotics.
   a) Draw the plate and use the results to explain which is the most effective antibiotic.
   b) What would you expect to happen on the control plate?

	Effectiveness of antibiotic in %			
organism	A	B	C	D
S. aureus	91	100	91	82
S. epidermidis	100	100	82.5	40
S. haemolyticus	92	100	92.5	20.8

Learning outcome

After completing the work in this topic you will be able to:

- understand the limitations of the use of antibiotics:
  - the reasons for their ineffectiveness against viruses
  - the problems arising from their over-use, in terms of the rapid evolution of resistant strains of bacteria by mutation and natural selection

What's in a name?

The word antibiotic comes from two Greek words: 'anti' meaning against and 'bio' meaning life. It is used to describe any substance produced by a microorganism that can kill or inhibit the growth of a different microorganism. The method of action may be by preventing proper cell wall formation, or by preventing DNA or protein synthesis. A microorganism must have these structures or perform these activities if an antibiotic is to have any effect on them. Viruses are not cells and do not have metabolic processes of their own. Therefore they do not have any of the structures or processes that an antibiotic is targeted at. It is for this reason that antibiotics are ineffective against viruses. Since antibiotics will not destroy viruses, they are of no use to someone who has influenza, for example. However, they will destroy the *Streptococcus* bacteria which cause throat infections, so would be useful to someone suffering from a serious throat infection.

'Try anything to make me better, doctor'

Many people who visit their doctor are not satisfied unless they leave with a prescription (Figure 13.79). In some cases this is necessary, for example if symptoms appear to be getting worse or the patient is elderly or very young. However many sore throats, colds and other fairly minor ailments will be cleared up naturally by the body's own defence mechanisms. It is particularly important that antibiotics are not prescribed unless absolutely necessary, as their over-use directly leads to resistant strains of bacteria being produced.

For as long as antibiotics have been in use, the bacteria have been fighting back. Although antibiotics do not cause bacterial resistance, their presence gives resistant bacteria an advantage. The non-resistant ones will be killed by the antibiotic, but the resistant ones may live to fight another day. Continued use of an antibiotic favours the survival of the resistant bacteria because the antibiotic will kill all the non-resistant ones. In most cases, the odd few resistant bacteria that survive a course of antibiotics will be killed by the patient's immune system. However, problems arise when people with weak immune systems do not manage to kill all the antibiotic-resistant bacteria. These may then have a chance to multiply and even be passed on to other family members or close contacts.

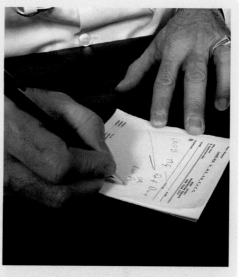

Figure 13.79 A Doctor writing a prescription.

Did you know?

We are most familiar with the genus *Penicillium* because some species, such as *Penicillium notatum* and *Penicillium chrysogenum* produce the antibiotic penicillin. However, members of this genus are also responsible for the familiar green and blue moulds which grow on citrus fruits and other stored products such as cheese and bread. *Penicillium roquefortii* is used to produce blue-veined cheese.

13.15 Limitations of antibiotics

Did you know?

Hospitals are a major reservoir of resistant bacteria. People who are admitted to hospital often have an infectious disease, which will be treated with antibiotics. Some of the bacteria that these patients brought with them may be resistant strains. These can easily multiply in the absence of all the other bacteria which have been killed by prescription drugs. This reservoir of resistant bacteria includes some that contain plasmids with resistance to more than one antibiotic. In an outbreak of tuberculosis (TB) in the United States between 1990 and 1992 over 140 patients had a strain of TB which was resistant to treatment even with a combined dose of three different antibiotics.

Key Facts

- Antibiotics are ineffective against viruses because viruses do not have a common cell structure or their own metabolic processes so there is nothing for the antibiotic to disrupt.
- Antibiotics should only be prescribed when essential.
- Bacteria may become resistant to one or more antibiotics.

How do the bacteria become resistant in the first place?

Some bacteria may have been naturally resistant to a particular antibiotic, whereas others have become resistant as a result of a mutation, i.e. a change in the bacterial chromosome. One method of resistance to antibiotics is for the bacteria to be able to produce the enzyme penicillinase. With this, the bacteria can break up the penicillin molecules, making them ineffective against its cell wall.

Other bacteria may have acquired their antibiotic resistance by exchange of genetic material with bacteria that were already antibiotic resistant.

What can be done to prevent the spread of antibiotic resistance?

There is evidence to support the link between the high use of antibiotics and the spread of antibiotic resistance. Ever higher doses of antibiotic now have to be prescribed to combat diseases that were once easily cured by much smaller doses (Figure 13.80).

In some countries it is possible to buy antibiotics over the counter at a chemist. This allows irresponsible people to take them for conditions that they are unsuitable for, without a doctor's advice.

As well as stopping the use of antibiotics for minor illnesses, we must also continue to look for new antibiotics to replace those to which bacteria have become resistant.

When antibiotic treatment is essential, but resistance seems likely, doctors may prescribe a combination of two or more antibiotics. The aim of this is to reduce the possibility of infectious bacteria, resistant to one of the antibiotics in the combination, surviving.

Another approach is to consider the ways in which antibiotics are used for non-clinical purposes. Pigs, cattle and poultry frequently have antibiotics added to their food to increase their growth rate and to prevent diseases developing. As long ago as 1969 a dramatic increase in the number of resistant strains of bacteria in the gut of these animals was reported. Some of these resistant bacteria will eventually be ingested by humans. European agricultural regulations prohibit antibiotics that are needed for human medical treatment from being used in animal feed. However, this is not the case everywhere else in the world.

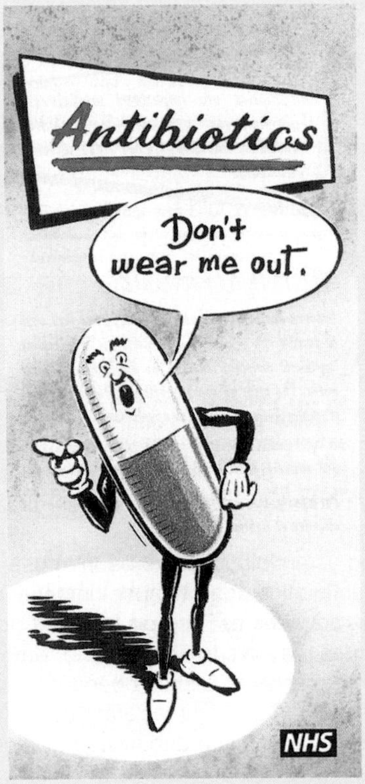

Figure 13.80 An NHS leaflet to encourage people to reduce antibiotic use.

Questions

1   Copy and complete:
Antibiotics should not be prescribed to people who have an illness caused by a .... or to people who only have .... ailments. They are useful for killing or preventing the growth of ...., especially in children or .... people.

2   a) Why should we all try to use fewer antibiotics?

   b) Make a list of ways that we could reduce the use of antibiotics.

3   Antibiotics have been used to control bacterial diseases for some time. Erythromycin was first available in the U.K. in 1954 to control infection, caused by *Staphylococcus* bacteria, in young babies. The graph in Figure 13.81 shows the development of erythromycin resistance in bacteria.

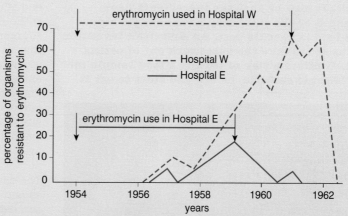

Figure 13.81

a) What important event took place in the bacterial population sometime during 1956?

b) What decision did Hospital E and Hospital W take concerning the use of erythromycin in 1959 and 1961 respectively?

c) What effect did the action taken in 1959 and 1961 have on the percentage of organisms resistant to erythromycin?

d) If resistance is inherited and the decision taken in (b) had not been taken, what long-term change in the *Staphylococcus* population would take place?

4   Find out more about the over-use of antibiotics by visiting www.antibiotics-info.org/

... more at www.modularscience.co.uk

If it glows, don't eat it!

Science Today

Many of you will have eaten a mouthful of food that tastes a bit peculiar at some time in your lives. It may be that the ingredients have changed or the taste may have changed because the food is past its best. An American invention looks set to take the guesswork out of eating out. It offers a way of testing a food sample for pathogenic bacteria, before you start to eat it.

Normally, the testing of suspect food would involve a sample being sent off to a laboratory from where, after a delay of at least 24 hours, a result would be sent out. Meanwhile, someone may have been infected or, worse still, have passed the infection on.

The new gadget, called ImmunoFlow, uses antibody technology to give an on the spot result. A small sample of the suspect food or drink is poured into the device. Solid food has to be ground up with a little water first. A battery-operated pump then pushes the sample into the testing chamber.

Inside the testing chamber there are hundreds of glass beads, each coated with millions of antibodies specific to a particular bacterium e.g. Salmonella. The food poisoning bacteria bind to the antibodies so remain fixed on the glass beads while the remaining materials are pumped on through to avoid clogging the beads. Another set of antibodies are now added. These have been labelled with a luminescent marker. This second set of antibodies have been chosen so that they will bind to any antibody–bacteria pairs trapped on the glass beads. The surface of the beads will now glow in any regions where Salmonella bacteria are present.

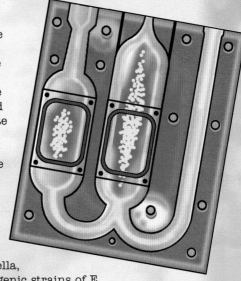

At the moment, the glow is not bright enough to measure without a photon counter, a machine that will detect and record these minute emissions of light. These counters are currently about the size of a PC, but smaller versions are on the way.

The device is so sensitive that it can detect Salmonella, Listeria and pathogenic strains of E. coli even when there are only 100 cells per millilitre. What's more, it can do the test in 15 to 30 minutes, which could save valuable time in preventing a food poisoning outbreak.

At first, this device is only likely to be used by food-processing companies, but once the photon counter has been made smaller and the whole device made more portable, it could be used in the home. It would allow us to test milk or meat that has been lying in the fridge for several days. We could find out if food-poisoning bacteria were present in the food without taking the risk of tasting it.

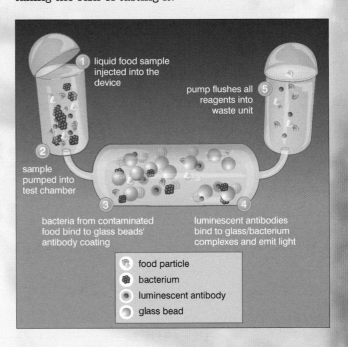

1 liquid food sample injected into the device

2 sample pumped into test chamber

3 bacteria from contaminated food bind to glass beads' antibody coating

4 luminescent antibodies bind to glass/bacterium complexes and emit light

5 pump flushes all reagents into waste unit

- food particle
- bacterium
- luminescent antibody
- glass bead

1.   The diagram shows the first stage of a virus attack on bacterium.

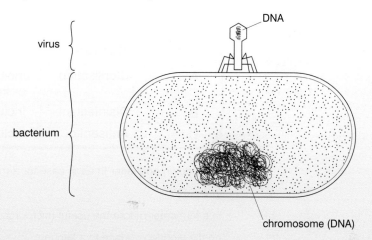

(a)   The virus has just made contact with the bacterium.

(i)   What happens immediately after this?   (1)

(ii)   Describe the final stage when the bacterium is destroyed.   (1)

(b)   Use words from the box to complete the following sentences.

cytoplasm	membrane	wall	protein	coat

On the outside of the bacterium there is a ....

On the outside of a virus there is a ....

(2)

(c)   In some ways viruses seem to be non-living and in other ways they seem to be alive.

Complete the table to show which processes viruses and bacteria can do (✓) and which they cannot do (✗). The first one has been done for you.

	Nutrition (feeding)	Respiration	Reproduction
viruses	✗		
bacteria	✓		

(4)

(Total 8 marks)

Edexcel GCSE Science: June 2002, paper 2F, no. 3.

2. Some microorganisms are harmful.

Different methods can be used to kill them.

Letter	Method	Information
A	Sterilisation	Includes the use of chemicals or heat or irradiation
B	Disinfectant	Includes the use of chemicals
C	Antiseptic	Includes the use of chemicals

Write down **one** letter in each case for a method to kill microorganisms

(a) in a cut (1)

(b) in a fermenter before the useful microorganisms are added (1)

(c) on the worktop surface in a kitchen (1)

(d) on a surgeon's scalpel (1)

(e) on food as a method of food preservation (1)

(Total 5 marks)

Edexcel GCSE Science: June 2001, paper 2F, no.1.

3. Athlete's foot is a skin infection caused by a fungus.

Disinfectant footbaths at swimming pools help to prevent the spread of athlete's foot by killing spores on people's feet. In one year, many people using a swimming pool developed athlete's foot. It was suggested that the disinfectant in the footbath was too dilute.

Describe how you could find out if the survival of spores is affected by the concentration of disinfectant.

You could use the following apparatus and materials.

sterile bottle of water
fungal spores
disinfectant
sterile pipette
Bunsen burner
Petri dishes with lids, containing sterile nutrient agar
incubator with thermometer
roll of sticky tape
wax pencil

(Total 5 marks)

Edexcel GCSE Science: June 2002, paper 4H, no. 1 & paper 2F, no. 5.

Aerobic	Needing oxygen to live. Most bacteria are aerobic, but many can survive without oxygen if they have to.
Anaemic	A lack of red blood cells, causing a person to feel weak and tired.
Anaerobic	Not needing oxygen. Some bacteria and other decomposers are anaerobic.
Antibiotic	A chemical substance that kills bacteria.
Antibiotic resistance	The antibiotic resistance genes of a bacterium make it resistant to (not killed by) antibiotics. Antibiotic resistance is passed on in the plasmids when bacteria reproduce.
Antigens	Foreign substances that have entered the body.
Binary fission	Reproducing by the parent splitting in two.
Bacteria	A group of microorganisms which play an important role in nutrient recycling, disease transmission and industrial processes.
Broad-spectrum antibiotics	Antibiotics which act on a wide range of bacteria
Capsid	The outer protein coat of a virus. It protects the genetic material from damage and helps the virus break into host cells.
Capsule	A thick protective layer around a bacterial cell in addition to its cell wall.
Cell wall	The tough, rigid outer layer of a bacterial cell, that gives protection and helps maintain the cell's shape.
Chemotaxis	A movement made in response to a chemical stimulus. White blood cells known as phagocytes move towards chemicals secreted by invading bacteria. A movement away from a chemical stimulus is also chemotaxis.
Chlorinated	Water is chlorinated when it has chlorine added to it to kill bacteria and make the water safe to drink or bathe in.
Cholera	A serious, often fatal, illness caused by bacteria transmitted in water.
Clone	A genetically exact copy of a cell or an organism.
Cure	Treatment given to a person with an illness, to kill the bacteria or viruses causing their disease.
Diarrhoea	One of the symptoms of illness caused by pathogenic bacteria living in the intestines. It might be caused by a 'tummy bug' or by a more serious disease such as cholera.
Donor cell	The name given to the cell which supplies the DNA to be moved to another organism in genetic modification.

Dormant	A organism is dormant if it is alive but not moving, growing or reproducing. Bacteria remain dormant as endospores.
Effluent	The liquid part of sewage, left after the sludge has settled out.
Electron microscope	A microscope that uses high energy beams of electrons instead of light. It has very high magnification and is useful for looking at very small objects in detail, such the structure of microorganisms.
Endemic	A disease is endemic if the disease, or its vector is always found in a particular area.
Endospores	The name given to spores of bacteria that are surrounded by a thick, protective coat to survive extreme heat, dryness, pH level, and the effects of radiation and toxic chemicals.
Enzymes	A biological catalyst. One of a group of proteins that help speed up the rate of chemical reactions in an organism.
Epidemic	An outbreak of disease that affects a much large number of people in a community than would normally be expected.
Escherichia coli (*E. coli*)	A type of bacterium naturally present in our intestines. Most *E. coli* bacteria are harmless but a few strains of *E. coli* are pathogenic and cause disease.
Exponential growth	The increase in numbers of bacteria which happens when one bacterium splits in two, then they each split in two and so on. The total number of bacteria keeps doubling.
Flagella (sing. flagellum)	Long hair-like structures that can be moved to allow the bacterium to move towards or away from different chemicals.
Flash pasteurisation	Pasteurising milk by heating it to 71.7°C for 15 seconds then cooling it rapidly to 3°C.
Fusing	Joining together two different types of cells to produce a new cell with the characteristics of both original cells.
Genetically modified organism	Organisms that have had their genetic code altered artificially. Plasmids are often used to transfer a chosen section of DNA into a bacterial cell.
Hormones	Chemical messenger molecules that are transported in the blood from where they are made to their target cells, thus producing a change.
Host	The organism that has a pathogenic microorganism living inside it is called a host.
Hybrid	A cell formed from two different cells which have been joined together; or an organism formed from parents of different species.

Hyphae (sing. hypha)	The individual tubes or hollow threads making up the mycelium of a fungus.
Immune	A person is immune to a disease if they do not catch the disease even when exposed to the viruses or bacteria which cause it.
Infection	The illness caused by a pathogen reproducing inside the body of another organism. It can be local (like an infected cut) or affect the whole body (like influenza)
Intensive rearing	Housing large numbers of animals in a small area. This provides ideal conditions for *Salmonella* to spread.
Light microscope	A microscope which uses light to view an object. It does not give as high magnification as an electron microscope.
Limiting factor	If an essential factor is in short supply, causing the rate of, e.g., growth to slow down, that factor is said to be a limiting factor.
Memory cells	Small, long-living clones of the plasma cells produced to destroy particular pathogens.
Mitochondria (sing. mitochondrion)	Rod-shaped structures found in the cytoplasm of cells. It is here that the chemical reactions of aerobic respiration take place.
Monoclonal antibodies	Antibodies which have been produced by clones of identical hybrid cells called hybridoma cells.
Mutations	Any changes in the amount or arrangement of DNA in a cell.
Mycelium	The branching network of fine threads making up many fungi, such as *Penicillium* and bread moulds.
Narrow-spectrum antibiotics	Antibiotics which only act on only one or a few species of bacteria. They are useful for targeting a limited range of bacteria.
Nucleoid	The 'nucleus' of a bacterial cell. It is a tightly coiled double-stranded loop of DNA containing chromosomes.
Nucleus	The part of a bacterial cell containing the DNA. Unlike the nucleus in a plant or animal cell, it does not have a membrane around it.
Pandemic	An outbreak of disease that affects people over many countries. A pandemic is a world-wide epidemic.
Parasite	An organism which lives in or on another organism of a different species, known as its host. The parasite benefits but the host suffers harm.
Pathogens	Microorganisms that cause disease.
Penicillium	The mould fungus used to produce the antibiotic penicillin.
Phagocytosis	The process by which cells take up large particles from their environment. It is used by certain white blood cells to surround and destroy bacteria.
Phases	One of the main stages of growth of a population of bacteria. The phases are lag phase, log or exponential phase, stationary phase and death phase.

Plasmids	Circular pieces of DNA in a bacterium, which are separate from the main DNA. The bacterium can survive without the DNA in its plasmids.
Plasmodium	A parasitic microorganism that causes malaria in man.
Prevention	Protecting people from illness by preventing them catching the disease.
Primary immune response	The destroying of a new pathogen by lymphocytes and plasma cells.
Protoctista	One of five kingdoms (phyla) of living things. It contains organisms which do not easily fit into fungi, plants, animals or bacterial kingdoms, such as large algae (seaweeds) and single celled creatures such as *Amoeba* and *Plasmodium*.
Protozoa	A single celled organism belonging to kingdom Protoctista. It is a term that is now less commonly used in classification.
Salmonella	Species of bacteria which commonly cause food poisoning.
Secondary immune response	This happens when a pathogen invades a body for the second time. Memory cells multiply rapidly and produce the exact antibodies needed to destroy that particular pathogen.
Secondary infection	Infection caused by bacteria or viruses invading tissues already infected by a different pathogen.
Septum (sing. Septa)	The extension of the cell wall that partly grows across the hyphae in some fungi, dividing the hyphae into cell-like regions.
Slime layer	A slightly sticky layer on the outside of a bacterial cell wall. It prevents the bacteria from drying out and helps bacteria stick together in clumps.
Sludge	The solid part of sewage that settles out at the bottom of a sedimentation tank.
Spoilage organisms	Organisms which cause food to decay.
Sporangia	The black swellings containing fungal spores (sing. sporangium) that are produced when fungi reproduce.
Spores	Spores are produced in large numbers for asexual reproduction. They may lie dormant until conditions are favourable for growth.
Stimuli (sing: stimulus)	A change in an organism's internal or external environment to which it responds.
Substrate	The material that a bacterium or fungus is living on. This may be the host cell or a supply of chemical nutrients in a laboratory culture.
Toxins	Poisons produced by pathogenic bacteria in our bodies.
Vaccine	Medicines (usually injections) developed to give people immunity to a disease, to prevent them catching it and becoming ill.
Vectors	A vector of a disease is the means of transmitting the disease to people. The female mosquito is the vector for malaria. People are infected with malaria by malarial parasites contained in a female mosquito's saliva.

Biotechnology is a relatively modern word with a long history. Some people would consider its origins to be in the activities of the first human civilisations. They may have discovered many techniques for prolonging the life of food or adding new flavours quite by accident, but once these methods had been discovered, new ones may have been tried out. These ancient methods of preserving food and modifying its taste have evolved into our modern food industry. In this module we look at the production of yoghurt and soy sauce. Now found in every supermarket, these had much simpler origins as traditional Middle Eastern and Oriental products before they were mass produced. We see how increasing knowledge of the activities of microorganisms has enabled us to grow them in vast fermenters, producing materials such as mycoprotein.

With increasing frequency, we hear about the application of new biological techniques to both plant and animal reproduction. It is just over 50 years since the structure of DNA was discovered. Today, scientists are modifying the genetic make-up of an organism. The techniques of gene transfer to make human insulin and the genetic modification of plants to withstand adverse conditions are both studied in the module.

The first human heart transplant in 1967 was world news; modern biotechnology offers us ways of growing organs for transplant. Perhaps the most controversial technique you will read about in this module is that of cloning mammals. We are moving from a world where biotechnology has brought us new vaccines and medicines, biological washing powders and biodegradable plastics, into one where major ethical barriers are about to be challenged. Are we ready to manipulate human life? Perhaps working on this module will help to formulate your views on how biotechnology should proceed.

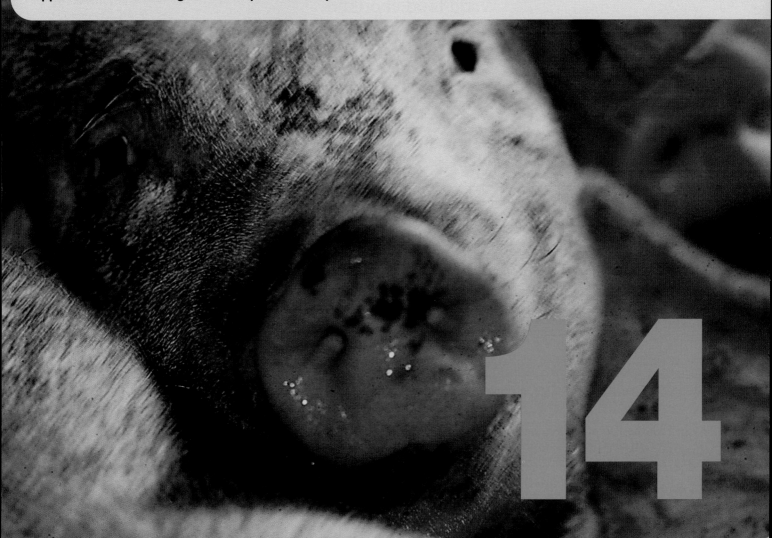

Biotechnology is far too broad a term to define exactly, but a good working definition is 'the use of organisms and biological processes to provide food, chemicals and services to meet the needs of humans'.

World food shortage

In many parts of the world, food is in short supply. The reasons for this are not simple – a mixture of economic, political and social factors are to blame. The solutions are similarly complex. Protein, in particular, is in short supply for combinations of the following reasons:

- animal protein is expensive to produce and requires refrigerated transport if it is produced elsewhere and transported to where it is needed
- global fish stocks are dwindling, reducing another source of animal protein
- vegetable protein sources are limited in areas of infertile soil, drought or other adverse climatic conditions

In terms of energy efficiency, it makes sense to feed the world directly using protein from microorganisms. If this is fed to animals first, then the animals used as food, some of the food's valuable energy will be lost along the way in keeping the animal alive and warm. New foods, such as **Quorn**[TM], made from the fungus **Fusarium** may be a solution. But it is very important that novel food materials such as this are acceptable in terms of taste, appearance and texture. The nutritional value of food that no-one will eat is zero! Aid workers have found that just trying to add protein powders produced by microorganisms to local traditional food is not as straightforward as it might seem. Consider whether you would be willing to eat your meal today if a relative stranger had sprinkled an unknown substance onto it first.

Another solution to the world food shortage may lie in the field of genetic engineering. Many more crops are being modified to increase their yield and to be resistant to insect pests and pathogenic fungi. It has been estimated that about one-third of the world's agricultural crops are currently destroyed by pests. Grain crops, such as maize or wheat may be genetically altered to enable the use of atmospheric nitrogen in the way peas and beans naturally can. This makes them less dependent on chemical fertilisers. If crops that will currently only grow in subtropical regions of the world could be modified to grow in the more temperate climates of Europe they would not need to be imported, leaving a more equal world-wide distribution. However, this raises an economic issue if

their original country of origin is relying on their export to Europe for income.
In Scotland, genetically engineered salmon are already being farmed. These fish have the potential to grow up to ten times faster than ordinary salmon. This too could be a way forward for world food supplies, but at present consumers are still very wary of GM foods.

What is fermentation?

The word 'fermentation' can be used in two ways. Originally it was only used to describe the way in which some organisms or cells obtained energy from organic materials without the need for oxygen. More recently, fermentation has started to be used to describe any process that includes the breakdown of food by microorganisms regardless of whether oxygen is used or not. Therefore, a more comprehensive definition is shown in Figure 14.01.

Fermentation is used as a way of modifying raw fresh food. As you can see from the definition, the growing medium is chemically changed. So, after fermentation, a foodstuff has different properties to the original plant or animal material. Its flavour or texture may have changed. It may be more palatable or easier to digest and its nutritional content may have changed. Often the pH of the food is lowered (i.e. it becomes more acidic) during fermentation. This will improve the keeping qualities of the product. This pH change, and some of the other changes, often makes the food safer by reducing the number and range of microorganisms that can grow on it, or by removing potential toxins.

> fermentation: any process in which microorganisms use an external food source i.e. one outside their cell, to obtain energy.
> In doing this they chemically change the medium that they are growing in.
>
> fermenter: a vessel used to cultivate micro organisms - a type of bio reactor

Figure 14.01 A modern definition of fermentation.

The industrial fermenter

Many biological processes can be carried out in a fermenter. It can be used for the bulk culture of microorganisms or plant cells with the aim of providing as near as possible the optimum conditions for their growth. From Module 13, you may already be familiar with antibiotic production using a fermenter.

Most industrial fermenters are huge – capacities of about 200 000 litres are common. However the particular process to be carried out in them will have first been tested on a much smaller scale to find the nutrient requirements and environmental conditions needed to produce the required product (Figure 14.02). These requirements are then scaled up and adapted as necessary to use in a larger vessel.

Fermenters are usually made of stainless steel. They need to be able to withstand any pressure increases as the reaction proceeds and must be non-corrosive as this would contaminate the contents. Stainless steel provides a hard, smooth surface which can be steam sterilised inside and out.

Figure 14.02 A fermentation laboratory.

1 Aseptic precautions

Fermentation processes exploit a particular microorganism, often a specific strain that has been singled out for its ability to produce exactly the required product (Figure 14.03). Conditions that are as close to optimum as possible for this organism will have been provided. Unfortunately these could also be ideal conditions for many other unwanted microorganisms. These unwanted competitors might interfere with the fermentation by:

• killing the desired microorganism, for example by inhibiting its chemical reactions
• destroying the products of the reaction
• providing toxins which might contaminate the products of the reaction

The fermenter itself, including all the pipe-work, must therefore be sterilised for 30 to 60 minutes using steam and all nutrients going into it must also be sterile. The air supply to the fermenter must pass through a filter that can prevent any air-borne microorganisms entering the reaction chamber.

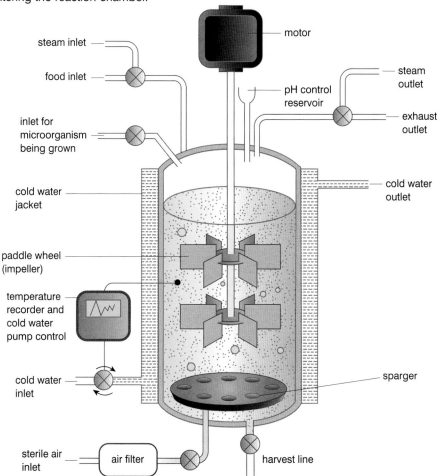

Figure 14.03 Diagram of a fermenter.

2 Oxygenation

If the microorganisms being grown in the fermenter are aerobic (i.e. require oxygen) a supply of oxygen will need to be pumped into the fermenter. With such large numbers of microorganisms growing and dividing rapidly, any dissolved oxygen will quickly be used up.

By reducing the size of the bubbles (Figure 14.04), more oxygen can be encouraged to dissolve. However, a compromise has to be made between this aim and the fact that tiny bubbles entering very rapidly may cause foam to be produced.

3 Agitation

In all fermentation processes, the aim is to ensure that the organisms in all parts of the fermenter receive the same, optimum conditions. To achieve these uniform conditions the contents must be continuously stirred. This will distribute oxygen, nutrients and heat within the fermenters, as well as preventing pockets of the product building up and causing localised pH changes. Mechanical paddle like stirrers, called **impellers** do the stirring. With so many microorganisms present, these must be able to withstand the mechanical stress of being pulled through quite a viscous medium.

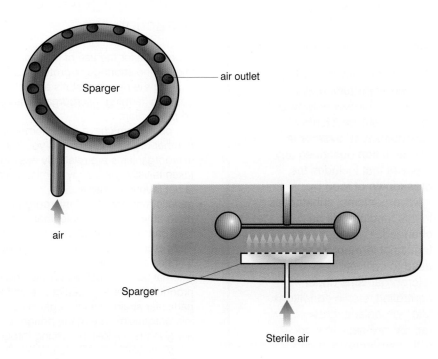

Figure 14.04 The sparger used in a fermenter to make air enter as small bubbles.

4 Nutrients

The sterile culture medium used in the fermenter will vary according to the organism being cultured. In addition to the oxygen supply being pumped into the watery medium, a carbon source and a nitrogen source must be added. In mycoprotein production, for example, mineral ions including potassium, magnesium and phosphate will also be supplied.

5 Temperature and pH

Biological systems are very sensitive to relatively small changes in temperature and pH. Most fermenters will therefore be fitted with devices that continually monitor and automatically adjust the temperature and the pH within the fermenter. A jacket is fitted to the outside of the fermenter through which refrigerated water is circulated for cooling. A drop in temperature may slow the reaction but an increase in temperature could have more of an impact on the process, as the microorganisms or the product may be irreversibly damaged by the heat. With such a large number of microorganisms respiring, there would be a relatively higher rate of heat production than heat loss; hence the need for this cooling system.

Did you know?

A bacterial population can double in number every 20 minutes. If there are no limiting factors, this means that a single bacterium, with a biomass of only 10^{12} g would produce 2.2×10^{25} tonnes of biomass – 4000 times the mass of our planet – within 2 days. Looked at another way, a single bacterium, in an environment with no limiting factors, could produce 10^{11} times its own biomass of protein alone in a single day.

Key Facts

- World shortages of food, especially protein, may be helped by biotechnology, but there are still problems of acceptability to overcome.
- Fermentation describes any process that includes the breakdown of food by microorganisms; substances in this medium will be changed.
- Industrial fermenters are used to cultivate microorganisms under controlled, sterile conditions.
- Microorganisms grow rapidly, are easy to work with, can grow on cheap substrates and can be produced independently of the external climate.

The advantages of using microorganisms for food production

The potential for the use of microorganisms to help in the global food shortage, in particular the shortage of protein, has already been discussed. The associated problems of making the new foodstuffs acceptable may well be overcome in the future. If this is the case, then 'farming' microorganisms has many advantages over conventional methods of food production:

- microorganisms have a phenomenal population growth rate when compared to that of other organisms (see Did you know?)
- microorganisms are relatively easy to house and handle. If aseptic precautions are taken initially, the colony of microorganisms can then be monitored by machinery – it is not labour intensive
- genetic modification of microorganisms is much easier to do, and to many people more ethically acceptable, than modifying more complex organisms
- food can be produced from microorganisms independent of the external climate. Plant crops are still much more governed by the seasons or the region of the world that has a suitable climate
- external factors, such as climate, do not affect the quality or quantity of the end product. An equally predictable and reliable product could be produced from a particular strain of microorganisms in Bristol or in Bombay
- microorganisms are at the bottom of the food chain. Energy from the nutrients they are given is not lost in passing through a series of other organisms before it reaches a human consumer. Coupled with the fact that microorganisms can be grown on waste materials from other processes, this makes them very energy efficient. Waste materials, which might otherwise be disposed of, are relatively cheap to obtain, thus reducing the relative cost of microorganism-produced foods

Questions

1 Copy and complete:

In many parts of the world .... is in short supply, especially .... New foods such as Quorn™ from the .... called *Fusarium* may help solve this problem. Genetically engineering crops to .... their yield and their resistance to damage by .... may also help.

2 Explain what is meant by each of the following terms:

a) fermentation

b) fermenter

c) culture medium

3 Read the 'Did you know?'. A single bacterium would not actually produce this much protein. Suggest why.

4 A group of students are going to visit a laboratory where microorganisms are cultured in fermenters.

a) Imagine that you are their teacher. Design a question sheet which the students could answer while they were there. Ask questions such as 'How big are the fermenters?', 'Why are aseptic precautions taken?' etc.

b) Make an answer sheet for them to mark it from when they return to school.

... more at www.modularscience.co.uk

Yoghurt
biology

Learning outcome

After completing the work in this topic you will be able to:

- explain the role of bacteria in the production of yoghurt from milk by the conversion of lactose to lactic acid

Yoghurt is a semi-liquid product made from fermented milk. It was probably first made in the Middle East, perhaps originally by accident. Milk that had unintentionally become sour in the heat may have been tasted rather than discarded. If people then went on to transfer samples of the sour milk into their fresh milk, they had started the foundations of what is now a very popular product. These people were using biotechnology – they were using the bacteria in the sour milk to trigger a process of converting milk to yoghurt – and as a result were altering its taste, texture, pH and keeping qualities. Although they may not have been aware that bacteria were responsible for the fermentation, they were effectively selecting the most suitable strains of bacteria for the job. If the ferment tasted disgusting they would be unlikely to use samples from it. If it tasted good, samples might be used to start several other fermentations, thus increasing the availability of the most suitable bacteria for producing their favourite taste or texture.

Modern yoghurt

Milk that is to be used to make yoghurt will be heat treated before use. A temperature of 85–95°C for 15–30 minutes is suitable. This is necessary to kill any bacteria that could compete with the yoghurt-making bacteria during the fermentation process.
At this stage the milk is also **homogenised** – a process which disperses its fat content by making it into smaller globules. At this point the milk will be too hot to add the starter culture of bacteria without killing them, so it must first be cooled to about 40–45°C.
Milk contains the sugar **lactose**. The starter culture that is now added will contain a particular strain of lactic acid bacteria, *Lactobacillus* sp., which will ferment the lactose to produce lactic acid.

A second type of bacteria, shown in the photograph, are also present in the starter culture (Figure 14.05). The activities of the two species of bacteria enhance one another by each producing materials which stimulate the growth of the other.
As lactic acid is produced, the pH of the culture decreases until it reaches about 4.3 to 4.6. This will have taken between 3 and 6 hours at an incubation temperature of 40–45°C. The yoghurt must then be cooled to about 5°C to virtually stop the fermentation. Fruit, flavouring or colourings may now be added, although in 'set' yoghurts these are often added during incubation to avoid destroying their characteristic smooth texture later on by stirring them (Figure 14.06). The yoghurt is then packaged and despatched. Many supermarket yoghurts are pasteurised before or after packaging to extend their shelf life (Figure 14.07).

Did you know?

Yoghurt type foods and drinks are given different names throughout the world. Here are just a few of them:
- buttermilk
- kefir
- lassi
- raita
- yakult

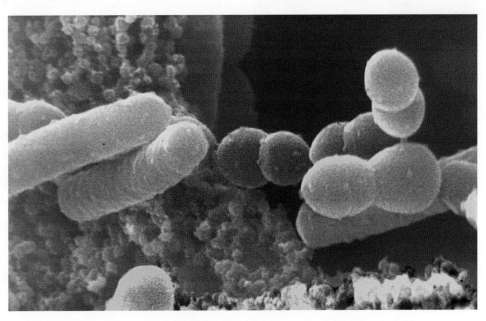

Figure 14.05 Yoghurt bacteria: *Streptococcus thermophilus* and *Lactobacillus bulgaricus*.

Did you know?

Did you know?

Yoghurt is a good way to tell the age of your teachers! It is widely available in supermarkets now but was not common in the UK until the late 1960s. So, anyone aged over 45 may not have tasted yoghurt until they were into their teens. Even then, it was probably strawberry, banana or raspberry Ski yoghurt. That was the extent of the choice of flavours and brands that were readily available!

Figure 14.08 Ski yoghurt advert.

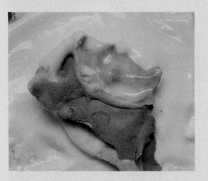

Figure 14.09 Fungus growing on a pot of yoghurt.

Figure 14.06 Different types of yoghurt.

A closer look at the bacterial activity

Some people are lactose-intolerant; in other words they need to avoid this sugar that is found in milk. *Lactobacillus* bacteria break down the lactose in milk to lactic acid so, providing additional milk solids are not added to thicken the finished yoghurt, it is ideal for lactose-intolerant people. It is also a popular milk product with many other people because it is more easily digested than whole milk.

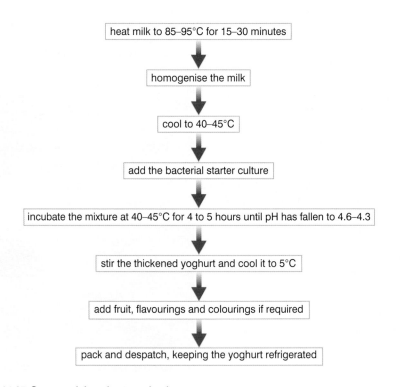

heat milk to 85–95°C for 15–30 minutes

↓

homogenise the milk

↓

cool to 40–45°C

↓

add the bacterial starter culture

↓

incubate the mixture at 40–45°C for 4 to 5 hours until pH has fallen to 4.6–4.3

↓

stir the thickened yoghurt and cool it to 5°C

↓

add fruit, flavourings and colourings if required

↓

pack and despatch, keeping the yoghurt refrigerated

Figure 14.07 Commercial yoghurt production.

As we have seen, when the bacteria ferment the lactose to produce lactic acid, the pH becomes more acidic. This increasing acidity restricts the reproduction and activity of the lactic acid bacteria as the reaction proceeds but also has the advantage of helping to prevent the growth of any contaminant organisms. The effect of the lactic acid on the milk proteins helps to thicken the yoghurt. It also gives yoghurt its characteristic, slightly sour, flavour.

Key Facts

- Milk contains the sugar lactose.
- Specific lactic acid bacteria ferment lactose to produce lactic acid.
- Competition from other bacteria must be prevented by killing them by heating the milk to 85–95°C.
- Fermentation takes place best at 40–45°C.
- As lactic acid forms, the acidity increases. This reduces the bacterial activity and helps prevent growth of contaminant organisms.
- Lactic acid gives yoghurt its characteristic, slightly sour, flavour.

1 Copy and complete:

Yoghurt is made from .... which has been fermented using bacteria. These bacteria convert ...., which is the sugar found in milk, to .... This takes place at a temperature of ....to.............. °C. As lactic acid forms, the pH of the mixture ....

2 a) How are bacteria, apart from those in the starter culture, prevented from growing in the milk?

b) Why is it important that these bacteria are not allowed to grow?

c) Why is the milk cooled before the starter culture is added?

d) How does yoghurt get its sour flavour?

3 a) Make a survey of the types of yoghurt available locally. Do any of them give details of the bacteria they were made with?

b) Find out more about the yoghurt-type foods mentioned in the 'Did you know?'

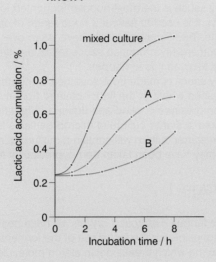

Figure 14.10

4 The graph in Figure 14.10 shows lactic acid production by two strains of bacteria, labelled A and B. Describe any differences in activity between A and B when they are separate and when they are in a mixed culture. Suggest a reason for this.

5 Visit www.generalmills.com/ Yoplait to find out more about yoghurt.

... more at www.modularscience.co.uk

Soy sauce is the most popular fermented food in China, Japan and much of the rest of Asia. It is used to flavour a huge range of dishes (Figure 14.11). It has an acidic, salty taste. Traditionally, it would have taken over 18 months to produce, but modern commercially produced sauce takes less time! It is the application of biotechnology that has allowed this to happen.

Soy sauce is made from soya beans together with a starchy crop. This is often roasted, crushed wheat or the flour obtained from it. The soya beans have been first soaked and then pressure cooked and drained. When the soya and the wheat (flour) have been mixed, a starter culture of microorganisms is added.

The starter culture will contain a mixture of mould fungus and bacteria. This may be fresh or may have been taken from a previously fermented batch.

Figure 14.11 Bottles of soy sauce.

Did you know?

Soya beans are a good source of protein. One hectare of soya beans can yield 162 kg of protein. The same area would yield 9 kg if used for beef production.

Did you know?

Soy sauce is rich in the amino acid called glutamic acid. The widely used food additive monosodium glutamate is the salt of this amino acid. Look out for it on the ingredients list of your favourite snack food. It is very commonly used as a flavour enhancer.

Stage 1

The fungus *Aspergillus oryzae* will have been part of the starter culture and is largely responsible for the first stage of the fermentation (Figure 14.12). It releases one type of enzyme which breaks down starch molecules into smaller sugar molecules and another which breaks down the proteins, which are present in large amounts in the soya beans. This stage takes place in aerobic conditions. Shallow containers are used to ensure that oxygen can reach as much of the mixture as possible.

This fermentation lasts from 3 days to a week at a temperature of about 28–30°C. A strong salt solution is then added to the mixture. This will act as a preservative as well as helping to extract liquid from the remaining solids. It will now be transferred to deep tanks or large vats for stage 2 of the fermentation process.

Stage 2

The anaerobic conditions in the large, deep fermentation tanks are ideal for the growth and reproduction of the yeast and other microorganisms that were present in the starter culture, such as *Lactobacillus* bacteria. The large starch and protein molecules in the original soya beans and wheat were broken down into smaller molecules in stage 1. These can now be used by the yeast and bacteria as a food source. The yeast produces alcohol and contributes to the flavour of the final sauce, as well as acting as a preservative. A variety of bacteria are involved in this second stage. Some produce lactic acid, which lowers the pH.

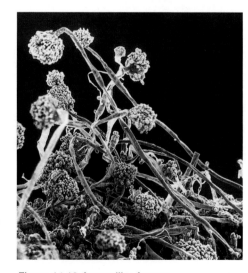

Figure 14.12 *Aspergillus* fungus.

This fermentation continues for about 3 to 6 months. It is then left for another 4 to 5 months to 'age'. The finished products are then filtered and the solids are removed leaving a dark brown liquid, which is the soy sauce. This is then usually pasteurised. It may need filtering again before bottling in sterile bottles.

The sauce is now acidic in taste, salty and mildly alcoholic (Figure 14.13). It is also rich in amino acids. Variations to the flavour can be made by modifying the fermentation conditions, or altering the species of microorganism in the starter culture (Figure 14.14).

Figure 14.13 Soya beans (inset) and assorted soya products.

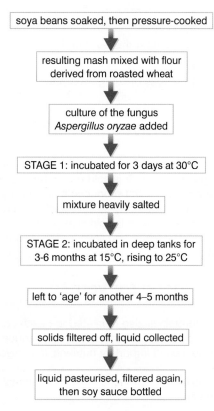

soya beans soaked, then pressure-cooked

↓

resulting mash mixed with flour derived from roasted wheat

↓

culture of the fungus *Aspergillus oryzae* added

↓

STAGE 1: incubated for 3 days at 30°C

↓

mixture heavily salted

↓

STAGE 2: incubated in deep tanks for 3-6 months at 15°C, rising to 25°C

↓

left to 'age' for another 4–5 months

↓

solids filtered off, liquid collected

↓

liquid pasteurised, filtered again, then soy sauce bottled

Figure 14.14 Soy sauce production.

Key Facts

- Soy sauce is made from soaked, boiled soya beans, which are fermented in two stages.
- In the first stage a starchy ingredient, such as roasted crushed wheat, or the flour from it, is added to the beans.
- The fungus *Aspergillus oryzae* is responsible for the first stage ferment which takes between 3 days and a week.
- After salting, yeasts and bacteria carry out the second stage for 3 to 6 months.
- The yeast produces alcohol; some of the bacteria produce lactic acid, which lowers the pH.
- The product is filtered and the liquid soy sauce is usually pasteurised, then put into sterile bottles.

Questions

1 Copy and complete
   Soy sauce is made from .... beans which have been .... and .... It is fermented in two stages. In the first stage, flour from .... is mixed with the bean mash. It is then fermented by the fungus .... After a few days the mixture is .... It is then fermented a second time by .... and .... The yeast produces .... One of the bacterial products is .... which lowers the pH. It is then .... and may be .... before it is ....

2 Soy sauce is described as being 'acidic, salty, rich in amino acids and mildly alcoholic'. Explain how each of these four properties has been given to the sauce during its production.

3 Soya beans are a valuable crop in many parts of the world. Find out more about:
   a) what soya beans are like
   b) what products, other than soy sauce, are made from soya beans
   c) why sales of soya milk are gradually increasing in the UK

4 Although the details of soy sauce production differ from those in yoghurt manufacture, both are fermented. Make a table of similarities and differences in the production method.

5 Find out how beer is made. In what ways is it similar to soy sauce production and in what ways does it differ?

... more at www.modularscience.co.uk

Mycoprotein

What is mycoprotein?

Mycoprotein is a food material which is manufactured by growing a species of the fungus *Fusarium*. It is sold under the brand name Quorn™ (Figure 14.15). When the mycoprotein is first produced it has a fairly bland taste, however it is very versatile because it can easily be flavoured, coloured and processed in a variety of ways. A popular way that it is sold is as a substitute for meat, especially to vegetarians who want the chewy texture and flavour of meat without actually eating an animal. Mycoprotein 'chicken' pieces and minced 'beef' are on sale in most supermarkets.

Is it 'good for you'?

Mycoprotein is also marketed to health-conscious people and those who are at risk from heart disease or need to control or reduce body mass. Apart from having an all-round distribution of important nutrients in it, mycoprotein is especially chosen because it has:

• little fat content, none of which is animal fat
• no cholesterol
• high protein content
• high dietary fibre content
• useful amount of minerals and B vitamins, particularly zinc and vitamin B12

Figure 14.15 Quorn™ products.

Nutritional analysis of freshly harvested Quorn™ mycoprotein

Constituent	Mass (g per 100 g)
Protein	11.8
Dietary fibre	4.8
Fat	3.5
Carbohydrate	2.0
Sodium	0.24
Cholesterol	None
Water	75.0
(the remaining mass will be a variety of vitamins, minerals and nucleic acids)	

How is mycoprotein produced?

Mycoprotein is manufactured by growing the mycelial fungus *Fusarium* in huge fermenters which run continuously for periods of 6 weeks at a time (Figure 14.16). The fermenter will be sterilised with steam before each new batch is started to avoid contamination by unwanted organisms, which could ruin the product and compete with the *Fusarium*. The nutrient supply will be heat sterilised and the air supply filtered for the same reasons.

Although the basic principles of operation are the same, the fermenters used to grow mycoprotein differ slightly from those used for antibiotic production and many commercial microbial fermentations. Instead of the paddle stirring type, an air lift or 'loop' fermenter is used (Figure 14.17).

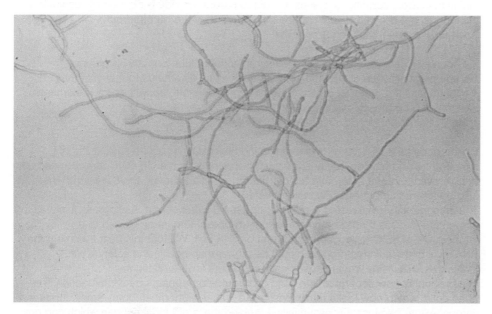

Figure 14.16 *Fusarium* fungus.

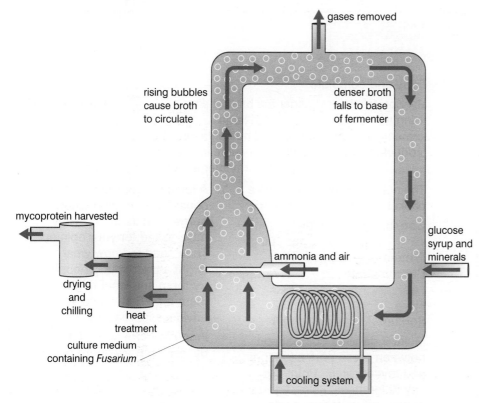

gases removed

rising bubbles cause broth to circulate

denser broth falls to base of fermenter

mycoprotein harvested

drying and chilling

heat treatment

culture medium containing *Fusarium*

ammonia and air

glucose syrup and minerals

cooling system

Figure 14.17 An air lift fermenter.

Did you know?

Although beef contains more protein than mycoprotein, it doesn't contain any dietary fibre and, even if the beef is lean, it has the higher fat content.

Did you know?

The air lift fermenters used to produce mycoprotein can be 40 m high. That's a similar height to Nelson's column.

Key Facts

- Mycoprotein is made by growing the fungus *Fusarium*. It is marketed as Quorn™.
- Mycoprotein contains little fat, none of which is animal fat, and no cholesterol.
- It is high in protein, dietary fibre and vitamin B12.
- Mycoprotein can be flavoured, coloured and shaped to resemble meat products.
- An air lift fermenter is used, which is sterilised and has sterile nutrients added during the 6-week block of processing time.
- Filtered air is pumped in to provide oxygen for aerobic respiration; waste gases are removed. The air circulates the fermenter contents.
- The final product must have excess RNA destroyed by heat before it is dried, processed and sold.

In this type of fermenter, the contents are kept mixed by a supply of compressed air which is pumped in at the base of the fermenter. This not only agitates the mixture inside, circulating it around the fermenter, but also supplies and distributes oxygen to maintain aerobic conditions. Gases, including carbon dioxide produced by respiration of the fungus, are allowed to leave at the top, where they are pumped out.

Apart from oxygen, the fungus requires:

- a source of carbon – usually glucose syrup which will be about 95% glucose
- a source of nitrogen – supplied as ammonia (which also helps to maintain the pH)
- mineral ions e.g. potassium, magnesium and phosphate, as well as trace elements
- a growth promoter to encourage long hyphae to grow
- the B vitamin biotin

Optimum conditions for growth are maintained by checking and adjusting the pH, temperature and oxygen content. If the temperature is kept at 30–32°C, the biomass will double every 5 hours if no other factors become limiting. During the 6-week run there will also be a steady input of additional nutrients.

The mycoprotein is harvested steadily during the 6-week period. As soon as it leaves the fermenter it passes through a heat treatment process. It must be heated to a temperature of 65°C to reduce the amount of RNA in it. Without this heat treatment the RNA level of the finished product would be higher than health and safety limits. Excessive RNA levels would cause health problems for the consumer.

The product is now separated into solid and liquid components by centrifugation. The dried solid, which now looks rather pastry-like, has a slight mushroomy smell. It has a fibrous texture because it is essentially a tangled mass of fungal hyphae which can now be pressed, cut, coloured and/or flavoured according to its future use.

Questions

1 Copy and complete

   Mycoprotein is sold under the brand name .... It is produced using the fungus .... in large .... fermenters. The fermenter and nutrients must be .... before production starts. This usually occurs in batches which run for .... weeks before the fermenter is cleaned out again.

2 The nutritional information on a packet of pork sausages reads:

Constituent	Mass (g per 100 g)
Protein	15.1
Carbohydrate	7.7
Fat	23.3
Fibre	0.2
Sodium	0.8

   Make a detailed comparison between these pork sausages and mycoprotein. Point out any differences, using figures to support your comments.

3 A local burger restaurant is considering putting Quorn™ burgers on its menu. They have asked for your opinion. They need to know what might attract young people to try them and what might put them off. What would your advice, with reasons, be?

4 Find out more about Quorn™ by visiting www.quorn.com

When the scientists James Watson and Francis Crick discovered the structure of DNA – deoxyribonucleic acid, Francis Crick announced to his mates in the pub, 'we have discovered the secret of life'. He wasn't exaggerating – they had (Figure 14.18). DNA controls the joining together of amino acids to make proteins in a cell. Much of our soft tissue is made of protein. Hair, nails and skin are almost entirely protein. Without DNA in control, none of these structural proteins could be replaced if they were damaged. Our skin would not grow as we grew up and hair and fingernails would never need cutting. Perhaps the one about hair and fingernails seems an advantage, but that list is only the start. All the enzymes responsible for chemical reactions in the body are made of protein. Hormones, the chemical messenger molecules, are made of protein; blood contains proteins. Without the ability to make proteins our body could not function. But what is also critical is that EXACTLY the right protein must be made. The chemical structure of any protein needed by the body must be identical every time it is produced. DNA ensures that this happens.

Figure 14.18 Watson & Crick.

A recap on DNA structure

Our genes carry the instructions for making proteins. Genes are made of DNA, a molecule with a double helix structure that has the ability to replicate itself. If you were to unwind the double helix, you would find a ladder-like structure of pairs of chemicals called bases: adenine (A), thymine (T), cytosine (C) and guanine (G) (Figure 14.19). These link together to form base pairs, always with the same chemical partner i.e. A with T and C with G. So, if you know the base sequence down one side of the DNA molecule, you can work out the other. This genetic 'alphabet' of just four bases is enough to code the thousands of proteins that exist in living organisms. Proteins are large, complex molecules, made up of long chains of amino acids. There are just 20 different amino acids to build with.

The order of bases

The sequence of bases on the DNA molecule is actually a code. Three bases in a row correspond to a particular amino acid. So the order of the bases on a section of DNA determines the order that amino acids will be joined together to make a particular protein. Change the order and you change the protein that is assembled.

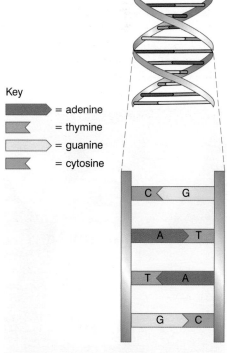

Key

= adenine
= thymine
= guanine
= cytosine

Figure 14.19 The structure of DNA showing the pairing between the four bases – adenine (A) with thymine (T) and cytosine (C) with guanine (G).

Gene transfer

We have seen that the base coding on DNA is in a particular sequence and that the order of the bases determines the order of amino acids in the protein they join to make. Therefore, if we could 'crack' the code, we could make proteins of our own choice. This is what scientists do when they transfer genes.

The human hormone insulin is a protein (Figure 14.21). It regulates the levels of glucose in the blood. People who are unable to produce enough insulin suffer from a form of diabetes. They have to have daily injections of insulin. From the 1920s insulin could be obtained from animals for diabetics to use, first dogs, then later cattle and pigs. However the insulin from these animals is not identical to human insulin so could have side effects. Human and cattle insulin differ by two amino acids; human and pig insulin by just one. The other drawback was that, to maintain a continuous supply of insulin, many animals had to be killed.

Figure 14.20 Frederick Sanger.

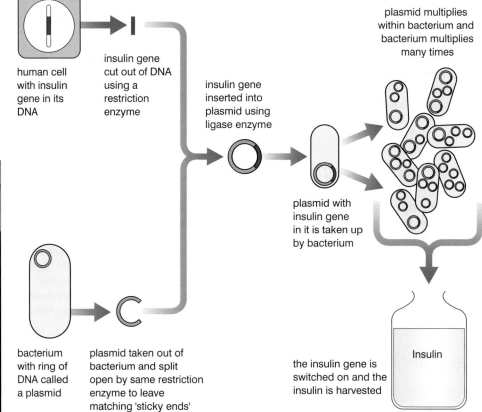

human cell with insulin gene in its DNA

insulin gene cut out of DNA using a restriction enzyme

insulin gene inserted into plasmid using ligase enzyme

plasmid multiplies within bacterium and bacterium multiplies many times

plasmid with insulin gene in it is taken up by bacterium

bacterium with ring of DNA called a plasmid

plasmid taken out of bacterium and split open by same restriction enzyme to leave matching 'sticky ends'

the insulin gene is switched on and the insulin is harvested

Insulin

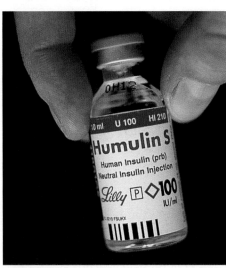

Figure 14.21 Human insulin made by genetic modification.

Figure 14.22 The main steps in the production of human insulin using genetically modified bacteria. Plasmid greatly enlarged to show detail.

Today almost unlimited quantities of insulin can be harvested from genetically engineered microorganisms for use by diabetics all over the world (Figure 14.22).

Humulin was produced using *E.coli* bacteria but since then other microorganisms, for example bakers' yeast (*Saccharomyces cerevisiae*), have also been genetically modified to produce insulin. The advantages of using microorganisms to produce insulin are:

• much larger quantities can be produced than could be obtained from animal sources
• the insulin produced this way is identical to human insulin
• large numbers of animals do not have to be killed to obtain the insulin
• laboratory-produced insulin is relatively cheap compared to rearing animals, once the equipment is in place

Key Facts

• The structure of DNA is held together by linked base pairs, adenine with thymine and cytosine with guanine.
• DNA controls the joining together of amino acids to make a particular protein in cells.
• The order of the bases decides the order in which the amino acids will be assembled.
• Sections of DNA which code for certain proteins, e.g. insulin, can be transferred from human cells to microorganisms such as bacteria or yeast.
• The cutting and joining of the DNA section is done using enzymes.
• The clones of genetically modified bacteria are grown in huge fermenters.
• Insulin produced this way is identical to human insulin and can be used instead of killing pigs and cattle.

Questions

1   Copy and complete:

DNA controls the joining together of .... in a cell to make .... There are four chemical bases in DNA molecules. These are given the letters ...., ..., ... and .... The order of these on the DNA molecule determines the order that the .... will be assembled in to make a particular ....

2   Copy and complete:

Insulin is a .... which is needed to control the level of .... in our blood. Insulin can now be made using genetically .... bacteria. This synthetic insulin can be given to people who have .... instead of insulin from animals such as .... or ....

3   Explain how human insulin is produced, step by step, using bullet points.

4   Some base sequences on one DNA strand are listed below. Copy and complete the table by working out what the other strand will read in each case. The first one is done for you.

One strand	Other strand
a) CGGTACCTA	GCCATGGAT
b) TACGACCTA	
c) AGCTTCAAT	
d) AATCAGCTA	

5   Visit www.lillydiabetes.com where you can find information on the milestones in our knowledge of insulin.

modularscience.co.uk

... more at www.

We saw in the previous section that a DNA molecule stores information about the sequence of amino acids needed to make a particular protein. Here we look in detail at this code and how it is used to synthesise a protein. Each of the 20 amino acids has a 3-base code on the DNA. This is known as a triplet of bases or a **codon**. Some codons code for specific amino acids, others code for 'punctuation marks' such as 'start here' or 'stop here'. Several codons may code for the same amino acid.

Copy CAT

Although DNA carries the coded information, one small section of DNA would not be able to produce enough protein to supply the whole cell's needs. The code must be copied. Each of the copies can then be used to produce proteins. The DNA is rather like the library reference copy. It is the master template from which all the copies are made. These copies are made with messenger RNA (mRNA).

What is mRNA?

RNA stands for ribonucleic acid. RNA molecules differ from DNA molecules:
- they are single stranded not double stranded
- instead of the base thymine (T), RNA has the base uracil (U). Uracil and thymine molecules are similar in shape and size, so uracil will pair with adenine (A) just as thymine does

Messenger RNA is a copy of part of the genetic code on the DNA. The process of copying the DNA code to form mRNA is called **transcription**. The mRNA carries coded information in the same way as DNA but the order of bases on a mRNA molecule will be a mirror image of their order on the DNA molecule (Figure 14.23).

DNA template	mRNA codon	Corresponding amino acid
AAA	UUU	phenylalanine
GTC	CAG	glutamine
ACG	UGC	cysteine
GTG	CAC	histidine
TTG	AAC	asparagine
GAG	CUC	leucine
CAC	GUG	valine

The mRNA molecules are much shorter than DNA molecules so they can fit through pores in the membrane that surrounds the nucleus where they were made. Once out of the nucleus and in the cytoplasm, they go to the **ribosomes**. Here, attached to the ribosomes, the mRNA code is used to assemble the amino acids that it codes for.

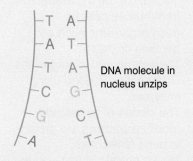

DNA molecule in nucleus unzips

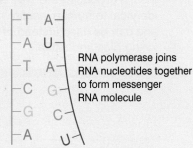

RNA polymerase joins RNA nucleotides together to form messenger RNA molecule

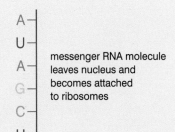

messenger RNA molecule leaves nucleus and becomes attached to ribosomes

Figure 14.23 mRNA transcription.

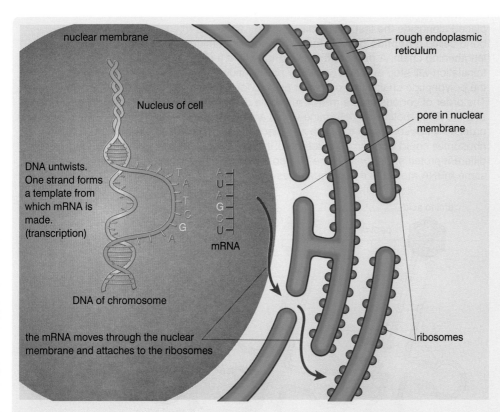

Figure 14.24 Detail of cell showing mRNA taking the genetic code out of the nucleus to the cytoplasm.

Transfer RNA

Near the ribosomes, molecules of another type of RNA, known as transfer RNA (tRNA) will be present. tRNA is the chemical that transfers the required amino acids to the ribosomes. Each of the 20 amino acids has its own specific tRNA molecule. The tRNA molecule is arranged in a clover leaf shape. Three bases stick out from one of the 'leaves'.

Starting at one end of the mRNA code, each three base codon is translated. For example, if the mRNA codon is CAG (see table on page 78), the amino acid glutamine will be brought by the tRNA. The tRNA molecule which brings the glutamine will have this amino acid at one end and the 3-base anticodon GTC at the other end.

The anticodon on the tRNA and the codon on the mRNA match so the amino acid is put in place. The second mRNA codon is now translated in the same way. A second amino acid is brought by its tRNA and

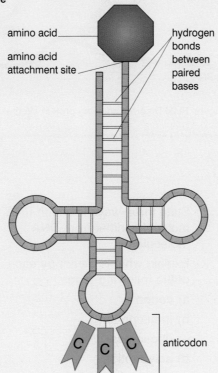

Figure 14.25 The structure of tRNA.

Key Facts

- Each amino acid is coded for by a triplet of bases on the DNA molecule called a codon.
- In the nucleus of a cell, the DNA code is copied onto mRNA. Multiple copies may be made.
- DNA has the bases A, C, G and T but RNA has A, C, G and U.
- mRNA copies leave the nucleus and attach to the ribosomes in the cytoplasm.
- tRNA brings the correct amino acid specified by the first mRNA codon.
- Each codon in turn specifies another amino acid to be brought by tRNA.
- These amino acids are linked by peptide bonds to form polypeptide chains which can then form proteins.

placed alongside the first. A chemical bond called a **peptide bond** is formed to hold the amino acids together in an ever-lengthening chain. A **polypeptide** is being built. If a stop codon is reached, the translation will stop and that particular polypeptide is now finished. As they are formed, the polypeptide chains join or fold or twist to form protein molecules.

The order of codons on the mRNA molecule determines which tRNA molecules bind to it and the tRNA molecules determine which amino acids are brought together and in what order. Any ribosome can translate any piece of mRNA. Therefore, a group of 30 ribosomes could work on 30 different mRNA molecules at the same time, producing 30 different proteins. Or, these same 30 ribosomes might be working on 30 copies of the same mRNA molecule if large quantities of a particular protein were needed.

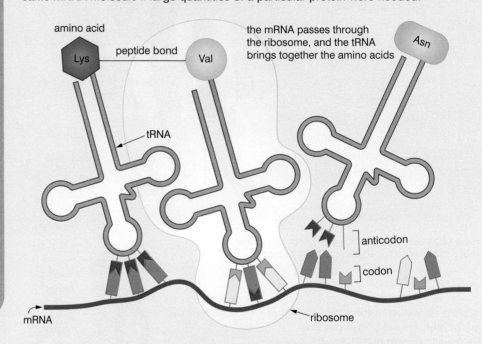

Figure 14.26 Diagram showing protein synthesis on the ribosomes (translation)

Questions

1 Copy and complete:
RNA stands for .... Messenger RNA (written as ....) is a copy of part of the genetic code on the .... The order of bases on a mRNA molecule will be a .... image of their order on a .... molecule.

2 State three ways in which RNA molecules differ from DNA molecules.

3 Explain what is meant by each of the following terms:
a) codon
b) transcription
c) ribosomes
d) polypeptide

4 Explain the role of each of the following in protein synthesis:
a) DNA
b) mRNA
c) tRNA
d) peptide bond

... more at www.modularscience.co.uk

GM plants

Most of the fruit, vegetables and cereals that we eat have come from plants which have been bred specially for food production. Traditionally this would have been a trial and error process. Simple observations such as 'I don't like the flavour of this type, so I won't grow it again' would have led to some species not being grown while other more palatable varieties would be allowed to set seed and be re-grown next season. Similar judgements about texture, colour or keeping qualities will also have been made over the years. Now that scientists have an increasingly detailed knowledge of genetic mechanisms, they are able to identify and alter individual genes which give plants particular characteristics. Selected genes can be transferred from one species to another. This field of biotechnology is known as genetic modification and the plants produced are genetically modified (GM) plants.

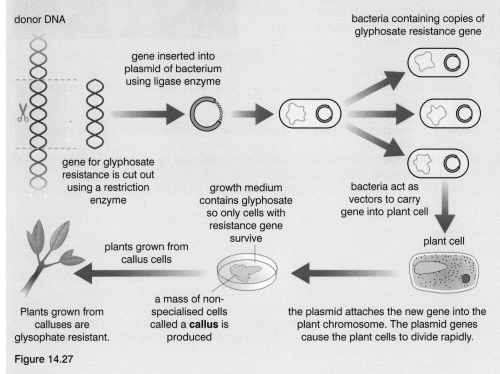

donor DNA

gene inserted into plasmid of bacterium using ligase enzyme

bacteria containing copies of glyphosate resistance gene

gene for glyphosate resistance is cut out using a restriction enzyme

growth medium contains glyphosate so only cells with resistance gene survive

bacteria act as vectors to carry gene into plant cell

plants grown from callus cells

plant cell

Plants grown from calluses are glysophate resistant.

a mass of non-specialised cells called a **callus** is produced

the plasmid attaches the new gene into the plant chromosome. The plasmid genes cause the plant cells to divide rapidly.

Figure 14.27

Crop trials

In the UK a number of GM crop plants such as oilseed rape, sugar beet and potatoes have been grown in trial sites to find out more about their potential use. Significant numbers of people have objected to this being done. Some consider that genetic modification should not be done at all. Others think that more should be done in the laboratory or in closed greenhouses before field trials start.

In other parts of the world GM crops are past the field trials stage and are in full commercial production. Therefore some products on sale in UK supermarkets have GM ingredients in them such as GM soya and GM maize. Tomato purée made from GM tomatoes is also on sale in the UK.

What are the advantages of GM crops?

• Fewer pesticides used
Many people want farmers to use fewer chemicals on their crops. Insect-resistant GM crops can lead to a reduction in the use of insecticides.
Example: Corn borers are insect pests of maize. They enter the maize stalk and eat the plant from inside. In many countries they are a major threat to the maize crop and it can take up to six insecticide sprayings to control them. A type of maize known as **'Bt maize'** has been modified to make it produce a protein from the bacterium *Bacillus thuringiensis*. This protein kills the corn borer, so one spraying of insecticide is all that is needed, just to kill any other insect pests.

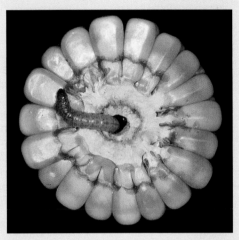

Figure 14.29 A corn borer on a maize cob.

• Fewer herbicides used
Herbicides are used to stop weeds growing in crop fields where they would compete with the crop.

Example: The herbicide glyphosate is an effective weedkiller against a broad range of weeds but it cannot be used on conventional soya during the growing season as it would kill the soya as well as the weeds. Instead, repeated spraying with several different herbicides is needed. Herbicide-tolerant GM soya (Figure 14.27) is resistant to glyphosate so farmers can use glyphosate to control weeds in the growing season without killing the soya crop. In 1000 fields of herbicide tolerant soya beans, the reduction in herbicide use was reported to have been 10–40% depending on the region and growing conditions.

• Increasing yields
Making crops resistant to insect pests and disease and reducing competition from weeds should lead to greater crop yields worldwide because fewer crops will be destroyed.

Example: Nematode worms destroy crops worth around £40 billion worldwide every year. One solution may be to modify crops to carry a gene to stop worms reaching sexual maturity.

• Increased nutritional quality
Rice has been genetically modified to enhance its vitamin A and iron content. In countries where rice is often the only staple food, many people die or become unwell due to iron and/or vitamin A deficiency. This is particularly common in children and their mothers.

• Extending shelf life
With 24-hour supermarkets we expect to find fresh fruit and vegetables of uniform quality sitting on the shelves just waiting for us to buy them, be it day or night. Many people will judge by the appearance – if it looks appetising they will buy it. So there is a market for

Figure 14.28 Customers want to know which products have GM ingredients.

fruit and vegetables which have a long 'shelf life' and which continue to look freshly picked despite having undergone long journeys which would make us humans feel rather the worse for wear.

Example: Tomatoes soften as they ripen, so traditionally they would have been picked when very under-ripe. They would then be transported to their destination and artificially ripened just before being sold. This does not produce as much flavour as a naturally ripened tomato. GM tomatoes have been given an additional artificial gene which prevents the softening. This means that growers can leave the tomatoes to ripen naturally on the plants and pick them when they are riper, and more flavoursome. The gene preventing softening gives the ripe tomatoes an extended life of several days compared to a normal tomato. Enough time to get the ripe, flavoursome GM tomato to its point of sale still at its best.

Figure 14.30 Tomatoes soften as they ripen.

What are the disadvantages of GM crops?

A number of advantages of GM crops have been listed, but to many people their potential for environmental damage is too large a price to pay for any advantages these crops may have. If the environment is damaged, it will be a point of no return. We will not be able to 'put it right'. The ways in which environmental damage could occur are not precisely known, because fortunately the trials and growth of GM crops has so far been closely monitored. But it takes just one unruly player to ruin a team's chances; the same could be said of GM technology.

• Loss of beneficial insects
There is concern that the toxin produced by Bt maize to kill corn borers will travel through the food chain and kill beneficial insects such as lacewings and ladybirds. Also, if GM crops become increasingly more effective at killing their target insects, other organisms which eat these insects will starve. This could reduce biodiversity, i.e. there would be fewer different species.

• Effects on the soil
Genetic modifications, such as Bt toxin in plants, may affect the way in which the GM plant decomposes in the soil. As yet we know little about their effects on fungi and other microorganisms.

• Effects on humans
Many people do not want their food genetically modified just as they may not want it to contain chemical additives. GM crops have not been around long enough for any long-term health studies to be undertaken, so we do not know if eating crops which are insect resistant could have long-term dangers for our own health.
One study has found that the lifespan and fertility of ladybirds was reduced when they were fed on aphids that had eaten GM potatoes carrying an anti-aphid protein. Parents are particularly concerned that these GM crops may have a cumulative effect over their child's lifetime, or interact with one another or the child's own genes to trigger illnesses such as cancer.

Did you know?

In August 2002, six African countries on the brink of starvation, refused to take food aid because it was GM food. Three of the countries insisted that the GM crops being sent must first be milled to prevent the seeds being planted by African farmers. Zambia's agriculture minister said, "We cannot be so irresponsible so as to risk the lives of innocent people. We don't need to engage in biotechnology at this stage."

"I was given some GM maize seeds by Monsanto and they have done very well. I am very pleased. They save time and money," said George Phanto, a farm leader from KwaZulu Natal province.

But Samuel Togo, a Tanzanian farmer who came to Johannesburg with an African grassroots organisation, was more cautious. "I have heard of GM seeds. I do not understand them, but I do not think they are good. I want to farm organically because it is better for the soil".

Figure 14.31 This product contains GM soya.

Key Facts

- GM crop plants are being grown in field trials in the UK but not as commercial crops, as in other parts of the world.
- GM soya, GM maize and GM tomato puree are seen in supermarkets, but are appropriately labelled.
- GM crops may lead to fewer pesticides and herbicides being used, higher yields, increased nutritional quality and longer shelf life for food.
- Objections to GM crops include loss of beneficial insects and unknown long term effects on the soil and to human and animal consumers.
- People are concerned that the novel genes may pass from GM crops to similar wild species or to organic crops.
- It would be a major problem if herbicide-resistant genes were transferred to weeds.

• Jumping genes

This is the major area of concern. Will the 'new' genes that have been inserted into the plants 'escape' into other plants that they were not intended for? Fields of bright yellow oilseed rape can be easily spotted around the UK. Odd plants growing outside the boundaries of these fields are also a common sight. GM rape has been found to cross with wild turnips (a close relative) to produce hybrids that are able to breed and have inherited the herbicide tolerance.

Genes which give pesticide or herbicide tolerance are the biggest potential problem if they do 'escape'. In general, people are less worried about genes for extra vitamins or delayed ripening escaping to other plants. But if a weed became herbicide tolerant it would survive herbicide spraying just as the crop would. If it was not spotted and killed some other way (e.g. by uprooting) it may go on to reproduce and produce a large number of herbicide-resistant weeds.

• Using buffer zones

The transfer of genes from a GM crop to a non-GM crop is increased if the two crops are next to each other and reduced the more they are separated. Isolating GM crops by putting 'buffer zones' all around them may be a solution, but pollen can be carried by wind or insects. Bees can carry pollen a number of kilometres. So the ideal width of a buffer zone is still controversial, especially when a GM crop is being grown near an area which is being farmed organically. To be sold as 'organic', crops must be totally GM free.

Terminator technology

If GM crops were prevented from producing viable seeds by inserting 'terminator genes', the problem of genes escaping into the environment may be reduced. This would mean seed from one year's crop could not be saved for planting the following year, instead new seed must be bought. This may be an acceptable compromise for the wealthy few, but in developing countries seed saving from year to year is an economic necessity.

Questions

1 Copy and complete:

   A genetically modified plant has had selected .... from another species given to it. This may give it resistance to .... or ...., increase its nutritional .... or extend its ....

2 There are advantages and disadvantages of genetic modification. Copy and complete the table below:

Genetic modification of plants	
Advantages	Disadvantages

3 Many supermarkets have information leaflets to explain genetic modification to their customers. Design your own leaflet for supermarket customers to give them balanced information on genetic modification so that they can decide how they feel about it.

4 Organise a class debate with speakers who are for and against GM. Use your answers to questions 2 and 3 as a starting point.

... more at www.modularscience.co.uk

Learning outcome

After completing the work in this topic you will be able to:

- evaluate the potential for using transgenic animals including the production of 'designer milk' such as milk containing human antibodies, low cholesterol milk

Animals that have been given genes from another species are called **transgenic organisms**. A particular interest has been taken in transgenic mammals because they can be used to produce substances useful to humans and even have the potential to produce organs suitable for transplanting into humans.

Figure 14.32 A fluorescent transgenic mouse. This mouse glows green under blue light because it contains a green fluorescent protein taken from a glowing jellyfish. This genetic engineering technique could be used to mark cancer cells in human patients to follow their movement around the body.

How are transgenic animals formed?

The most common method of making transgenic mammals is to inject DNA that codes for the required protein into a plasmid. This is then put into the nucleus of an embryo that has been fertilised *in vitro*. It is a very delicate procedure, done using a micropipette. The embryo is then allowed to develop to a 16-cell embryo in laboratory culture before being transferred into a **surrogate mother**. Here it continues to develop until it is ready to be born.

'Designer milk'

Transgenic technology can be used to exploit the phenomenal milk production capability of the mammary glands of mammals. In 1993, Tracey made headlines as the world's first transgenic lamb. As a fertilised egg, she had been given some human genes. When she

Did you know?

Tracey, the transgenic sheep, was able to make milk containing 35 g per litre of the AAT protein she had been modified to make. A large flock of about 2000 transgenic ewes like Tracey could supply enough AAT to meet the current demands of every hospital in the world.

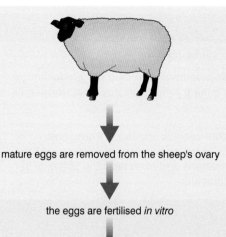

mature eggs are removed from the sheep's ovary

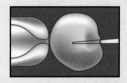

the eggs are fertilised *in vitro*

plasmids containing the AAT gene are injected into fertilised egg cells using a micropipette

embryos develop to the 16-cell stage and are then inserted into ewes that will become surrogate mothers

many embryos have to be inserted to establish a successful pregnancy

Figure 14.33 The stages in transfer of a human gene into a sheep.

became an adult sheep she was able to produce milk containing a valuable human protein called AAT (alpha-1-antitrypsin) which can be used to treat human lung diseases such as emphysema and cystic fibrosis. The production of Tracey was a biotechnological milestone because she not only looked like a 'normal' sheep, she was also able to go on to reproduce. She produced two lambs, one of which inherited her ability to produce AAT milk. This shows that the genetic modification can be passed on, although as yet not reliably. Tracey has shown that human proteins can be manufactured in other mammals and 'harvested' from their milk. This has potential for many different genetic modifications:

- milk that contains specific antibodies
- low cholesterol milk for people with special dietary needs
- milk containing the blood clotting Factor VIII used to treat haemophilia

The drawbacks of transgenic animals

Apart from the huge ethical issues already mentioned, there are further problems which still have to be overcome. These include:

- not all attempts at establishing a pregnancy in the surrogate ewes are successful – many embryos die

Figure 14.34 Tracey the transgenic sheep

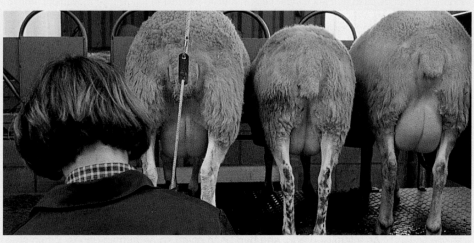

Figure 14.35 Transgenic sheep awaiting milking. The milk contains AAT protein.

- not all cells will take up the human genes
- it is difficult to extract some of the 'designer proteins' from the milk and purify them to the high standards required for medical use
- conditions such as BSE in cattle and scrapie in sheep are very similar to CJD in humans. There is a worry that mammals containing a mixture of their own genes and human ones might increase the risk to humans of contracting CJD or similar conditions

Why not use microorganisms?

Many of the proteins produced using transgenic animals would be too complex for bacteria to produce. Yeasts and some plants could do some of the 'construction work' but the precision needed to make a protein suitable to use for human medical applications can only be reliably achieved using mammals. Mammalian cell cultures could be used to produce some products. This is known to be safe and reliable but high in cost and produces only small quantities of the required protein at a time. Inserting the human gene for producing a certain protein into the genome of another mammal would produce much greater quantities of the required product and, once research costs have been overcome, would be relatively cheap. The big drawback is, of course, the ethical hurdle. Putting human genes into other animals opens up a lot of debate. Add to this the idea of putting transgenic animal organs into humans and you are left with an area of science which many people do not want us to enter. Or, if we do, they want it to be carefully regulated.

Key Facts

- Transgenic animals are animals which have been given genes from another species.
- The donor eggs are fertilised *in vitro* and then injected with the 'new' gene.
- The embryos are cultured for a short time in a laboratory then inserted into a surrogate mother.
- Transgenic animals such as sheep containing human genes, can be used to produce 'designer milk'.
- 'Designer milk' may contain human proteins needed for medical use, such as antibodies or clotting factors. Milk low in cholesterol can also be produced this way.

Questions

1   Copy and complete:
   Animals that have been given genes from another species are called ....
   .... The world's first transgenic sheep was called .... She was able to produce .... containing a human protein. This technology can be used to produce milk that is low in .... to help people avoid a heart attack.

2   a) List the advantages and disadvantages of using transgenic animals containing human genes.

   b) In your opinion, do the advantages outweigh the disadvantages or vice versa?

3   Organise a group or class debate on the use of transgenic organisms. As well as your ideas from question 2, you could also consider:

   a) should scientists be able to patent transgenic animals or even human genes?

   b) would we consider putting animal genes into humans?

   c) how many human genes is it acceptable to put into a sheep at once?

   d) should transgenic animals only be produced for human medical purposes?

4   Visit www.roslin.ac.uk or www.ppl-therapeutics.com for more information about transgenic animals.

... more at www.modularscience.co.uk

Micropropagation

Learning outcome

After completing the work in this topic you will be able to:

- describe the process of tissue culture (micropropagation) where very small pieces of plants (explants) are grown *in vitro* using nutrient media; describe the advantages of the process in producing virus-free stock and commercial quantities of plants, quickly

Did you know?

The oil palm is an important tropical crop which is used for making margarine and soap. Plantations of oil palms developed by micropropagation have now been growing in Malaysia since 1977.

Figure 14.36 A cloned grapevine growing in a culture tube.

Figure 14.37 An orchid growing in nutrient jelly in a laboratory flask.

The growing of microorganisms under controlled conditions has been studied with reference to, for example, antibiotic production. The same principles can be used to culture cells or tissues from plants and animals. Laboratory conditions must be able to provide the correct balance of nutrients, ideal temperature conditions and, if appropriate, correct lighting. Providing these 'ideal' conditions for the culture of the required cells inevitably provides ideal conditions for the growth of unwanted microorganisms. The containers and their contents must therefore all be sterile before use.

What is micropropagation?

Micropropagation involves growing small plants, called **plantlets**, from single plant cells or pieces of plant tissue using sterile laboratory techniques. All plant cells have the ability to produce a genetically identical copy of their parent plant. The information to do this is coded in the DNA present in every cell nucleus. All the plantlets produced from the original cell or piece of tissue will be genetically identical i.e. they will be **clones**. The sterile conditions in which they have been grown make them free of disease too.

What use is micropropagation?

Some plants which are hybrids i.e., a cross between two species, are naturally sterile, so are unable to reproduce. Being a hybrid, they may well have useful characteristics from the two plants that were crossed to make them better than either of the parent species. Micropropagation can be used to produce clones of these hybrids by using, for example, small pieces of leaf tissue from them. For some plants this is the best way if conventional cuttings have failed. With rare, or endangered species, micropropagation may be the last chance of reproducing them if more conventional methods have failed.

Micropropagation is also used to produce large quantities of pot plants for commercial growers. The quality and characteristics of the plantlets produced is under much greater control if a good quality parent plant is used. Similarly, large quantities of flowers for sale as cut flowers and orchids can be cloned in this way.

Micropropagation can be used to produce plants which are free of pathogens such as viruses, e.g. carnations and potatoes.

How are the plantlets grown?

A plant with the desired characteristics is chosen. A small part of the chosen plant is taken. This piece is known as an **explant** and could be almost any part of the plant, for example a root tip, a shoot tip, a piece of leaf or stem. The explants are sterilised and then put into a growth-medium. This will

Figure 14.38 Roots and shoots have developed on these genetically identical Sundew plants.

contain sucrose, amino acids and a variety of minerals as well as growth-promoting chemicals. The plants are said to be growing *in vitro*, literally 'in glass'. A mass of cells called a callus develops, followed by shoots as the plantlet develops.

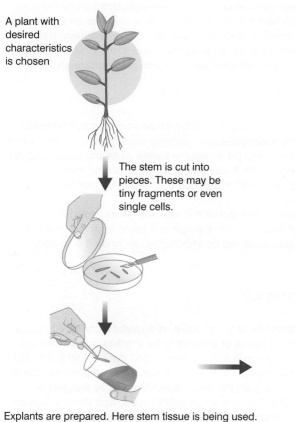

A plant with desired characteristics is chosen

The stem is cut into pieces. These may be tiny fragments or even single cells.

Explants are prepared. Here stem tissue is being used. Using sterile conditions, the explant is transferred to a culture vessel, which contains a growth medium

Roots appear and the plantlets can be planted into pots of sterile compost

Figure 14.39 The stages in micropropogation.

Key Facts

- Micropropagation is a form of tissue culture where whole plants (plantlets) are grown from single plant cells or small pieces of plant tissue.
- The small pieces of tissue, called explants, are grown in laboratory glassware on sterile nutrient media.
- Each plantlet that forms will be genetically identical to the original plant i.e. a clone.
- Large quantities of identical, virus-free, plants can be grown this way. It is also ideal for cloning large quantities of plants for sale which are of equal quality every time.

Questions

1 Copy and complete:
Micropropagation is used to grow plantlets from single .... or small pieces of .... These small pieces are called .... They are grown on .... in laboratory glassware. The glassware and its contents must be .... before use.

2 Explain what is meant by each of the following terms:
a) micropropagation
b) nutrient medium
c) *in vitro*
d) explant
e) plantlet

3 Suggest any disadvantages of micropropagation.

4 Look at www.rbgkew.org.uk to find out more about micropropagation. Select schools education and then in science and horticulture search for micropropagation.

... more at www.modularscience.co.uk

Learning outcome

After completing the work in this topic you will be able to:

- describe the stages in the production of cloned mammals, such as Dolly the sheep: the introduction of a diploid nucleus from a mature cell into an enucleated egg cell, stimulation of the diploid nucleus to divide by mitosis; evaluate the risks associated with later embryonic development; describe the social and ethical concerns of cloning mammals (including the possibility of cloning human body parts for transplant surgery)

When we think of great scientific discoveries, we often picture scientists in a laboratory with rows of test tubes, flasks or microscope slides, perhaps searching for a new cure for disease. So in February 1997 when media photographers were all taking photographs of a 7-month-old, white-nosed lamb in a barn it was perhaps not surprising that many people were unaware of the major landmark in science that had been reached. Dolly the sheep had made her film premiere.

Animals had been cloned in the pre-Dolly era, but this was something special. Dolly was a fully formed lamb who had been created from a single cell taken from a 6-year-old ewe. Many people had thought that this would be impossible, so when it was done it caused quite a stir.

A wolf in sheep's clothing?

Cloning, as you will see in other sections of this module, is a useful technique to allow large numbers of genetically identical plants or animals to be produced in a relatively short time. But the production of Dolly made both scientists and the general public stop and re-consider what might now be possible in the future. For a start, the whole idea of what it means to grow old was suddenly up for discussion. When Dolly was just 6 months old, her DNA, which had been taken from an adult sheep, was already 7 years old. The basic ideas about life which everyone was used to were suddenly under question because of both the scientific potential and the ethical issues of this milestone. There were almost immediate calls for a ban on human cloning in a number of countries such as the United States, Switzerland and China.

The sheep unfolds

Research scientists started experimenting on frog embryos and tadpoles as far back as 1952. They were able to produce cloned tadpoles and even adult frogs, but they found that the older the frog cell used as the DNA donor, the less likely that the clone from it would develop normally. In fact, when donor cells from an adult frog were used, no frog clone would develop further than the tadpole stage. Results with mice, typical laboratory animals of the time, were even more disappointing with nothing but an early embryo being suitable for use as the donor cell. The idea of a mature adult cell being used as the donor, as was the case with Dolly, seemed an unachievable goal.

The breakthrough

Many new scientific discoveries often happen as a result of years of work by groups of scientists working in different ways on a variety of subjects. This is exactly how Watson and Crick 'cracked' the structure of DNA and how Alexander Fleming's chance

Figure 14.40 Dolly the cloned sheep

observations resulted in the antibiotics we use today. Dolly represented the tip of the iceberg – the outcome of years of diverse scientific work which just had one piece of its jigsaw missing. The missing piece was a procedure called **nuclear transfer**. Once this had been perfected, all the other steps were in place.

What is nuclear transfer?

Nuclear transfer is when the complete nucleus of one cell, known as the donor cell, is absorbed into an **enucleated** egg cell i.e. one whose own nucleus has been removed. This egg cell is known as the recipient cell. Some preliminary experiments led to an assortment of cloned sheep being produced from a variety of donor cells in the 1990s. However the goal was to achieve what was thought to be impossible – a cloned sheep from an ADULT donor cell.

Figure 14.41 The microneedle (right of screen) is about to be used to inject an egg cell.

'Doing a Dolly'

The team of scientists who developed Dolly worked at the Roslin Institute in Edinburgh in partnership with a local biotechnology company called PPL Therapeutics. The team took cells from the udder of a 6-year-old ewe. These were grown in a laboratory culture and monitored carefully until they appeared to be at a similar stage in cell activity to the enucleated eggs that their nuclei would be given to. A total of 277 enucleated eggs were used; a single udder cell nucleus was transferred into each one. Only one went on to produce a healthy living animal; the sheep we know as Dolly. Researchers will now be watching Dolly to see if her 'old' DNA will make her age prematurely. There are already signs that at 5 years old Dolly has started to develop a form of arthritis in her left hind leg. This would be more typical of an older animal.

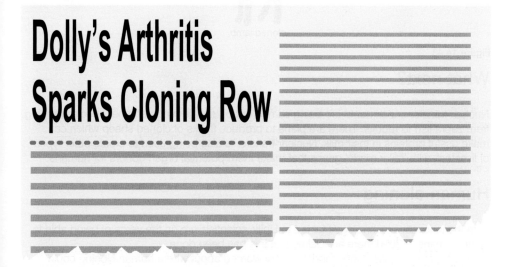

Dolly's Arthritis Sparks Cloning Row

Figure 14.42 Is Dolly starting to show her age?

Details of the procedure used to create Dolly

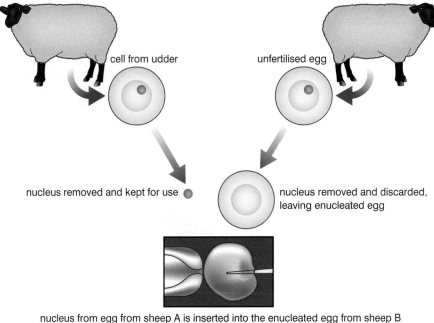

cell from udder

unfertilised egg

nucleus removed and kept for use

nucleus removed and discarded, leaving enucleated egg

nucleus from egg from sheep A is inserted into the enucleated egg from sheep B

after laboratory culture to the 16-cell stage, the embryos are placed in the uterus of a surrogate mother

cloned lamb

Figure 14.43

Did you know?

This is a quotation from 'Brave New World', a science fiction book written in 1932 by Aldous Huxley.

'Under the microscopes, their long tails furiously lashing, spermatozoa were burrowing head first into eggs; and, fertilised, the eggs were dividing …… and breaking up into whole populations of separate embryos.'
'….. in the Decanting Room, the newly unbottled babes uttered their first yell …..'.

Lords back ban on human cloning

Figure 14.44 Parliament have to make new laws that keep pace with new developments in cloning technology.

What next?

Nuclear transfer experiments are being carried out on a wide range of other species ranging from zebra fish to rabbits. There are plans to produce flocks of cloned sheep which can make useful proteins in their milk. Nuclear transfer is also being used to create other types of livestock with 'tailor-made' genes that make them potential organ donors for humans.

Human cloning

With the innovative technology that led to Dolly, scientists are on the verge of being able to clone humans. Indeed there are claims that this has been done.
Many people are, quite understandably, very worried about where human cloning could lead. Suddenly science fiction is starting to look worryingly close to being science fact.
The 1990 Human Fertilisation and Embryology Act has limited British scientists' research on

donated embryos up to 2 weeks old. However in 1998 the two research 'watchdog' organisations called for this law to be relaxed so that research on the stem cells of early embryos could take place. These are the body's 'master' cells. Depending on the chemical signals they are given, stem cells can develop into any of the body's specialised tissues. Scientists want to take stem cells from early embryos and control their growth and development so that they can be used to build any cell or tissue type that is needed for transplant. An embryo cloned from a patient would be able to supply stem cells which could be used to grow tissue that was compatible with the patient. This would overcome the problem of transplant tissue rejection. This is known as therapeutic cloning. In January 2001 the UK law was relaxed to take account of scientists' wishes and thus the UK became the first country to legalise the creation of cloned human embryos. However reproductive cloning of babies – where an embryo clone is produced and put into a woman's uterus – still remained illegal.

Some people might argue that human cloning would be wonderful. Think of the potential for a clone of David Beckham, or a clone of your favourite band. You wouldn't have to worry about concerts being sold-out; clones of the singers could be sent to unlimited venues! If human cloning were allowed, the exact circumstances in which it could be done would have to be made law. This is very much easier said than done. It would be hard to decide who was a suitable person to be used as a donor. Perhaps the Queen or the Pope might be regarded as more suitable donors than members of a terrorist organisation or a dictator. There may be people in your class, or teachers at your school, that you would not mind having cloned but there may also be people of whom you think 'one is more than enough'.

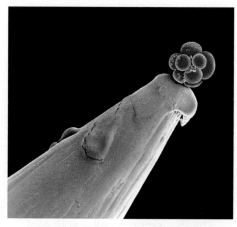

Figure 14.45 Electron micrograph of a 10-celled human embryo on the tip of a pin.

Replacement body parts

A more serious use for cloning techniques would be to 'grow' replacement body parts. Body parts grown from your own cells would not be seen as 'foreign' by your immune system. There is currently a huge shortage of organs for transplant. Growing organs as required might be a solution. There is more information about how pigs may be used for replacement body parts in Science Today at the end of the module. Inevitably, human cloning techniques would not just be available to scientists who were only working for good purposes. People who had a particular political or religious cause could employ scientists with sufficient knowledge of cloning to clone them an army or a replacement individual if a leader was under threat. It would be very difficult to decide what was a 'good' purpose when drawing up legislation to control cloning.

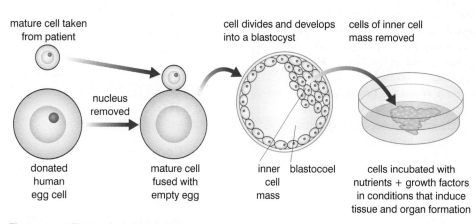

mature cell taken from patient

nucleus removed

donated human egg cell

mature cell fused with empty egg

cell divides and develops into a blastocyst

inner cell mass

blastocoel

cells of inner cell mass removed

cells incubated with nutrients + growth factors in conditions that induce tissue and organ formation

Figure 14.46 The basic principles for growing human tissue.

The risks

Aside from the ethical issues, one of the major reasons for there being such interest in Dolly is the prospect of using the knowledge gained in the project to rapidly produce genetically identical cattle from chosen stock. However this has led to another area of concern. Will herds become so genetically similar, all over the country, that an outbreak of disease affecting one herd will affect almost all the national stock. However, similar concerns were raised when artificial insemination began to be widely used. This has not proved to be a major problem where strict controls and records are kept. In the plant kingdom, a very large proportion of the world's grapes, bananas, pineapples and potatoes are produced from cloned stock.

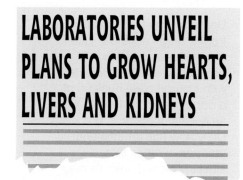

LABORATORIES UNVEIL PLANS TO GROW HEARTS, LIVERS AND KIDNEYS

Figure 14.47 Many of the planned uses of cloning are controversial.

But there may be risks in getting more mature cloned mammals along the way. The problems of producing adult frogs in the early days may yet carry over into mammalian cloning. Mammals cloned from adult donor cells are inevitably being produced from older DNA (see Dolly and arthritis). To date, the percentage effectiveness of nuclear transfer has been very low if we look at the number of nuclear transfers to eggs and the number of mature adults produced.

The table below shows typical numbers of live births resulting from nuclear transfer in mammals. The results from 3 sets of trials are shown. The first line of the table is the data for the trial which produced Dolly.

Type of donor cell	Number of donor cells injected	Number developing into embryo	Number of live births
Sheep – adult cell – mammary gland	277	29 / 277	1 / 29
Sheep – embryo cell – epithelial	128	31 / 128	2 / 31
Sheep – embryo cell – epithelial	258	44 / 258	1 / 44

A variety of factors are probably responsible for the high failure rate. These include:

- variation in efficiency between labs
- source and quality of recipient eggs used
- methods of embryo culture
- donor cell type
- transferred nucleus 'working' inadequately
- failure of stimulated fertilisation

Did you know?

Natural cloning of humans occurs when identical twins are formed. About 1 in every 270 pregnancies in the UK produces identical twins. It occurs when the first formed group of cells after fertilisation divide into two separate groups before implantation.

Key Facts

- Dolly the sheep was created from a single adult cell taken from a 6-year-old ewe.
- An enucleated cell is injected with the complete nucleus of a donor cell – this is known as nuclear transfer.
- Dolly now has arthritis and there are worries that similarly cloned animals may age prematurely.

Questions

1 Copy and complete:
Dolly the sheep was cloned from an adult .... taken from a ....-year-old ewe. This was the first time an .... cell had been successfully used. A technique called nuclear .... was used. This is when the complete .... of one cell, which is known as the .... cell, is inserted into an .... egg cell.

2 Explain what is meant by each of these terms:
a) clone
b) enucleated
c) nuclear transfer
d) premature ageing

3 Write a paragraph to answer each of the following:
a) Why was Dolly such headline news compared to other sheep?
b) Why do some people want human cloning banned?
c) Are there circumstances when you think cloning of humans would be acceptable? Make it clear whether you mean whole humans or just parts.

... more at www.modularscience.co.uk

Learning outcome

After completing the work in this topic you will be able to:

- understand the collection, dilution and storage of cattle semen from genetically suitable bulls and its use in artificial insemination

Artificial insemination (AI) is a method of putting semen into a female to fertilise her ova without the male animal being present. His semen will have been collected beforehand.

Figure 14.48 A bull does not have to be kept on a farm using AI.

AI originally began as a way of overcoming sterility, but in the early 20th century studies were undertaken to look at its potential for improving farm animals. It is now a routine procedure on dairy farms with the vast majority of dairy cattle being produced in this way.

Semen collection

A bull is chosen for particular qualities that would help to improve the genetic make-up of a herd. The bull is induced to ejaculate into an artificial vagina. This can be done by allowing him to mount either a tethered live partner, which can be a bull or a cow, or a mechanical dummy animal. However his penis must enter the artificial vagina, so it is important that this is positioned appropriately and that it simulates the feel of a real cow's vagina.

Figure 14.49 Semen being collected from a bull as it tries to mate.

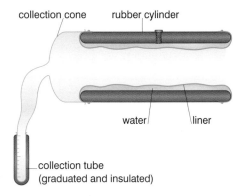

Figure 14.50 A section through an artificial vagina used to collect bull semen for AI.

The artificial vagina is made up of a stout external rubber casing with an inner lubricated rubber sleeve. Between these two layers will be water at about 45°C.

Once ejaculation has taken place, the semen is collected in an insulated tube. It must be checked for contamination by blood, pus or faeces. A sample will also undergo microscopic examination to check that the sperm appear normal and in sufficient concentration. Semen is usually collected from a particular bull about four times a week.

Dilution of the semen

Semen is diluted using an 'extender' which is typically a mixture of:

- milk or egg yolk, to protect against cold shock when the semen is initially cooled below body temperature
- glycerol, to act rather like an 'antifreeze' preventing the formation of ice crystals in the sample which would damage it
- a buffer, to prevent changes in pH which might otherwise be caused by, for example, lactic acid being produced by the sperm's chemical activities
- glucose and/or other sugars, to provide an energy source for the sperm and to keep balanced concentrations inside and outside the sperm to prevent excessive water loss or uptake
- antibiotics, to kill pathogens

The extender nourishes and protects the sperm during storage and distribution and also dilutes it around 50 times. This has the effect of making the products of one ejaculation enough for many inseminations. Any further dilution and the sperm count in each sample would fall too low.

Packaging and storing the semen

Semen is packed into plastic straws, each holding 0.25 cm³ of semen. The filling and labelling of straws is done by machinery. The straws will then be stored in liquid nitrogen at −196°C.

Inseminating the cow

AI can be carried out by a vet or other qualified person but many farmers will also be licensed to conduct AI on their own herd after appropriate training. The farmer will have chosen in advance which semen they want to buy, taking into account information that they will have seen or read about the bull it came from. This could be in farming literature, catalogues for AI centres or, increasingly, on the internet.

Figure 14.51 The semen is stored frozen in liquid nitrogen.

The required number of straws of the chosen semen will be delivered to the farm. Before use, the straws are thawed in warm water for a few seconds to reactivate the sperm. The straw is then fitted into a special insemination gun (catheter) which is inserted into the cow's vagina. It will be positioned so that the semen will be deposited beyond the cervix. The procedure must be timed so that when the cow is inseminated, the sperm will reach the site of fertilisation a few hours after ovulation. This involves close monitoring of the cows by their herdsman to recognise the critical time.

Figure 14.52 Farmers can order semen straws using the internet.

Why use AI?

AI has a number of advantages over natural breeding:

- **Choice of bull:** farmers have access to semen from bulls that they might not otherwise be able to afford. The semen may be from bulls overseas – frozen semen can be transported anywhere. The bulls are of known quality, so AI gives a farmer access to the genes of the best possible bulls which will improve the genetic make-up of a herd.
- **Disease control:** disease can be spread by sexual contact. To prevent epidemics, such as foot and mouth, livestock movement will be stopped if an outbreak occurs. Very tight controls are kept on the health of the donor bulls and the hygiene at all stages of the AI process to reduce the risk of disease.

Figure 14.53 A farmer artificially inseminating dairy cattle.

Did you know?

Each semen straw will contain around 20 million spermatozoa.

Key Facts

- AI is used to put semen into a chosen female without the chosen male donor being present.
- In cattle, it can be used to improve the genetic make-up of a herd.
- Semen, collected using an artificial vagina, is diluted and stored in liquid nitrogen.
- Farmers choose semen straws for purchase by examining the reproductive history of a number of bulls.
- Using AI means the farmer does not commit to the expense and hazards of keeping a bull; there is more choice of pedigree and less risk of disease.

- **Cost effectiveness:** a semen straw for AI can cost from £10 upwards depending on the bull required. A bull may cost £10 000 to buy, plus the cost of rearing it. If a farmer makes a wrong choice over a bull for AI straws, the loss is negligible compared to the wrong choice of a bull for purchase. Even if a good purchase is made, the bull may have a relatively short life span if disease or accident strikes.
- **Flexibility:** AI means that several bulls can sire the calves in a particular herd so that a mixture of characteristics is maintained. Or market conditions may favour a change; for example, years ago customers wanted creamy milk, but now this is much less popular.
- **Safety:** bulls can be aggressive and potentially dangerous. Although temperament will differ between breeds, AI is much less risky than a member of the public being chased across a field by your bull!

How are bulls chosen for AI?

A company offering semen for AI will have a varied list of bulls on offer. Some will be proven sires whose semen has been used over a period of years to inseminate high quality cows and the performance of the calves they produce has been measured. Other semen will be advertised as coming from 'Young Evaluation Sires'. The quality of semen from these bulls is still being monitored and data will be being collected to evaluate their offspring. Bulls of lesser quality may be culled but a 'successful' bull may continue to sire offspring well beyond its natural life.

Questions

1 Copy and complete
   AI is an abbreviation for
   .... AI can
   be used to improve the
   genetic quality of a herd by
   using .... from high
   quality bulls. The semen is
   purchased in ....
   which were kept frozen in
   .... at
   ....°C until needed.

2 'Norfolk Diamond' is a pedigree bull whose semen is collected 3 times a week, every week in a particular year.

   a) How many semen samples will be collected from this bull in a year?

   b) If we assume that just 10 straws are produced from each semen sample, how many straws will be produced in a year from this bull?

   c) 'Norfolk Diamond' was used for AI from 1986 to 1994 inclusive. How many calves could he have sired during this time?

   d) Suggest why your answer to c) may not be accurate.

4 Visit www.avoncroft.com to look at images and data on bulls whose semen is available for purchase.

5 Design your own advertisement for a particular bull's qualities to encourage a breeder to purchase his semen for AI.

... more at www.modularscience.co.uk

Surrogacy

Learning outcome

After completing the work in this topic you will be able to:

- explain how offspring with desired characteristics can be produced by stimulation of ovulation in genetically suitable cows using hormone treatment, *in vitro* fertilisation of these ova and implantation of the resulting embryos into surrogate mothers

Artificial insemination is a way of controlling the genetic input of the male animal to the offspring. Control over the female input can also be manipulated to allow, for example, more offspring from a particular cow to be produced.

Manipulating ovulation

Figure 14.54 Each cow ovarian follicle being held here contains a single immature egg.

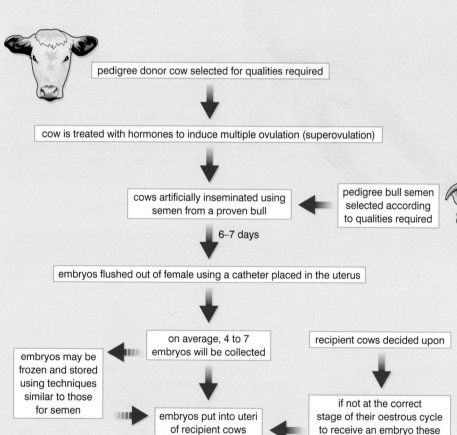

pedigree donor cow selected for qualities required

↓

cow is treated with hormones to induce multiple ovulation (superovulation)

↓

cows artificially inseminated using semen from a proven bull ← pedigree bull semen selected according to qualities required

↓ 6–7 days

embryos flushed out of female using a catheter placed in the uterus

↓

on average, 4 to 7 embryos will be collected

recipient cows decided upon

embryos may be frozen and stored using techniques similar to those for semen

↓

embryos put into uteri of recipient cows (surrogate mothers) ← if not at the correct stage of their oestrous cycle to receive an embryo these cows will be hormone-treated first to ensure that they are

↓ 40 weeks

calves born

Figure 14.55 Flowchart showing how embryo calves with specific characteristics can be produced by manipulating reproduction.

Did you know?

Scientists have used a domestic cat as a surrogate mother for an African wildcat. The frozen wildcat embryo was the first successful inter-species transfer. One of the scientists, speaking about the cat, said 'They may think they have an ugly-looking baby, but it smells like them and they know they have given birth to it, so it must be theirs'. They hope to extend this technique to save rare species.

On average a cow produces only two or three calves in her lifetime. Therefore a single cow, however desirable her features, cannot naturally contribute very greatly to the gene pool of the whole herd. However recent developments in biotechnology have already begun to improve this rate.

A cow will normally produce only one ovum during each 21-day oestrous cycle. If the number of ova released could be increased, the potential offspring numbers could also be increased. This can now be done using hormone treatment.

The cows which receive the fertilised embryos do not need to be such high-quality cows as the cow which donated the ova, as they will have no genetic input into the calves. Their uterus is simply being used as a place for the embryos to develop. This is described as surrogacy, i.e. these cows are surrogate mothers.

In vitro fertilisation (IVF)

Key Facts

- Selected cows, with good characteristics, are given hormone treatment to cause multiple ovulation (superovulation).
- These groups of ova can be fertilised inside the superovulating cow by AI.
- Alternatively, the ova can be removed and fertilised *in vitro*.
- Quality sperm will be used for fertilisation.
- The resulting embryos are gestated in surrogate mothers who have no genetic input into their calves.

Figure 14.56 A scientist "twins" a calf egg using a glass scalpel and a microscope.

Rather than artificially inseminating the superovulated cow to fertilise her ova, the unfertilised eggs can be removed and fertilised in a laboratory using the chosen semen.

The fertilised eggs are then cultured for a few days until they have divided and developed into early embryos. These embryos are then put into the uteri of the prepared surrogate mothers, as shown on the flowchart.

This procedure again allows the breeder to select the quality of both the male parent and the female biological parent of the calves.

Questions

1 Copy and complete:

A cow normally produces one .... during her .... day oestrous cycle. By giving the cow .... treatment, she can be made to produce more ova each time she ovulates. This is called .... ovulation or ....ovulation.

2 Explain each of these terms:

a) superovulation

b) donor cow

c) *in vitro* fertilisation

d) surrogate mother

3 Suggest reasons why:

a) a surrogate mother is used instead of putting the embryos back into the donor cow

b) the surrogate mother does not need to have such a good pedigree as the donor mother

c) the surrogate mother has to be at a particular stage of her oestrous cycle when she receives the embryos

4 Suggest what good qualities the breeder might look for in the surrogate mother.

... more at www.modularscience.co.uk

Will pigs win by a knock-out?

Science Today

If you were dying of a heart disease would you accept a transplant? What if the replacement heart came not from another person but from an animal? What about if it came from a pig?

This scenario may sound comical and far-fetched but it is neither. A chronic shortage of organs for transplant means that thousands of people die every year waiting for a suitable donor. Now scientists are trying to breed animals to make up the shortfall and the most likely candidates are pigs.

Few people would enjoy the comparison but we are more similar to pigs than many think. We have similar physiology and importantly, similarly sized organs. Also, pigs are easy to breed and grow in controlled environments. And because pigs are already farmed for food, there are fewer objections about killing them for organs than there would be over doing the same thing with monkeys or dogs. In fact, heart valves harvested from pigs are already transplanted into people and pig cells have been used in experimental treatments for Parkinson's disease, diabetes and liver failure.

But the next stage: taking an entire pig heart or lung and wiring it up inside a person is far more difficult. One reason that there are so many people waiting for transplants from other people is that the donor and recipient tissue types have to match. Otherwise the immune system of the person receiving the foreign organ reacts and rejects the alien tissue. This is rare enough between people, transplanting organs from animals – a technique called xenotransplantation -- raises a whole new set of problems. Pig hearts would be rejected before the person had even left the operating table.

Scientists think they could overcome these drawbacks by stopping the pig organs triggering the human immune system. One of the biggest obstacles is that cells lining the walls of pig blood vessels have certain sugar molecules not found on the human cells. Human antibodies from the immune system recognise the sugars and bind to them. This sets off a reaction that eventually burst the cells and causes the organ to be rejected.

But in recent years scientists in America and Scotland have taken important steps towards overcoming this problem. Using genetic modification techniques they have cloned pigs that are missing the gene that helps build the sugar molecules. The missing gene is described as having been 'knocked out'. Scientists hope that these 'knock-out' pigs will take us a step nearer to making pigs whose organs and cells will not produce an immune response when transplanted into human patients.

But even if the immune response can be defeated in this way, the use of organs from pigs and other animals in people is still very controversial. Many other scientists are worried that viruses could jump from transplanted pig organs into humans, perhaps causing diseases that are impossible to cure. This has happened before -- the human disease AIDS probably started as a viral infection in monkeys.

Some studies in which humans were exposed to pig cells have suggested that pig viruses do not infect human cells. But not everyone is convinced. Other people point out that there could be more viruses that we do not know about. And some scientists say that just because a certain virus does not seem to harm the pigs does not mean it would be harmless to people.

1.   The diagram below shows a fermenter used to grow microorganisms.

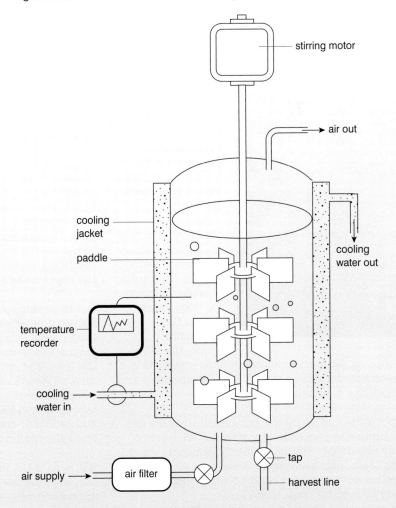

- stirring motor
- air out
- cooling jacket
- cooling water out
- paddle
- temperature recorder
- cooling water in
- air supply
- air filter
- tap
- harvest line

(a)   (i)   Describe how the temperature is kept constant in the fermenter.   (2)

(ii) Name ONE other factor that must be kept constant in the fermenter.   (1)

(b)   Explain why air is pumped into the fermenter.   (2)

(c)   Explain what would happen to the growth of microorganisms in the fermenter if the paddles stopped working.   (3)

(d)   Suggest why steam is used to sterilise the fermenter rather than disinfectants.   (2)

(e)   The list below shows six different microorganisms. Which TWO microorganisms are not grown in fermenters?

Fusarium   Lactobacillus   Salmonella   Aspergillus   Hepatitis B virus   Penicillium   (2)

(Total 12 marks)

Edexcel GCSE Science: June 1999, paper 2F, no. 7.

2.　Artificial insemination is used in the breeding of most cattle.

(a)　(i)　What is meant by the term **artificial insemination**? (2)

(ii)　Suggest how artificial insemination reduces the risk of disease in cattle. (1)

(b)　The diagram shows a section through an artificial vagina used to collect semen from a bull to use for artificial insemination.

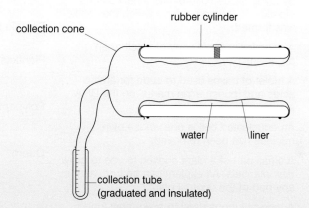

Explain how the structure of the artificial vagina makes it suitable for the collection of semen. (2)

(c)　The collected semen is diluted and stored.

(i)　Give the reason for diluting the semen. (1)

(ii)　Copy and complete the table to give the function or name of the substances in the liquid used to dilute the semen. (4)

Name of substance	Function of substance
glycerol (antifreeze)	
a chemical buffer	
	provides energy
	kills pathogens

(Total 10 marks)

Edexcel GCSE Science: June 2000, paper 4H, no. 4.

Bt maize	Maize which has been genetically modified to be resistant to an insect pest by producing a toxic protein. The gene for this toxic protein has been taken from a bacterium (*Bacillus thuringiensis*).	*In vitro*	An egg cell that has been fertilised artificially in the laboratory is said to have been fertilised 'in vitro'.
Callus	A clump of cells which have not specialised so are all identical. Each one can be grown, by using tissue culture, into a new plant identical to the parent from which the callus was formed.	Lactose	The sugar found in milk.
		Nuclear transfer	This is when the complete nucleus of one cell, the donor cell, is transferred to a different cell, whose nucleus has been removed.
Clone	A genetically exact copy of a cell or an organism.	Peptide bond	The chemical bond used to hold amino acids together in a long chain.
Codon	A triplet of bases used to code for amino acids and 'punctuation marks' on the DNA sequence.	Plantlets	Small plants developed from single plant cells or pieces of plant tissue using sterile laboratory techniques.
Enucleated	An enucleated cell is one whose own nucleus has been removed.	Polypeptide	The long chain, consisting of many amino acids, that is joined or folded or twisted with other polypeptide chains to make proteins.
Explant	A small part of a plant chosen to use to grow new plantlets. An explant can be from almost any part of the original plant.		
Fusarium	A type of fungus used to make new food products, such as Quorn™ mycoprotein.	Quorn	A new food made from the fungus *Fusarium*. Quorn™ is often used to make meat-free products such as vegetarian sausages and burgers.
Glyphosate	A powerful herbicide (weedkiller) sold under the trade names Roundup or Tumbleweed. It is one of the few herbicides that are non-toxic to animals and that quickly break down to harmless components.	Ribosomes	Tiny structures in the cytoplasm of a cell, where proteins are made from amino acids.
		Surrogate mother	When the embryo developing inside a mother is not genetically her own, but is an embryo implanted after *in vitro* fertilisation, the mother is a surrogate mother.
Homogenised	Milk that has been treated so that its fat content has been broken into smaller globules than normal and spread equally through all of the milk.		
		Transcription	The process of copying the DNA code to form mRNA. This makes copies of a cell's DNA to supply the cell's protein needs.
Impellers	Mechanical, paddle-like stirrers used to stir foods being fermented, to ensure nutrients, oxygen and heat are equally distributed throughout the mixture.	Transgenic organisms	Organisms that have been given genes from another species.

Reading the popular press can often lead people to the idea that chemistry is a source of everything bad. Many people use the word 'chemicals' to mean substances which are harmful, toxic, not 'natural', etc. Nothing could be further from the truth. 'Chemicals' can only be shorthand for 'chemical substances'. It only takes a moment for those who have studied chemistry to realise that we are made up of 'chemicals'; that all the foods we eat, good and bad for our health, are 'chemicals'; and that all fertilisers, whether man-made or produced by rotting vegetation, are 'chemicals'. Indeed we can only continue to live and breathe if the many chemical reactions taking place in our bodies continue to function correctly. So let us be in no doubt, 'chemicals' is a neutral word simply meaning 'chemical substances' and these can be used for good or ill, they can benefit our lives or make them more difficult, but we need them and the chemical reactions they produce to stay alive.

Having recognised that we need chemicals, we see how important chemists are. We rely on them to provide us with the right chemical substances for the right purposes. This means that we want them to be able to prepare the substances we need, produce pure products from manufactured or natural sources and be able to analyse products that have been produced to verify that they are pure and safe for the use intended.

This module investigates how salts can be produced and purified, how gases can be collected and how tests can be carried out to identify simple salts. Hard water is then used to exemplify what has gone before: we will consider how it is formed, its advantages and disadvantages to us, how we can find out what type of hardness is present and how, if we need to do so, we can remove the hardness from water. This all provides excellent examples of the way chemistry and chemists help us in our everyday lives. Finally we will look at calculations that, for example, enable us to prepare the appropriate quantities of substances for particular uses. It would be embarrassing to carry out a reaction to produce 1 tonne (1 000 000 g) of a substance if only 1 g was needed or vice versa!

15

Learning outcome

After completing the work in this topic you will be able to:

- understand and remember the rules for the solubility of salts in water

Did you know?

The reason that you instinctively expect to be able to help a substance to dissolve in water by heating the mixture is that the solubility of most substances increases with increase in temperature. However there are substances whose solubility decreases with increasing temperature and if you heat a solution of one of these substances in water, more solid will actually come out of solution as the temperature rises!

Why do we want to know?

It is very important to chemists to know whether substances are soluble or insoluble in various solvents. Any liquid may act as a solvent for solids (solutes) but the commonest solvent on Earth is water. Two simple everyday examples illustrate why it is important for chemists involved in manufacturing, to know whether a substance is soluble or insoluble in water.

- If sugar was insoluble in water, it would not sweeten tea.
- If paint used on cars was soluble in water, rain would remove all the paint from cars to expose the metal.

Salt solubility rules

Salts are a large group of important chemical substances and whether they are soluble or insoluble in water affects the methods by which they can be made, how they are purified and how they are used. How salts are made and purified will be discussed in later sections but, for the moment, we will try to arm ourselves with a system which enables us to see the name of a salt and immediately be able to predict whether it will dissolve in water or not.

As you probably know there are over one hundred known elements. These elements give rise to many millions of compounds. To try to memorise each compound's solubility individually would be a mammoth task. As usual in this situation, chemists look for useful generalisations to minimise the learning. You might think that a chemist could consult a computer data base to retrieve this information but, quite simply, there are not enough hours in the day for chemists to retrieve all information in this way and they must carry fundamental, frequently used pieces of information in their heads.

So what are the useful generalisations? You will find that the following rules cover all of the salts you meet in your GCSE course and almost all those you will meet if you continue to study chemistry at Advanced level.

Rules for solubility of salts in water

- all common sodium, potassium and ammonium salts are soluble
- all nitrates and common ethanoates are soluble
- common chlorides are soluble, except those of silver and lead
- common sulphates are soluble, except those of barium, lead and calcium
- common carbonates are insoluble except those of sodium, potassium and ammonium
- common hydroxides are insoluble except those of sodium, potassium and ammonium

In your GCSE course you will only meet the 'common' examples mentioned above.

How do we test?

You can do simple practical experiments to determine whether a salt dissolves in water (or any other solvent). In order to obtain reliable results it is important that you try to dissolve literally a few crystals of the salt under test in water. Two examples illustrate the

Figure 15.01 Evaporation of water from a solution using a sand tray.

importance of this. If you add a larger quantity of readily soluble, colourless salt crystals to water, you know it is soluble because the crystals disappear. If you add a similar quantity of purple potassium manganate(VII) crystals to 1 cm³ of water you know it is soluble because the water turns purple. Closer examination shows that the crystals of potassium manganate(VII) are still in the bottom of the test tube and there appear to be as many as originally. If you had a substance that dissolved to give a colourless solution, like the first one in this example, but only dissolved slightly, like the second one, and you used a large quantity of it in a test, you could easily decide, incorrectly, that the salt was insoluble.

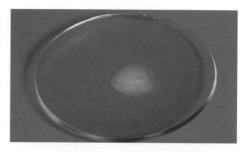

Figure 15.02 Deposit left after evaporation of water.

Are substances really insoluble?

You may also find it interesting to take a salt which you believe to be insoluble in water, shake a spatula full of it with water, then filter off a few drops of clear liquid onto a Pyrex watch glass. You can quickly evaporate off the water if you have a sand tray and some sand to put on it. Place the watch-glass on the sand and heat the sand in the tray with a Bunsen burner (Figure 15.01). If you do not have this apparatus simply leave the watch-glass in a warm place. When you examine the watch-glass after all the water has evaporated you will find a deposit of your original solid in a thin film on it (Figure 15.02). This shows that substances that we describe as 'insoluble' are actually very sparingly soluble. But don't let this stop you using the word 'insoluble'; all chemists do!

Figure 15.03 Coloured solutions.

How to describe solutions

One final point to note about solutions. Look at the solutions in Figure 15.03 below
• All the solutions are '**clear**', that is you can see through them
• Only the first one is '**colourless**', that is it has no colour
Don't confuse these two words.

Finally remember that there is no such thing as a 'white solution'. If a liquid looks white and you cannot see through it, it must be a 'suspension', that is a solution with a solid dispersed in it.

Key Facts

• The rules for solubility of salts in water.

Questions

1 Learn the rules for solubility and then, without looking at the rules, state whether the following substances are soluble or insoluble: in each case quote the rule which has enabled you to decide (in some cases there may be two relevant rules; if so state both).

a) potassium nitrate

b) sodium chloride

c) lead chloride

d) ammonium phosphate

e) copper(II) sulphate

f) silver chloride

g) lead sulphate

h) lead nitrate

i) potassium hydroxide

j) cobalt nitrate

k) zinc carbonate

l) iron(II) hydroxide

m) barium sulphate

n) calcium ethanoate

o) uranium nitrate.

2 'Substances that are called "insoluble" are actually "very slightly soluble."'

Describe and explain a practical experiment to show that this is true for the 'insoluble' substance calcium sulphate.

... more at www.modularscience.co.uk

Learning outcomes

After completing the work in this topic you will be able to:

- choose a suitable method of soluble salt preparation
- describe how to prepare a solution of a given soluble salt
- describe how to obtain a pure, solid salt

Reactions that make soluble salts

Three general reactions can be used to make soluble salts

ACID + METAL = SALT + HYDROGEN
(For this reaction to work as shown the acid must be hydrochloric or dilute sulphuric acid and the metal must be above hydrogen in the reactivity series. This reaction must not be used with highly reactive metals such as the group 1 metals, where the reaction would be explosive.)

ACID + BASE = SALT + WATER
(A base is the oxide or hydroxide of a metal)

ACID + CARBONATE = SALT + WATER + CARBON DIOXIDE

Obtaining pure soluble salts

We must now consider how these reactions can be carried out experimentally in the laboratory to produce pure, dry samples of soluble salts. At this point you may be wondering why it is so important that we produce **pure** products. To understand why, you only have to think of the dangers to our health if anything we eat, drink or take as a medicine is contaminated by a poisonous impurity! Chemists are rightly very concerned that what the label says is in a bottle is exactly that and only that.
In making pure salts, the first important point is to ensure that, as far as possible, all the reactants in solution are reacted and none is left in excess to contaminate the salt produced in the solution. There are two methods of doing this, depending on whether the substance being reacted with the acid (i.e. the metal, base or carbonate) is soluble or insoluble in water.

Excess method: used when the substance reacted with the acid is insoluble…

If the substance reacted with the acid to produce the soluble salt is insoluble in water, then excess of this substance is added to the acid. This makes sure all the acid reacts and means that the unreacted excess solid reactant can be filtered off to leave only the soluble salt in solution in the water. In most cases this will be the experimental method used because

- all metals used will be insoluble
- all bases used will be insoluble, except those of sodium, potassium and ammonium
- all carbonates used will be insoluble, except those of sodium, potassium and ammonium

You should have been able to predict the last two bullet points from your knowledge of the rules for solubility of salts in water!

Key Facts

- Soluble salts can be prepared by
  - acid + metal
  - acid + base
  - acid + carbonate.
- The excess method is used if the substance reacted with the acid is insoluble.
- The titration method is used if the substance reacted with the acid is soluble.
- Crystals of a soluble salt are obtained by evaporating its solution to the point of crystallisation and then leaving it to cool.
- The salt crystals usually contain water of crystallisation.

Titration method: used when the substance reacted with the acid is soluble…

If the substance reacted with the acid to produce the soluble salt is soluble in water, titration must be used to find the *exact* amount of reactants, dissolved in water, which must be mixed together to *just* react completely.

This method has to be used for the preparation of sodium, potassium or ammonium salts as the bases or carbonates used as reactants would all be soluble in water. Titration is a very important practical technique, which is not only used for the preparation of some soluble salts but also for other important chemical purposes. Therefore it is discussed in a separate section.

How do we produce pure solid salt from a solution?

No matter which of the two practical methods is used, if the preparation has been successful, the pure, soluble salt will be obtained dissolved in water. The soluble salt must now be recovered from the solution as a pure solid. When crystals of soluble salts are obtained from solution, the crystals usually contain **water of crystallisation**. It is very important that this water of crystallisation is not removed. Therefore the prepared salt solution must be heated gently (Figure 15.04) until, when a drop of solution is withdrawn on the end of a glass rod, crystals form as the drop cools (Figure 15.05). When this happens we say the solution has reached the **point of crystallisation**. At this stage the dish of solution is set aside to cool. The crystals which form are then filtered off (Figure 15.06), washed with a little water to remove any traces of impurities and dried between blotting or filter paper. In this way, pure, dry crystals of the salt, probably containing water of crystallisation, are obtained (Figure 15.07). If the solid was placed in a hot oven to dry, the water of crystallisation would be driven off.

Figure 15.04 Heating to the point of crystallisation.

Figure 15.05 Point of crystallisation.

Figure 15.06 Filtering off the crystals.

Figure 15.07 Crystals.

Questions

1 Give the names of two reactants you could use to prepare each of the following soluble salts:

a) zinc sulphate

b) copper(II) sulphate

c) sodium chloride.

2 For each of the following pairs of reactants, state:

(i) the name of the soluble salt that would be produced

(ii) whether it would be prepared using the excess method or the titration method, **giving a reason for your answer.**

a) potassium hydroxide and dilute sulphuric acid

b) magnesium and dilute sulphuric acid

c) lead carbonate and dilute nitric acid.

3 You are provided with a sample of solid magnesium carbonate, which is insoluble in water, and dilute sulphuric acid. Describe, giving experimental detail, how you would try to obtain some pure, dry crystals of magnesium sulphate.

Learning outcomes

After completing the work in this topic you will be able to:

- explain why it is necessary to use titration to prepare some soluble salts

- describe how to carry out an accurate simple acid–base titration

Uses of titration

As indicated in the previous section, titration provides a practical method for determining the exact volumes of two solutions of reacting substances that should be mixed to give complete reaction. Not only can the results of such experiments be used to produce pure solutions of soluble salts dissolved in water but they can also be used to calculate the concentration of one reacting substance in its solution if the concentration of the other reacting substance in its solution is known.

For the moment let us assume that we are using titration to prepare a solution of a soluble salt in water by reacting a solution of a soluble base (an alkali) with a solution of an acid. This can be done by finding how much acid solution is needed to react with an accurately known volume of the solution containing the alkali (although the solutions could be used the other way round).

Measuring an accurate fixed volume of one solution

A known volume of alkali solution is taken using a pipette. Liquid is drawn into a pipette using a pipette filler (Figure 15.08). (Up to about 40 years ago liquids were drawn into pipettes by sucking with the mouth! Can you imagine the dangers of harmful liquids in the mouth, let alone the germs that could be passed from one user to the next?) The pipette should have been cleaned with detergent, tap water then pure water before finally rinsing it with some of the alkali solution, which should then be allowed to run away to waste. If this final rinsing was not carried out and the alkali solution was taken into a pipette which was wet with water, the original alkali solution would be diluted and the experiment would be useless. To take the exact volume of alkali solution required, it is most important to adjust the bottom of the meniscus of the solution so that it coincides exactly with the mark on the pipette (Figure 15.09). The volume of pipette most usually used in laboratories is a 25 cm^3 but laboratories carry a stock of all the different sizes of pipettes they need (Figure 15.10).

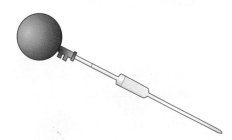

Figure 15.08 25 cm^3 pipette fitted with a pipette filler.

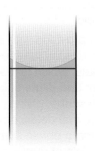

Figure 15.09 Bottom of meniscus coincides with mark.

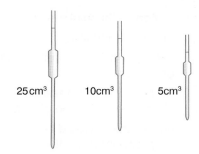

25 cm^3 10 cm^3 5 cm^3

Figure 15.10 A different pipette for each volume.

This solution is carefully transferred, without losing any of it, to a clean conical flask, which has been washed with detergent, tap water and pure water.

Measuring the variable volume of the other solution

The acid solution is placed in a burette which has been washed with tap water, then pure water and finally a little of the acid solution, which was then allowed to run away to waste. The burette is then filled with acid solution and a little solution is allowed to run out, by opening the tap, to allow the tip of the burette below the tap to fill (Figure 15.11). The reading on the burette is taken by looking where the bottom of the meniscus is on the scale. Check that you agree with the volume recorded for the acid in the burette shown in Figure 15.12.

How to find when the reaction is just complete

One problem remains. As we run the acid solution into the alkali solution, how will we know when exactly the correct quantity of acid has been added? The answer is that we can take advantage of the fact that alkalis and acids turn acid–base indicators different colours. Here is a table showing some indicators you might have used.

Figure 15.11 Solution in a burette.

Figure 15.12 Reading 0.65 cm^3

indicator	colour with alkali	colour with acid	colour at end point
litmus	blue	red	purple
methyl orange	yellow	pink	orange
phenolphthalein	magenta	colourless	just colourless

(Litmus is a poor indicator for titration experiments because the colour change is difficult to see accurately and so it is best to use one of the other two indicators if they are available. Universal indicator is useless to show the end point of a titration because it goes through a series of colour changes as the alkali solution becomes weaker and it is not clear which colour change shows the correct end point.)

How to do an accurate titration

One or two drops of the chosen indicator are added to the alkali solution in the flask. The acid is then added a little at a time (Figure 15.13) until the colour of the liquid in the flask changes permanently. The reading on the burette is then taken and the volume of acid added is calculated. You will probably find that you overshoot the end point slightly on your first titration and this is usually regarded as a rough titration which gives you an approximate idea of where the end point will occur. The conical flask is then washed thoroughly with tap water and pure water and the whole process repeated more accurately (Figure 15.14). The process should be repeated as many times as necessary to obtain two readings that agree to 0.1 cm^3. The average of these two readings only is the volume of acid solution required to just completely react with the alkali in the pipetted solution.

Did you know?

Titrations are carried out on nuclear submarines to check that sea water taken in is being effectively purified for other uses on board. (These are not titrations of alkali with acid but involve the addition of silver nitrate solution to react with chloride ions.)

Preparing and analysing

Key Facts

- In a titration:
  a fixed volume of one solution is measured in a pipette;
  the variable volume of the other solution is measured in a burette;
  the end point of the titration is shown by the change in colour of an added indicator;
  the determined volumes are finally mixed *without indicator* to obtain a pure salt solution.

Figure 15.13 Acid–base titration using methyl orange indicator.

Figure 15.14 Solution at end point.

Obtaining pure crystals of the salt

If a solution from one of the above titrations was evaporated to the point of crystallisation the solution would be coloured by the indicator and so would the final crystals of salt. Therefore to prepare pure crystals, a further volume of the alkali solution is pipetted and the determined volume of acid solution (i.e. the average of the two titration volumes which agree) is added but this time without indicator. The solutions are then mixed with a glass rod. Crystals of the solid salt are then obtained as described on page 109.

Questions

1 In a titration, what piece of apparatus is used to:
  a) measure a fixed volume of a solution
  b) measure a variable volume of solution needed for complete reaction
  c) contain the liquid mixture during the titration?

2 Two students carried out an experiment to prepare a pure solution of sodium sulphate from sodium hydroxide solution and dilute sulphuric acid. First they titrated 25.00 cm³ portions of sodium hydroxide solution with the dilute sulphuric acid using methyl orange indicator. In the first rough titration they used 26.00 cm³ of acid and in the next two titrations 25.60 cm³ and 25.50 cm³. Next they mixed a further 25.00 cm³ with the correct amount of acid but without adding indicator to prepare their solution.
  a) Calculate the volume of acid the students should have added in the final stage.
  b) Explain why it was necessary to mix the required volumes without indicator.

3 You are provided with aqueous solutions of potassium hydroxide and hydrochloric acid, a 25 cm³ pipette, methyl orange indicator and any other apparatus you require. Describe, in detail, how you would carry out an experiment to obtain pure, dry crystals of potassium chloride.

... more at www.modularscience.co.uk

Reactions to make insoluble salts

The method used to prepare insoluble salts is very different from the methods used to prepare soluble salts. This time there is only one type of reaction and one practical method; so life is much simpler, if you know the rules for solubility of salts in water!
All simple salts are composed of one type of cation and one type of anion.The insoluble salt is made by mixing solutions containing two dissolved substances, one which contains the cation of the insoluble salt and the other which contains the anion of the insoluble salt. When these two solutions are mixed the insoluble salt usually forms immediately as a **precipitate**; the other product remains in solution.
Imagine that we are trying to prepare an insoluble salt with the formula MX. This can be made by mixing solutions containing substances with the formulae MY and NX. The resulting reaction is

MY (aq)   +   NX (aq)   =   MX (s)   +   NY (aq)

The reacting substances, MY and NX, are usually salts.
For example, silver nitrate solution and sodium chloride solution can be used to prepare the insoluble salt, silver chloride.

silver nitrate (aq)   +   sodium chloride (aq)   =   silver chloride (s)   +   sodium nitrate (aq)

$AgNO_3$ (aq)   + $NaCl$ (aq)   = $AgCl$ (s)   + $NaNO_3$ (aq)

Figure 15.15a   Figure 15.15b   Figure 15.15c

However in some cases an acid can be used to provide the required anion.
For example barium chloride solution can be reacted with dilute sulphuric acid to form

insoluble barium sulphate.

| barium chloride (aq) | + | sulphuric acid (aq) | = | barium sulphate (s) | + | hydrochloric acid (aq) |
| $BaCl_2$ (aq) | + | H_2SO_4 (aq) | = | $BaSO_4$ (s) | + | 2HCl (aq) |

Figure 15.16a   Figure 15.16b   Figure 15.16c

If insoluble hydroxides are being prepared an alkali will need to be used to provide the required hydroxide ions.
For example, copper sulphate solution would have to be reacted with an alkali such as sodium hydroxide solution to produce insoluble copper hydroxide.

| copper sulphate (aq) | + | sodium hydroxide (aq) | = | copper hydroxide (s) | + | sodium sulphate (aq) |
| $CuSO_4$ (aq) | + | NaOH (aq) | = | $Cu(OH)_2$ (s) | + | Na_2SO_4 (aq) |

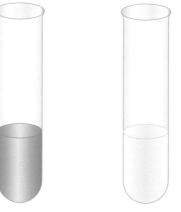

Figure 15.17a   Figure 15.17b   Figure 15.17c

Obtaining pure insoluble salts

The insoluble salt is then filtered off and washed with water to remove the other product and any unreacted reactant. Insoluble salts do not have any water of crystallisation and therefore can be dried in a hot oven, usually at about 200°C, to drive off all the water as vapour. (A lower temperature would have to be used if the insoluble salt decomposed at 200°C or a lower temperature.)
Further examples should make sure that you know how to prepare insoluble salts.

Lead iodide is insoluble…

It can be prepared by mixing lead nitrate solution and potassium iodide solution.

lead nitrate (aq) + potassium iodide (aq) = lead iodide (s) + potassium nitrate (aq)

$$Pb(NO_3)_2 \text{ (aq)} + KI \text{ (aq)} = PbI_2 \text{ (s)} + KNO_3 \text{ (aq)}$$

Zinc carbonate is insoluble…

It can be prepared by mixing zinc sulphate solution and sodium carbonate solution.

zinc sulphate (aq) + sodium carbonate (aq) = zinc carbonate (s) + sodium sulphate (aq)

$$ZnSO_4 \text{ (aq)} + Na_2CO_3 \text{ (aq)} = ZnCO_3 \text{ (s)} + Na_2SO_4 \text{ (aq)}$$

Now you should be able to use the rules for solubility of salts to choose an insoluble salt. Then work out a reaction to prepare it that ought to work. After your teacher has approved your reaction as safe to carry out, you may be able to carry it out to see if it works. Sometimes a reaction that should work will not do so. There is always an explanation for this and such unexpected results stress that chemistry is essentially a practical subject. It is all very well to design reactions on paper but 'the proof of the pudding is in the eating'; do they actually work in practice?

Ionic equations for reactions making insoluble salts

You will learn about ionic equations in Section 15.08 and they are extremely useful for these reactions.
Consider the preparation of silver chloride. It can be prepared by reacting any soluble silver salt with any soluble chloride in solution or even with dilute hydrochloric acid. Each of these reactions will have its own individual, full, balanced equation. **However, they all share the same ionic equation**

$$Ag^+ \text{ (aq)} + Cl^- \text{ (aq)} = AgCl \text{ (s)}$$

Similarly the ionic equation for the preparation of barium sulphate is always

$$Ba^{2+} \text{ (aq)} + SO_4^{2-} \text{ (aq)} = BaSO_4 \text{ (s)}$$

and the ionic equation for the preparation of copper hydroxide is always

$$Cu^{2+} \text{ (aq)} + 2OH^- \text{ (aq)} = Cu(OH)_2 \text{ (s)}$$

Did you know?

'Barium meal', given to people with stomach problems needing X-ray investigation, contains the insoluble salt barium sulphate. Barium ions block X-rays and therefore show the stomach lining. Barium salts are poisonous and so it is essential to use an insoluble barium salt.

Key Facts

- Use the rules for solubility of salts in water.
- Insoluble salts form as precipitates.
- An insoluble salt is made by mixing two solutions, one containing its cations and the other containing its anions.

Questions

1. Revise the rules for solubility of salts if you have forgotten them, and then without consulting the rules copy and complete the following table.

salt	soluble / insoluble	reason
lead chloride		
calcium sulphate		
zinc carbonate		
iron(III) hydroxide		

2. For each of the following insoluble salts:
   (i) state one substance you would use to prepare the salt
   (ii) state the other substance you would use to prepare the salt
   (iii) give the balanced equation for the reaction.
   a) lead sulphate
   b) calcium carbonate
   c) iron(II) hydroxide
   d) lead chloride
   e) nickel hydroxide, $Ni(OH)_2$.

3. Lead iodide is a yellow solid which is insoluble in water.
   a) Choose the reagents you would use to prepare lead iodide.
   b) Write a word equation for the reaction.
   c) Write a balanced equation for the reaction.
   d) Describe, giving full experimental details, how you would use your chosen method to prepare pure, dry lead iodide. Include all you would see during the experiment.

... more at www.modularscience.co.uk

Learning outcomes

After completing the work in this topic you will be able to:

- understand the three methods available to collect gases
- choose the best method to collect a given gas
- know how to test for some gases
- recall the dangers associated with some gases

Unlike solids and liquids (except those that evaporate quickly), which stay in the container in which we put them, gases escape quickly from uncovered containers. Containing them and experimenting with them provides an interesting practical challenge.

Collecting gases

There are three main methods of collecting and containing gases:

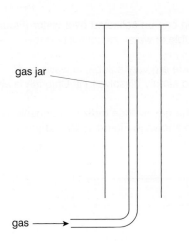

Figure 15.18 Upward delivery.

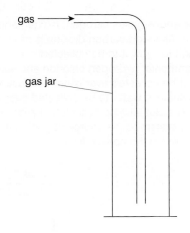

Figure 15.19 Downward delivery.

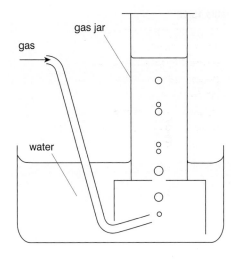

Figure 15.20 Over water.

Method of collection	Property enabling method to be used
upward delivery	gas lighter (i.e. less dense) than air
downward delivery	gas heavier than air
over water	gas insoluble in water

Table 15.01

The method we use depends on the physical properties of the gas, as shown in Table 15.01.

If you have a table of relative atomic masses and you know the formula of a gas, it is easy to work out whether the gas will be lighter or heavier than air. Air is mainly made up of nitrogen and oxygen. The relative molecular mass of nitrogen is 28 and of oxygen is 32.

Therefore a gas with a relative molecular mass less than 28 will be able to be collected by upward delivery (Figure 15.18) and a gas with a relative molecular mass more than 32 will be able to be collected by downward delivery (Figure 15.19). Table 15.02 shows how this works for a few examples.

gas	molecular formula	relative molecular mass	method of collection
nitrogen	N_2	$2 \times 14 = 28$	not by upward or downward delivery
oxygen	O_2	$2 \times 16 = 32$	not by upward or downward delivery
hydrogen	H_2	$2 \times 1 = 2$	upward delivery
ammonia	NH_3	$14 + (3 \times 1) = 17$	upward delivery
hydrogen chloride	HCl	$1 + 35.5 = 36.5$	downward delivery
carbon dioxide	CO_2	$12 + (2 \times 16) = 44$	downward delivery
sulphur dioxide	SO_2	$32 + (2 \times 16) = 64$	downward delivery
chlorine	Cl_2	$2 \times 35.5 = 71$	downward delivery

Table 15.02

Of the above gases nitrogen, oxygen and hydrogen can be collected over water (Figure 15.20). Although carbon dioxide is moderately soluble in water, its solubility is low enough to allow it to be collected over water also.

But ammonia, hydrogen chloride and sulphur dioxide are very soluble in water and cannot be collected over water because they would simply dissolve in it. Chlorine is also too soluble in water to be collected over water.

All gases can also be collected in a gas syringe. The gas syringe must be connected in a sealed system to the source of gas. In the example shown in Figure 15.21 the gas is generated in the conical flask.

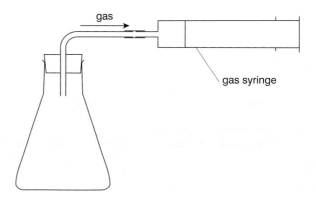

Figure 15.21 Collection in a gas syringe.

Tests for gases

If a reaction is producing a gas and we have collected the gas, we may need to identify it. Although this can be done using instruments, in the laboratory we need a quick and easy method to find out which gas is present. The tests and results for the six most common gases are shown in Table 15.03.

gas	colour	odour	test for gas	observation for positive test
hydrogen	colourless	odourless	apply a lighted splint	burns; if mixed with air with a squeaky pop
oxygen	colourless	odourless	apply a glowing splint	relights the glowing splint
carbon dioxide	colourless	odourless	pass through limewater	limewater turns milky; white precipitate formed
ammonia	colourless	pungent	test with damp red litmus paper	red litmus paper turns blue
			test with hydrochloric acid	white fumes
hydrogen chloride	colourless; fumes in moist air	pungent	test with damp blue litmus paper	blue litmus paper turns red
			test with ammonia solution	white fumes
sulphur dioxide	colourless	pungent; burning sulphur	test with blue litmus paper	blue litmus paper turns red
			test with potassium dichromate solution on filter paper	yellow potassium dichromate paper turns green

Table 15.03

Hazardous gases

Colourless gases can spread without being seen. Therefore if there are hazards associated with a gas, we must be aware of the hazards and take appropriate precautions to prevent accidents. All the above gases, except those that occur in air, have hazards associated with them. These hazards and the appropriate precautions are shown in Table 15.04.

gas	hazard	precaution
hydrogen	flammable	keep all naked flames away from the area where the gas is being collected
ammonia	toxic	collect gas in a fume cupboard
hydrogen chloride	toxic	collect gas in a fume cupboard
sulphur dioxide	toxic	collect gas in a fume cupboard

Table 15.04

A fume cupboard is a cupboard, usually with an upward sliding front, that is connected to an extractor fan (Figure 15.22). Fumes from experiments carried out in fume cupboards are drawn away from the practical worker and out of the laboratory.

Figure 15.22 Fume cupboard.

Did you know?

Although ammonia is toxic, it is the active ingredient in smelling salts. The bottle contains ammonium carbonate, which decomposes in the bottle, even at room temperature, to give a little ammonia. When the ammonia is inhaled it causes a reflex which produces faster breathing.

Key Facts

- Gases with relative molecular mass < 28 can be collected by upward delivery.
- Gases with relative molecular mass > 28 can be collected by downward delivery.
- Gases which are insoluble in water can be collected over water.
- All gases can be collected in a gas syringe.
- Tests for hydrogen, oxygen, carbon dioxide, ammonia, hydrogen chloride and sulphur dioxide.
- Ammonia, hydrogen chloride and sulphur dioxide are toxic.

Questions

1 Copy out the table below and complete it. Ammonia has been done for you.

gas	formula	calculation of relative molecular mass	upward/ downward delivery	over water
ammonia	NH_3	$14 + (3 \times 1) = 17$	upward	X
methane	CH_4			
ethene	C_2H_4			
bromine vapour	Br_2			
hydrogen iodide	HI			

2 Identify each of the gases **A** to **E** from the description given:

a) **A** is a colourless, odourless gas which rekindles a glowing splint

b) **B** is a colourless gas which has a pungent smell and fumes in moist air

c) **C** is a colourless, odourless gas which turns limewater milky

d) **D** is a colourless, pungent smelling gas which turns damp blue litmus paper red

e) **E** is a colourless gas which turns damp red itmus paper blue.

3 Describe a test to confirm your conclusion about:

a) gas **B**

b) gas **D**.

... more at www.modularscience.co.uk

It is important for all of us that chemists are able to identify what is present in labelled packets that contain food, drink, medicines, etc. Today much of this analysis is carried out using instruments. However, these instruments are very expensive and are generally only available in places like universities, hospitals, large manufacturing firms, or other specialist laboratories. On a number of occasions simple chemical tests are still carried out to find out what is present.

If the substances to be identified are salts, they will be ionic and each simple salt will contain a cation and an anion. Simple analysis to find out what is present (qualitative analysis) is carried out for cations and for anions in two separate sets of tests.

What sort of test do we need?

An ideal test must:
- be able to be carried out quickly
- give us something to see when it is positive
- be unique for the particular ion – i.e. the positive result it gives must not be given by any other ion.

Tests for anions

In this section we will only deal with tests for **anions**. You remember that anions are negatively charged particles present in salts, alkalis and acids with positively charged cations. To test for most anions in your GCSE specification only two simple tests are needed:
- addition of dilute hydrochloric acid to the solid
- tests for individual types of anions on the unknown solid in solution.

Addition of dilute hydrochloric acid to the unknown solid…

Take enough solid to fill the hemisphere of a test tube. Add 1 cm depth of dilute hydrochloric acid to it. If vigorous effervescence occurs immediately, test the gas evolved by delivering it into limewater. If there is no immediate effervescence, warm the mixture and test any gas with potassium dichromate solution on a test paper. The results and conclusions are shown in Table 15.05.

Reagent used to test gas	Result of test	Gas evolved	Anion present in unknown solid
limewater	turns milky (or white precipitate formed)	carbon dioxide	carbonate
potassium dichromate solution	paper turns from yellow to green	sulphur dioxide	sulphite

Table 15.05

Test for anions in solution...

If no gas is evolved, even on heating, two tests must be carried out on separate samples of solution. To make the solution fill the hemisphere of a test tube with the unknown solid and add about 3 cm depth of pure water. (Pure water must be used to ensure that no other ions are added.) If the solid does not dissolve in water, repeat the process with dilute nitric acid.

About 1 cm depth of solution in a test tube should be used for each test. In each case an equal volume of a dilute acid is added followed by the testing reagent. The possible results are shown in Table 15.06.

Dilute acid added	Testing reagent added	Result of positive test	Name of precipitate	Anion present
hydrochloric acid	barium chloride solution	white precipitate	barium sulphate	sulphate
nitric acid	silver nitrate solution	white precipitate	silver chloride	chloride
		pale yellow precipitate	silver bromide	bromide
		yellow precipitate	silver iodide	iodide

Table 15.06

(In each of the above tests the dilute acid is added, before the testing reagent, to destroy other ions which might give the positive results shown).

The colour of silver bromide can be difficulty to identify and it is shown in Figure 15.23 with silver chloride and silver iodide

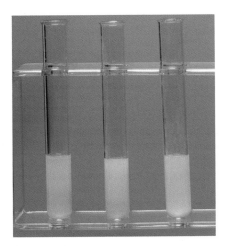

Figure 15.23 Precipitates of silver chloride, silver bromide and silver iodide.

If none of the above tests is positive then a solution of the unknown solid in water should be tested with red litmus paper. If the red litmus paper turns blue, the anion present is hydroxide and the unknown solid is a base.

The presence of hydroxide ions can be confirmed by mixing the unknown solid with an ammonium salt and testing the gas produced with damp red litmus paper. If the red litmus paper turns blue, ammonia is evolved and the unknown solid must be a base and probably contains hydroxide ions.

Questions

1 Identify the anion present in each of the solids, **F**, **G** and **H** from the experiment results below:

   a) When solid **F** was mixed with dilute hydrochloric acid, no gas was evolved, even on warming. **F** dissolved in water and when dilute hydrochloric acid, followed by barium chloride solution was added to its solution, a white precipitate was formed.

   b) Solid **G** effervesced on warming with dilute hydrochloric acid and the gas evolved turned potassium dichromate paper green.

   c) Solid **H** did not react with dilute nitric acid but when dilute nitric acid followed by silver nitrate solution was added, a pale yellow precipitate was formed.

2 Describe what you would **see** and give the **name** of the product you would see when each of the following reactions is carried out.

   a) Potassium carbonate was added to dilute hydrochloric acid.

   b) Ammonium chloride was dissolved in water, acidified with dilute nitric acid and mixed with silver nitrate solution.

   c) Barium chloride solution was added to copper sulphate solution which had been acidified with dilute hydrochloric acid.

3 Write balanced equations for the following reactions. In each case all reactants and products are named.

   a) Magnesium carbonate reacts with dilute hydrochloric acid to form magnesium chloride, water and carbon dioxide.

   b) Aluminium bromide reacts with silver nitrate to form silver bromide and aluminium nitrate.

   c) Potassium sulphate solution mixed with barium chloride solution forms barium sulphate and potassium chloride.

   When you have completed the equations fill in the state symbol after each formula.

4 Write equations for the following reactions.

   a) Carbon dioxide reacts with limewater to produce milkiness.

   b) Potassium iodide solution produces a yellow precipitate with silver nitrate solution.

   c) Potassium sulphite reacts with dilute hydrochloric acid on warming.

5 Write ionic equations for the reactions in questions 3 and 4.

Did you know?

In forensic science, many types of chemical analysis are used to solve medical and legal problems

Key Facts

- Test for carbon dioxide as test for carbonate ions.
- Test for sulphur dioxide as test for sulphite ions.
- Formation of silver halide precipitates as tests for halide ions.
- Formation of barium sulphate precipitate as test for sulphate ions.
- Red litmus paper as a test for hydroxide ions.

... more at www.modularscience.co.uk

Learning outcomes

After completing the work in this topic you will be able to:

- recall how to carry out a flame test
- recall the results for the cations that give positive flame tests
- recall the colour of precipitates produced by cations reacting with sodium hydroxide solution
- describe the test for ammonium cations

As with anions, the ideal test for a cation must:
- be able to be carried out quickly
- give us something to *see* when it is positive
- be unique for the particular ion – i.e. the positive result it gives must not be given by any other ion.

Tests for cations

In this section we will only deal with tests for **cations**. You will no doubt remember that these can be metal cations in salts and alkalis, ammonium cations in ammonium salts and hydrogen cations in acids. For most cations in your GCSE specification only two simple tests are needed:
- a flame test on the solid sample of the unknown salt
- addition of sodium hydroxide solution to a solution of the unknown salt.

Flame tests on solids…

Some cations give a colour to the Bunsen flame when one of their salts which is volatile at the temperature of the flame, is introduced into the flame. The volatile salt chosen is the chloride and the cation in the unknown salt is converted to its chloride by heating it with concentrated hydrochloric acid. The chloride sample is produced on a wire made of nichrome (an alloy of nickel and chromium which does not, itself, give a colour to the Bunsen flame) as follows. (A platinum wire gives more reliable results but platinum is too expensive for general use.)

Place a small sample of the unknown solid on the side of a watch glass. Carefully pour some concentrated hydrochloric acid into the middle of the watch glass. Heat a clean nichrome wire (pushed into a cork to protect your fingers) in a Bunsen flame until it glows red and then quickly put it into the acid and push it up into the unknown solid to form a sample of chloride on the wire. Return the wire to the outer part of a Bunsen flame and look to see if a colour is produced in the flame.

The results that might be produced are shown and listed in Table 15.07.

If the cation is identified as sodium or potassium, there is no further cation test to be done. If there is no positive flame test and if the cation is suspected to be calcium or copper the following test must be carried out.

Addition of sodium hydroxide solution to solutions…

The unknown solid must be dissolved to make a solution. To make the solution fill the hemisphere of a test tube with solid and add about 3 cm depth of pure water. (Pure water must be used to ensure that no other ions are added.) If the solid does not dissolve in water, repeat the process with dilute nitric acid.

To about 1 cm depth of this solution in a test tube, add dilute sodium hydroxide solution, drop by drop until a change occurs and then more rapidly until you are sure an excess of sodium hydroxide solution is present. The possible results and conclusions are shown in Table 15.08.

Photograph of flame produced	Colour of flame	Cation present in unknown salt
	daffodil yellow	sodium
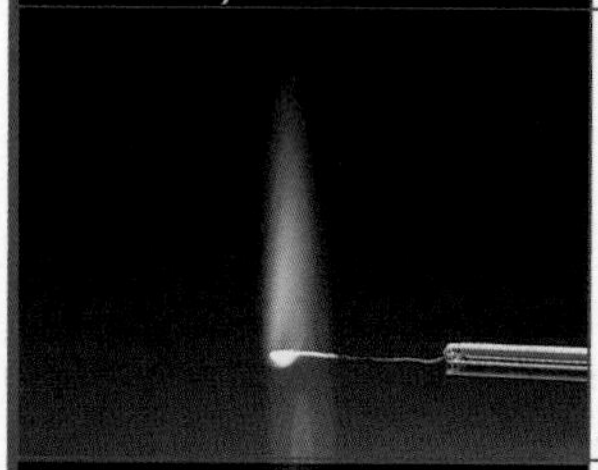	lilac	potassium
	orange-red	calcium
	blue-green	copper

Table 15.07

Did you know?

A hydrogen ion, H^+, would be a single proton with no surrounding electrons and therefore over a million times smaller than any other cation. Consequently, although we write it in equations, it does not actually exist as a single particle in normal laboratory reactions.

Key Facts

- Colour of flames produced by sodium, potassium calcium and copper ions.
- Colour of hydroxide precipitates produced by solutions of calcium, aluminium, copper, iron(II) and iron(III) ions with sodium hydroxide solution.
- Formation of ammonia as a test for ammonium ions.
- Blue litmus paper as a test for hydrogen ions.

Colour of initial precipitate	Behaviour in excess sodium hydroxide solution	Cation present
white	precipitate remains	calcium
white	precipitate dissolves to give colourless solution	aluminium
pale blue precipitate	precipitate remains	copper
pale green; turns red-brown if left in air	precipitate remains	iron(II)
red-brown	precipitate remains	iron(III)

Table 15.08

If the unknown substance gives neither a positive flame test nor a precipitate with sodium hydroxide solution, the mixture of it with excess sodium hydroxide solution must be boiled carefully and any gas evolved tested with damp red litmus paper. Take care not to allow the litmus paper to touch the top of the tube, which may be contaminated with sodium hydroxide solution. If the gas evolved turns the damp red litmus paper blue, the gas evolved is ammonia and the cation present in the unknown solid is ammonium.

If none of the above tests is positive then a solution of the unknown solid in water should be tested with blue litmus paper. If the blue litmus paper turns red, the cation present is hydrogen and the unknown solid is an acid.

Questions

1 Identify the cation present in each of the solids, **J**, **K** and **L** from the experiment results below.

   a) Solid **J** gives a bluish flame in a flame test. An aqueous solution of **A** gives a pale blue precipitate when sodium hydroxide solution is added.

   b) Solid **K** dissolved in water gives a white precipitate with sodium hydroxide solution and the precipitate dissolves in excess sodium hydroxide solution to give a colourless solution.

   c) An aqueous solution of solid **L** gives a colourless solution when sodium hydroxide solution is added but, on warming the mixture, a colourless gas which turns damp red litmus paper blue is evolved.

2 Describe what you would see when each of the following reactions is carried out.

   a) Potassium chloride on a nichrome wire is placed in a Bunsen flame.

   b) A clean nichrome wire is pushed through concentrated hydrochloric acid into calcium carbonate and then put into a Bunsen flame.

   c) Sodium hydroxide solution is added to copper sulphate solution.

   d) Sodium hydroxide solution is added to a solution containing a precipitate of aluminium hydroxide.

   e) Blue litmus paper is dipped into an acid solution.

3 Write balanced equations for the following reactions. In each case all reactants and products are named.

   a) Calcium chloride solution reacts with sodium hydroxide solution to give calcium hydroxide and sodium chloride.

   b) Iron(III) chloride solution reacts with sodium hydroxide solution to give iron(III) hydroxide and sodium chloride.

   c) Iron(II) sulphate solution reacts with sodium hydroxide solution to give sodium sulphate and iron(II) hydroxide.

   d) Aluminium sulphate solution reacts with sodium hydroxide solution to give sodium sulphate and aluminium hydroxide.

   e) Copper nitrate solution reacts with sodium hydroxide solution to give copper hydroxide and sodium nitrate.

   When you have completed the equations fill in the state symbols for each formula.

4 Write ionic equations for the reactions in question 3.

Ionic equations

Learning outcome

After completing the work in this topic you will be able to:

- write ionic equations

You have already learnt how to write balanced equations for chemical reactions. If the reaction is between ionic substances in solution there is a simpler type of equation that can be written, an **ionic equation**. Ionic equations only show the ions that are undergoing a change by giving new products or combining to form a solid, and ions that are being formed. The ions that are simply present at the beginning and the end of the reaction are left out of the equation as they are not changing.

Three examples will illustrate what we mean.

(a) Consider **sodium carbonate reacting with dilute hydrochloric acid**.

Sodium carbonate contains sodium ions, Na^+, and carbonate ions, CO_3^{2-}.

Hydrochloric acid contains hydrogen ions, H^+, and chloride ions, Cl^-.

When reaction occurs hydrogen and carbonate ions react to form carbon dioxide and water while the sodium and chloride ions remain in solution and are present at the end of the reaction as dissolved sodium chloride.

The ionic equation is therefore written as

$$CO_3^{2-} (aq) + 2H^+ (aq) = CO_2 (g) + H_2O (l)$$

(b) Consider **potassium sulphate solution reacting with barium chloride solution acid**.

Potassium sulphate contains potassium ions, K^+, and sulphate ions, SO_4^{2-}.

Barium chloride solution contains barium ions, Ba^{2+}, and chloride ions, Cl^-.

When reaction occurs barium ions and sulphate ions react to form barium sulphate as an insoluble precipitate while the potassium and chloride ions remain in solution and are present at the end of the reaction as dissolved potassium chloride.

The ionic equation is therefore written as

$$SO_4^{2-} (aq) + Ba^{2+} (aq) = BaSO_4 (s)$$

(c) Consider **magnesium reacting with dilute hydrochloric acid**.

Magnesium is a metal and exists as atoms.

Hydrochloric acid solution contains hydrogen ions, H^+, and chloride ions, Cl^-.

When reaction occurs, magnesium atoms react with hydrogen ions to form magnesium ions and hydrogen molecules while chloride ions remain in solution.

$$Mg (s) + 2H^+ (aq) = Mg^{2+} (aq) + H_2 (g)$$

How to write ionic equations

The problem many students have is deciding what to put into the ionic equation. Experienced chemists often find this difficult to explain because, over the years, they have gained an instinctive feel for what to put in and what to leave out when writing an ionic equation. Particularly in the early stages, you may find it easiest to follow the numbered rules given below, in order to arrive at a correct ionic equation:

1 write the word equation
2 under the appropriate words fill in the full formulae of covalent substances, elements and precipitates
3 check that all remaining substances are ionic (i.e. salts, strong acids or strong alkalis)
4 fill in under the ionic substances only the formulae of those ions required to complete the equation

Key Facts

- Before you write an ionic equation, you must know all the reactants and products.
- Full formulae of covalent substances, elements and precipitates appear in ionic equations.
- Only ions which are removed or produced appear in ionic equations.
- Ionic equations must balance from the point of view of charge as well as atoms.

5 balance the equation by ensuring that the same number of atoms of each element appears on both sides of the equation

6 check that the total charge on the left-hand side of the equation is equal to the total charge on the right-hand side of the equation.

Using the rules, the three ionic equations given above would be produced as follows.

sodium carbonate (aq) + hydrochloric acid (aq) = sodium chloride (aq) + carbon dioxide (aq) + water (l)

CO_3^{2-} (aq) + $2H^+$ = CO_2 (g) H_2O (l)

Carbon dioxide and water are covalent: all the rest are ionic

sodium sulphate (aq) + barium chloride (aq) = sodium chloride (aq) + barium sulphate (s)

SO_4^{2-} (aq) + Ba^{2+} (aq) = $BaSO_4$ (s)

Barium sulphate is a precipitate: all the rest are ionic

magnesium (s) + hydrochloric acid (aq) = magnesium chloride (aq) + hydrogen (g)

Mg (s) + $2 H^+$ (aq) = Mg^{2+} (aq) + H_2 (g)

Magnesium is an element, hydrogen is covalent: all the rest are ionic

Questions

1 Copy out each of the word equations below and, filling in each formula required under the correct word, write the ionic equation.

You may find it useful to follow the rules for writing ionic equations.

a) potassium carbonate (aq) + sulphuric acid (aq) = potassium sulphate (aq) + water(l) + carbon dioxide

b) copper sulphate (aq) + barium chloride (aq) = copper chloride (aq) + barium sulphate (aq)

c) zinc (s) + hydrochloric acid (aq) = zinc chloride (aq) + hydrogen(g)

2 Copy out each of the word equations below, fill in the correct state symbol after each substance and then, filling in each formula required under the correct word, write the ionic equation.

You may find it useful to follow the rules for writing ionic equations.

a) magnesium chloride + silver nitrate = magnesium nitrate + silver chloride

b) iron(II) sulphate + sodium hydroxide = iron(II) hydroxide + sodium sulphate

c) sodium sulphite + hydrochloric acid = sodium chloride + sulphur dioxide

3 For each of the following reactions write the

(i) word equation, with state symbols

(ii) ionic equation, filling in each formula under the correct word.

a) Copper sulphate solution reacts with sodium hydroxide solution to produce a blue precipitate.

b) Aluminium sulphate forms a white precipitate with sodium hydroxide solution.

c) Potassium hydroxide solution reacts with hydrochloric acid.

d) Calcium hydroxide solution reacts with nitric acid.

e) Zinc reacts with dilute sulphuric acid.

... more at www.modularscience.co.uk

Hard water – what is it and how is it formed?

biology **15.09** chemistry physics

Learning outcomes

After completing the work in this topic you will be able to:

- describe the behaviour of hard water with soaps and detergents
- understand why water is hard
- understand how hard water is formed

Hard and soft water

The water which falls as rain eventually reaches our homes. When it reaches us it is safe to drink and use but it is not pure water. Substances are dissolved in the water and most of these are salts which have been dissolved by the water as it soaks through rocks on its journey to the reservoirs. Some of these salts make the water **hard**.
If pure water and **hard water** (tap water in many parts of the country) are shaken with a small amount of soap solution you will see a difference.

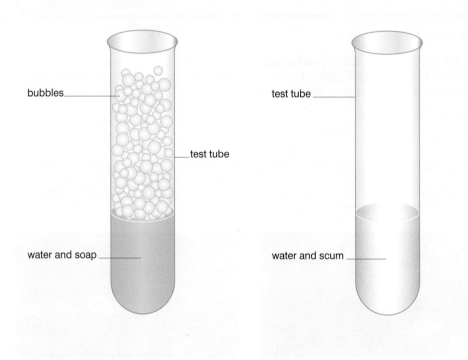

bubbles
test tube
water and soap

Figure 15.24 Pure water + soap.

test tube
water and scum

Figure 15.25 Hard water + soap.

The pure water produces a lather (Figure 15.24).
The hard water does not produce a lather with soap but instead forms a precipitate which we often call scum (Figure 15.25). You may have noticed scum form when you have a bath! Perhaps you were not as dirty as you thought!
Any water which produces a lather with soap and no scum is described as **soft water**.
If the same experiment is repeated with detergent instead of soap, the hard water, as well as the soft water, forms a lather.

Why is water hard?

The water is hard because it contains dissolved **calcium** or **magnesium salts**.
Another way of putting this is to say that the water is hard because it contains dissolved **calcium** or **magnesium cations**.
Examples of rocks which give rise to these dissolved salts are shown in Table 15.09

Rock	Important compound present in rock	Resulting soluble salt
limestone, chalk	calcium carbonate	calcium hydrogencarbonate
gypsum	calcium sulphate	calcium sulphate
Epsom salt	magnesium sulphate	magnesium sulphate
dolomite	calcium carbonate	calcium hydrogencarbonate
	magnesium carbonate	magnesium hydrogencarbonate

Table 15.09

You will notice that the calcium carbonate, present in limestone and chalk, dissolves in the water as calcium hydrogencarbonate. Insoluble calcium carbonate reacts with rain water to form soluble calcium hydrogencarbonate.

calcium carbonate	+	water	+	carbon dioxide	+	calcium hydrogencarbonate
$CaCO_3$ (s)	+	H_2O (l)	+	CO_2 (aq)	=	$Ca(HCO_3)_2$ (aq)

This reaction produces some magnificent scenery and creates an area which is often ideal for potholing (Figures 15.26 and 15.27).

Figure 15.26 Cave formed when limestone reacts with rainwater.

Figure 15.27 Potholer making use of a challenging tunnel formed when limestone reacts with rainwater.

Most of the limestone rock has dissolved by reacting with the rainwater, leaving the surrounding unaffected rocks to form the roofs, walls and floors of the caves and tunnels (Figures 15.26 and 15.27).

Action of soaps and detergents

The scum formed when hard water comes into contact with soap, is insoluble calcium and/or magnesium salt.

hard water	+	soap	=	scum	+	soft water
(containing soluble calcium/magnesium salt)		(soluble sodium/ potassium salt)		(insoluble calcium/ magnesium salt)		(containing soluble sodium/ potassium salt)

Soaps are sodium or potassium salts and therefore soluble in water. The anion of a soap is a long hydrocarbon chain with a $-COO^-$ end on it (Figure 15.28).

Figure 15.28 Soap anion.

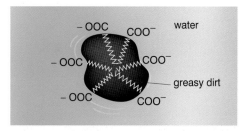

Figure 15.29 Soap anion enables grease and water to mix.

Figure 15.30 Grease and water do not mix.

The soap removes greasy dirt because the hydrocarbon part of the anion dissolves in the greasy dirt and the $-COO^-$ end dissolves in the water (Figure 15.29). Water on its own would have no effect on the greasy dirt (Figure 15.30) but the soap anions enable the grease to mix with the water and be washed away. If soap anions react with cations in hard water to form a scum the anions are removed, the soap is wasted and the anions are no longer available to remove greasy dirt.

No scum is formed when hard water comes into contact with detergents because the anions in detergents form soluble salts with the cations in hard water. Therefore even in hard water no detergent is wasted and the detergent anions remain in solution to remove greasy dirt.

Questions

1 The salts listed in Table 15.09 cause hardness in water.

a) List four other salts which you think would cause hardness if they were present in water.

b) Explain why you have chosen these salts.

2 Explain why there are large caves and tunnels in areas where the main rock is limestone. Include a balanced equation in your answer.

3 a) State and explain two problems that arise when soap is used in hard water areas.

b) State whether these problems arise if detergent is used instead of soap. Explain your answer.

... more at www.modularscience.co.uk

Permanent and temporary hardness

When hard water is boiled it does not always behave in the same way.

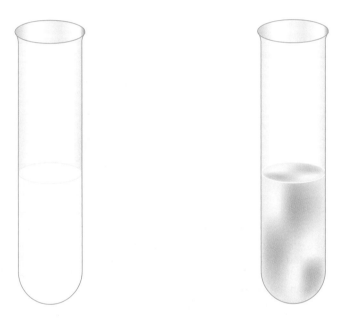

Figure 15.31 Test tube 1.   Figure 15.32 Test tube 2.

Some hard water is unaffected by boiling (see Figure 15.31). The hardness in this water is **permanent hardness**.

Other hard water becomes cloudy when it is boiled (see Figure 15.32) because an insoluble white precipitate is formed. The hardness in this water is **temporary hardness**. Permanent hardness is caused by any dissolved calcium and/or magnesium salts except hydrogencarbonates. Temporary hardness is caused by dissolved calcium and/or magnesium hydrogencarbonates.

Problems caused by temporary hardness...

The precipitate produced when water with temporary hardness is boiled, is formed because the calcium and/or magnesium hydrogencarbonates decompose forming insoluble calcium and/or magnesium carbonates. These carbonates form the scum.

calcium hydrogencarbonate	=	calcium carbonate	+	water	+	carbon dioxide
$Ca(HCO_3)_2$ (aq)	=	$CaCO_3$ (s)	+	H_2O (l)	+	CO_2(g)

Also

$Mg(HCO_3)_2$ (aq)	=	$MgCO_3$ (s)	+	H_2O (l)	+	CO_2 (g)

You can see examples of this reaction in your home, if you live in an area where temporary hard water is supplied.
- The shiny heating element in a new electric kettle soon becomes dull and covered in visible deposit which may break off and rattle around the kettle.
- A solid deposit quickly forms around the end of a dripping hot water tap.
- The white grouting between tiles in a shower cubicle soon looks dirty.

The solid deposit formed is sometimes called **scale**.

The scale is an insulator and on a heating element will be responsible for wasting electricity. In our homes and in industry a growing deposit of scale on the inside of hot water pipes may eventually block the pipe leaving a sealed system being heated and possibly causing an explosion!

Figure 15.33 Stalactites and stalagmites in caves at Guadalupe Cave, New Mexico.

Stalactites, stalagmites and petrifying wells

The decomposition of hydrogencarbonates to form solid carbonates also occurs (but much more slowly) in underground caves. The deposits grow very slowly down from the roof of the cave (stalactites) and up from the floor of the cave (stalagmites) and, particularly in areas where other salts (e.g. iron(III) salts) colour them, they producing amazing and beautiful effects (Figure 15.33).

In another example, people claimed to be able to turn soft objects, such as gloves, to stone! They simply hung the object under an overhang in a limestone area and waited for the hard deposit of carbonate to form. Areas where this happened were known as petrifying wells (Figure 15.34).

Estimation of temporary and permanent hardness of water

If the tap water in your area is hard you can find out the ratio of temporary to permanent hardness in it by titrating with a soap solution. Place 100 cm^3 of tap water in a conical flask. Fill a burette with soap solution and record the volume. Add the soap solution to the tap water 0.5 cm^3 at a time until, when you shake the flask, a permanent lather is formed. Record the volume of soap solution added (volume 1). Repeat the process with a fresh 100 cm^3 portion of tap water but this time boil it for 10 minutes. During this time replace any water lost as steam by adding pure water (not tap water) to keep the volume of water in the flask more or less constant. Allow the water to cool before adding the soap solution in the same way as before. Again record the volume of soap solution needed to produce a permanent lather (volume 2).

Figure 15.34 Petrified objects at Mother Shipton's Well, Yorkshire.

$$\frac{\text{temporary hardness}}{\text{permanent hardness}} = \frac{\text{volume 1} - \text{volume 2}}{\text{volume 2}}$$

Benefits of hard water

Hard water also has some benefits.
- The dissolved salts in hard water give the water a taste and dissolved calcium and magnesium hydrogencarbonates can decompose slightly, even at room temperature, to produce carbon dioxide, which gives the water a refreshing taste.
- Researchers are still investigating the possibility that people living in hard water areas seem to suffer less from heart problems than those living in soft water areas.
- Pipes in the plumbing systems of houses are usually made of copper nowadays, although they used to be made of lead. Both these metals can be attacked very slowly by the water supplied to our houses, forming small amounts of soluble copper or lead salts. These salts are poisonous and can, over a long period of time, damage our health. In hard water areas the solid deposit built up on the inside of a pipe prevents the water from reaching the metal of the pipe to produce the salts (Figure 15.35).

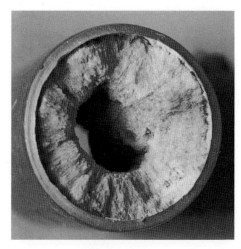

Figure 15.35 Deposit on inside of hot water pipe.

Preparing and analysing

Summary

Some of the problems and benefits associated with hard water are summarised in the table below.

Problems caused by hard water	Benefits of hard water
wastes soap by reacting with it to form a scum	has a more refreshing taste
forms deposit on heating elements which wastes electricity	may reduce the chance of heart disease
forms deposit on bases of spout-filled kettles which wastes gas	stops copper or lead of pipes forming poisonous soluble salts in the water
deposits scale in hot water pipes and this may block the pipes	

Table 15.10

Did you know?

Some stalactites grow down at a rate of about 1cm every three months whereas others may take thousands of years to grow by this amount.

Key Facts

- Temporary hardness can be removed from water by boiling; permanent hardness cannot.
- Temporary hardness is caused by dissolved calcium and/or magnesium hydrogencarbonates; permanent hardness is caused by any other dissolved calcium and/or magnesium salts.
- Temporary hardness deposits scale in hot water systems.
- A coating of insoluble carbonate scale on the inside of water pipes prevents soluble, toxic salts being formed in the water.

Questions

1 Give the name and formula of the ions which
   a) cause hardness in water
   b) are present in temporary hard water but not in permanent hard water.

2 a) Describe and explain what happens to temporary hard water when it is heated.
   b) Describe why the same thing does not happen in heated permanent hard water.
   c) Describe and explain fully two advantages and two disadvantages of hard water.

3 Explain how stalactites and stalagmites are formed in limestone areas.

4 When 100 cm³ of hard water is titrated with soap solution. 24.0 cm³ of the soap solution is added before a permanent lather is formed.

Another 100 cm³ of the hard water is boiled gently for 10 minutes and then titrated with the same soap solution. This time 16.0 cm³ of the soap solution is required to produce a permanent lather.
   a) Give the equation for the reaction that must be occurring when the hard water is boiled
   b) Calculate the ratio of temporary hardness to permanent harness in the water. Show your working.
   c) Write the ionic equation, including state symbols, for the reaction of hard water with soap, using X⁻ to represent the anion of the soap.

Water treatment

After completing the work in this topic you will be able to:

- understand that only temporary hardness can be removed by boiling
- understand that temporary and permanent hardness can be removed by adding sodium carbonate
- understand that temporary and permanent hardness can be removed by passing the water through an ion exchange column
- understand how water is treated to make it fit for domestic use

Softening of water

Although hard water is not always a problem, methods of removing hardness, called **softening**, are needed.
To soften water, a process must remove any calcium and magnesium ions.
There are a number of ways of doing this.
1 Temporary hardness only
  By boiling the hard water to decompose calcium and magnesium hydrogencarbonates to form insoluble calcium and magnesium carbonates.

$$Ca(HCO_3)_2 \ (aq) \quad = \quad CaCO_3 \ (s) \quad + \quad H_2O \ (l) \quad + \quad CO_2 \ (g)$$
$$Mg(HCO_3)_2 \ (aq) \quad = \quad MgCO_3 \ (s) \quad + \quad H_2O \ (l) \quad + \quad CO_2 \ (g)$$

2 Temporary and permanent hardness
  (i) By adding sodium carbonate. This is usually done by adding washing soda crystals (hydrated sodium carbonate) that used to be coloured and scented and sold as bath salts. Sodium carbonate dissolves in the water and reacts with the calcium and magnesium ions to form insoluble calcium and magnesium carbonates.

$$\text{e.g. } CaSO_4 \ (aq) \quad + \quad Na_2CO_3 \ (aq) \quad = \quad CaCO_3 \ (s) \quad + \quad Na_2SO_4 \ (aq)$$
$$MgSO_4 \ (aq) \quad + \quad Na_2CO_3 \ (aq) \quad = \quad MgCO_3 \ (s) \quad + \quad Na_2SO_4 \ (aq)$$

  (ii) By using an ion exchange column. This is a column packed with a substance in which the cations, usually sodium cations, are loosely held. As the hard water is slowly trickled down the column the calcium and magnesium ions replace the sodium ions in the substance packing the column. (Figure 15.36) The sodium ions are displaced into the water and so the water is softened (Figure 15.37).
  One advantage of softening by using an ion exchange column is that the column can easily be regenerated (i.e. made ready for further use) when it has given up virtually all its sodium ions. A concentrated solution of sodium chloride is poured down the column. This causes the reverse of the change that took place during the softening process and sodium ions go onto the column replacing the calcium and magnesium ions that have accumulated there. When this process is complete the column is ready for use again. At this stage some of you may think 'What is the point of this? The water used to regenerate the column has been made hard again!' The point is that the volume of water softened is far greater than the volume of water made hard in the regeneration process because a **concentrated solution** of sodium chloride was used.

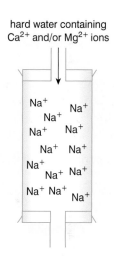

Figure 15.36 Hard water added to ion exchange column.

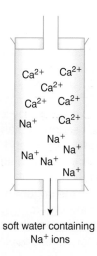

Figure 15.37 Soft water coming off ion exchange column.

Preparing and analysing

Ion exchange columns packed with acidic material are available and if water is trickled through these all the cations are exchanged for hydrogen ions. If an ion exchange column packed with base is then used, it will remove all anions except hydroxide ions and the result will be pure water. Remember this is needed for all analysis experiments.

Figure 15.38 Water deioniser.

Making water fit to drink

Whether it is hard or soft, the water that arrives via rivers and streams at a reservoir is not fit to drink. Before it comes to our homes it must be treated (Figure 15.39). The main stages are listed below.

Sedimentation. Aluminium sulphate is added to the water to coagulate small solid particles, causing them to stick together to form larger particles.

Filtration. Solid particles are removed in this stage but instead of using filter paper, the water is filtered through beds of gravel and sand.

Chlorination. Finally the water is treated with chlorine to kill the bacteria.

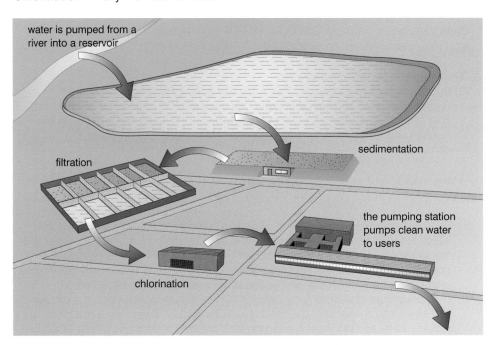

Figure 15.39 Water treatment.

How do we use water?

Water is vital for our survival and comfort. We can survive many days without food but only a comparatively short time without water. The water we drink in a day is only about 2% of what we use (Figure 15.40). An amazing 30% is flushed down the toilet with 45% used for washing ourselves, our clothes and the dishes!

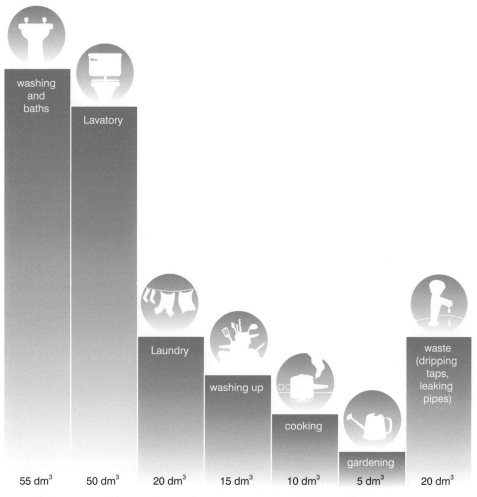

55 dm³   50 dm³   20 dm³   15 dm³   10 dm³   5 dm³   20 dm³

Figure 15.40 Typical amount of water used by one person in one day in Britain.

Key Facts

- Hard water can be softened.
- Temporary hardness can be removed by boiling.
- Temporary and permanent hardness can be removed by adding sodium carbonate.
- Temporary and permanent hardness can be removed by passing the water through an ion exchange column.
- Water must undergo sedimentation, filtration and chlorination to make it fit for domestic use.

Questions

1 Give the names of two

   a) ions which cause hardness in water

   b) substances which, dissolved in water, produce temporary hardness

   c) substances which, dissolved in water, produce permanent hardness.

2 Explain why temporary hardness is removed from water by boiling but permanent hardness is not. Include a balanced equation as part of your answer.

3 Describe how rainwater is treated to be supplied to our homes as relatively pure water. Your account should include descriptions of:

(i) substances present in the rainwater

(ii) substances which may enter the rainwater before it reaches a reservoir

(iii) processes used to treat the water at the waterworks, indicating what types of substances are treated at each stage.

... more at www.modularscience.co.uk

Calculations in chemistry

In this and the following sections on calculations in chemistry two aims are :
- to convince those of you who doubt your mathematical ability that you are able to deal with calculations in chemistry
- to help you to understand the ideas sometimes needed in calculations.

Those who may feel mathematics is not their strong point have little to fear from calculations in chemistry. If you understand the following simple, everyday example, you will be able to cope with the mathematical aspects of most calculations in chemistry at GCSE and even at Advanced Level.

$$4 \text{ oranges cost} = 80\,p$$
$$1 \text{ orange costs} = \frac{80}{4}\,p$$
$$3 \text{ oranges cost} = \frac{80 \times 3}{4}\,p$$
$$= 60\,p$$

Although the numbers in this example are very simple, the calculation has been set out line by line so that the argument is clear, for you and anyone marking it as an answer, to see. It is most important that you have a clear picture in your mind of what you are doing. It is also important that you show your method to whoever may be marking your answer so that, if you make a mathematical error (for example between the last two lines in this case), you will gain full credit for your correct chemistry. Note that the equals signs are used to separate the two related ideas in each line.

You will see these basic principles of setting out answers to calculations used in all the chemistry calculations in this book.

Having given you the confidence that you can cope with the mathematics required you need one extra chemical idea for some, but by no means all, chemical calculations. This is the idea of the mole (the chemical one not the biological one!).

The mole

The **mole** is simply another way of expressing the amount of something in chemistry. Let us return to our oranges example to give you the idea.

Oranges can be bought from a supermarket as a number, say 4 oranges; a mass, say 1000 g; or as a collection, say 1 bag (for the purposes of this example, one that contains four oranges).

Whether we ask for four oranges, 1000 g of oranges or 1 bag of oranges, we collect the same amount of oranges (Figure 15.41).

In chemistry it is exactly the same with particles (atoms, molecules, ions, formulae) of a given substance. We can specify a certain number of particles, these will have a certain mass and they will be a certain amount in moles.

The amount in moles and the mass of any specified particle in chemistry are connected by the following statement (the way in which these are connected to the number of particles is not required at GCSE, only at Advanced Level).

1 mol of particles of substance has mass = (relative particle mass) g of substance

(Note that just as we would write 'one centimetre' in the middle of a sentence but '1 cm' with a figure involved, we write 'one mole' in a sentence but '1 mol' when a number is shown.)

A few examples should show how the above statement is used. The figures used come from relative atomic masses (e.g. as shown on a periodic table).

1 mol hydrogen **atoms** (H) has a mass
= (relative **atomic mass** hydrogen) g
= 1 g

1 mol chlorine **molecules** (Cl_2) has a mass
= (relative **molecular mass** chlorine) g
= 2 × 35.5 g
= 71.0 g

1 mol water **molecules** (H_2O) has mass
= (2 × 1) + 16 g
= 18 g

1 mol sodium chloride **formula** (NaCl)
= (relative **formula** mass sodium chloride) g

has mass
= 23 + 35.5 g
= 58.5 g

Figure 15.41 Four oranges, 1000 g, 1 bag of oranges: all the same.

Strictly not only should the substance be specified when we mention moles but also the particles (as in the above examples). Thus '1 mol of chlorine' is potentially confusing. Does it mean '1 mol of chlorine atoms' (i.e. 35.5 g) or '1 mol of chlorine molecules' (i.e. 71.0 g)? (You are usually expected to take '1 mol of chlorine' to mean '1 mol of chlorine in its 'normal' form under room conditions, i.e. molecules'.)

It is interesting to realise that we can actually look at one (or more) moles of things. If we put 18 g of water in a glass, we have 1 mol of water molecules in the glass (Figure 15.42).

Figure 15.43 shows 1 mol of sulphur atoms (32 g), 1 mol of sodium chloride formulae (58.5 g) and 1 mol of hydrated copper sulphate formulae (249.5 g).

Figure 15.42 1 mol of water.

Figure 15.43 All the same amounts: 1 mol.

Key Facts

- Most calculations in chemistry are simple ratio calculations.
- The number of moles of something is simply a way of showing the amount of it.
- 1 mol of particles of a substance has a mass = (relative particle mass) g of the substance.
- Equal volumes of all gases, under the same conditions of temperature and pressure, contain equal numbers of molecules.
- 1 mol of molecules of any gas must occupy the same volume, under the same conditions of temperature and pressure.

Did you know?

All atoms have a mass in grams as well as a relative (atomic) mass that you are used to seeing and using. For example the mass of a hydrogen atom is 0.00000000000000000000000167 g. Is it any wonder we use **relative** masses?

Amounts of gases

Although we did not pursue the matter above we came to the conclusion that one mole of particles of anything would be a fixed number of particles. This idea helps us to understand Avogadro's Law which states

Equal volumes of all gases, under the same conditions of temperature and pressure, contain equal numbers of molecules
Putting these two ideas together we know that

1 mol of molecules of any gas must occupy the same volume, under the same conditions of temperature and pressure.

This volume is known as the **molar volume**.
The molar volume of any gas at room temperature and atmospheric pressure is 24 dm^3. Thus one mole of molecules of hydrogen, oxygen, chlorine, hydrogen chloride are all *different masses* of these gases but they all occupy the same volume at room temperature and atmospheric pressure, 24 dm^3 and this volume contains the same number of molecules of each of the gases.
Now you should be ready to tackle the calculations in the following pages, although you may need to refer back to this section from time to time in the early stages.

Questions

1   Use the relative atomic masses on your periodic table (or elsewhere) to calculate the mass in grams of 1 mol of:

a) potassium atoms, K

b) arsenic atoms, As

c) oxygen molecules, O_2

d) hydrogen chloride molecules, HCl

e) lithium chloride formulae, LiCl

f) calcium nitride formulae, Ca_3N_2

2   Use your answers to question 1 to calculate the mass in grams of:

a) 2 mol potassium atoms, K

b) 0.5 mol arsenic atoms, As

c) 10 mol oxygen molecules, O_2

d) 0.1 mol hydrogen chloride molecules, HCl

e) 0.2 mol lithium chloride formulae, LiCl

f) 4.5 mol calcium nitride formulae, Ca_3N_2

3   Use your answers to question 1 to calculate the number of moles of:

a) potassium atoms, K, in 39 g potassium

b) arsenic atoms, As, in 150 g arsenic

c) oxygen molecules, O_2, in 16 g oxygen

d) hydrogen chloride molecules, HCl, in 365 g hydrogen chloride

e) lithium chloride formulae, LiCl, in 4.25 g lithium chloride

f) calcium nitride formulae, Ca_3N_2, in 7.4 g calcium nitride

4   Given that the molar volume is 24 dm^3 at room temperature and atmospheric pressure, calculate volume, at room temperature and atmospheric pressure, of

a) 1 mol nitrogen molecules, N_2

b) 1 mol fluorine molecules, F_2

c) 2 mol oxygen molecules, O_2

d) 0.5 mol ammonia molecules, NH_3

e) 0.1 mol hydrogen sulphide molecules, H_2S

f) 10 mol hydrogen bromide molecules, HBr

5   Calculate the number of moles of molecules of each of the gases in the volumes given. All volumes are measured at room temperature and atmospheric pressure.

a) 24 dm^3 nitrogen

b) 24 dm^3 fluorine

c) 48 dm^3 oxygen

d) 12 dm^3 ammonia

e) 2400 cm^3 hydrogen sulphide

f) 120 cm^3 hydrogen bromide

modularscience.co.uk

... more at www.modular...

Why do we need to do calculations of quantities in chemistry?

When you do experiments in the laboratory you or your teacher decides the scale of the experiment. In most laboratory investigations the decision is simple and does not require a calculation: the amounts used are those that will conveniently fit in a test tube. However large–scale operations do need to be thought out very carefully. If ten times more chlorine than required were produced it would be difficult to find anything to do with the excess! So we need to be able to calculate how much reactants would be needed to produce a given mass of product, or volume of gaseous product.

How to do the calculations

In this section we will be considering three very closely related calculations. The biggest difficulty many pupils have is in recognising which calculation is which. Therefore each sub-section will begin by telling you how to recognise the particular type of calculation. There will also be a note about the use (or non-use!) of the mole concept. In each case an examination question will give relevant atomic masses and probably the equation for the reaction.

Mass relations calculations...

Recognition – given a mass, find a mass.
Mole note – it is not necessary to use the mole in this type of calculation.

Example
Calculate the minimum mass of calcium carbonate that must be reacted with excess dilute hydrochloric acid to produce 55.5 g of calcium chloride.

The answer is set out as follows:

$$CaCO_3 \quad + \quad 2HCl \quad = \quad CaCl_2 \quad + \quad H_2O \quad + \quad CO_2$$

40 + 12 + (3 × 16)   40 + (2 × 35.5)
= 100   = 111

111 g calcium chloride are produced from = 100 g calcium carbonate

1 g calcium chloride is produced from $= \dfrac{100}{111}$ g calcium carbonate

55.5 g calcium chloride are produced from $= \dfrac{100 \times 55.5}{111}$ g calcium carbonate

i.e. **minimum mass calcium carbonate needed = 50.0 g**

Note the following points about this answer:
- answers to most calculations in chemistry start from the equation
- under the equation we fill in only the relative masses of the amounts of two substances, the substance whose mass is given and the substance whose mass is to be found
- note that if the mass units are anything other than grams, only the units change.

Example
Thus
Calculate the minimum mass of calcium carbonate that must be reacted with excess dilute hydrochloric acid to produce 55.5 tonnes of calcium chloride.

The answer is set out as follows:

$$
\begin{array}{ccccccccc}
CaCO_3 & + & 2HCl & = & CaCl_2 & + & H_2O & + & CO_2 \\
40 + 12 + (3 \times 16) & & & & 40 + (2 \times 35.5) & & & & \\
= 100 & & & & = 111 & & & &
\end{array}
$$

111 tonnes calcium chloride are produced from = 100 tonnes calcium carbonate

1 tonne calcium chloride is produced from $= \dfrac{100}{111}$ tonnes calcium carbonate

55.5 tonnes calcium chloride are produced from $= \dfrac{100 \times 55.5}{111}$ tonnes calcium carbonate

i.e. **minimum mass calcium carbonate needed = 50.0 tonnes**

Volume relations (molar volume) calculations...

Recognition – given a mass, find a gaseous volume or given a gaseous volume, find a mass.
Mole note – the mole must be used in this type of calculation.

Example
Calculate the maximum volume of carbon dioxide that could be evolved when excess dilute hydrochloric acid is reacted with 50.0 g of calcium carbonate.

The answer is set out as follows:

$$
\begin{array}{ccccccccc}
CaCO_3 & + & 2HCl & = & CaCl_2 & + & H_2O & + & CO_2 \\
40 + 12 + (3 \times 16) & & & & & & & & 1 \text{ molecule} \\
= 100 & & & & & & & & \\
100\,g & & & & & & & & 1 \text{ mol molecules} \\
& & & & & & & & = 24\,dm^3 \text{ at r.t.p.}
\end{array}
$$

[r.t.p. = room temperature and pressure]

100 g calcium carbonate produce = 24 dm³ carbon dioxide

1 g calcium carbonate produces $= \dfrac{24}{100}$ dm^3 carbon dioxide

50.0 g calcium carbonate produce $= \dfrac{24 \times 50.0}{100}$ dm^3 carbon dioxide

i.e. **volume of carbon dioxide** $= $ **12.0 dm^3**

Note the following points about this answer:
- answers to most calculations in chemistry start from the equation
- under the equation we fill in only the relative mass of the substance whose mass is given or to be found and the number of molecules of the gaseous substance whose volume is to be found or is given
- note that if the mass units are anything other than grams, the conversion from those other units to grams must be carried out
  Therefore
  Example
  Calculate the maximum volume of carbon dioxide that could be evolved when excess dilute hydrochloric acid is reacted with 50.0 tonnes of calcium carbonate.

  Note 1 tonne = 1000 kg = 1 000 000 g

  The answer is set out as follows:

  $$CaCO_3 \quad + \quad 2HCl \quad = \quad CaCl_2 \quad + \quad H_2O \quad + \quad CO_2$$
  40 + 12 + (3 × 16)
  = 100

  1 molecule
  100 g 1 mol molecules
  = 24 dm^3 at r.t.p.

  100 g calcium carbonate produce $= $ 24 dm^3 carbon dioxide

  1 g calcium carbonate produces $= \dfrac{24}{100}$ dm^3 carbon dioxide

  1 tonne calcium carbonate produces $= \dfrac{24 \times 1000 \times 1000}{100}$ dm^3 carbon dioxide

  50.0 tonnes calcium carbonate produce $= \dfrac{24 \times 1000 \times 1000 \times 50.0}{100}$ dm^3 carbon dioxide

i.e. **volume of carbon dioxide** $= $ **12.0 × 10^6 dm^3 or 1.20 × 10^7 dm^3**

Avogadro's law calculations...

Recognition – given a gaseous volume, find a gaseous volume.
Mole note – it is not required in this type of calculation.
For these calculations you will need to know **Avogadro's** law which states:
Equal volumes of all gases, under the same conditions of temperature and pressure, contain equal numbers of molecules.

Example
Calculate the minimum volume of oxygen required for the complete combustion of 30 cm^3 of ethane, assuming all volumes are measured at the same temperature and pressure.

Did you know?

There are 1000 times more water molecules in a glass of water than there are oxygen and nitrogen molecules in the same volume of air, at room temperature and atmospheric pressure.

Key Facts

- If you are given a mass and asked to find a mass, the calculation can be done without the use of moles.
- If you are given a mass and asked to find a volume of gas, or vice versa, you must use the molar volume of gases.
- If you are given a gaseous volume and asked to find a gaseous volume, the calculation can be done without the use of moles.

$$2C_2H_6 \quad + \quad 7O_2 \quad = \quad 4CO_2 \quad + \quad 6H_2O$$

2 molecules   7 molecules

2 molecules ethane need   = 7 molecules oxygen

By Avogadro's law,

2 volumes ethane need   = 7 volumes oxygen

1 volume ethane needs $= \dfrac{7}{2}$ volumes oxygen

$30\,cm^3$ ethane need $= \dfrac{7 \times 30}{2}\ cm^3$ oxygen

i.e. **Minimum volume oxygen needed = 105 cm³**

Note the following points about this answer:
- answers to most calculations in chemistry start from the equation
- under the equation we fill in only the numbers of molecules of the two gases shown, the gas whose volume is given and the gas whose volume is to be found
- the temperature and pressure used make no difference to the calculation provided that they are the same at the beginning and the end of the experiment.

Questions

Mass relations calculations

1 What mass of sulphur is needed to react with 2.80 g of iron on heating?

   $Fe + S = FeS$

2 Calculate the maximum mass of magnesium chloride produced when 80.0 g of magnesium are reacted with dilute hydrochloric acid

   $Mg + 2HCl = MgCl_2 + H_2$

3 Calculate the mass of potassium hydroxide needed to neutralise 1.89 g of nitric acid

   $KOH + HNO_3 = KNO_3 + H_2O$

Volume relations calculations

4 3.00 g of magnesium ribbon is heated in steam until it catches fire. What is the maximum volume of hydrogen, measured at room temperature and atmospheric pressure, that can be produced?

   $Mg + H_2O = MgO + H_2$

5 What is the minimum mass of magnesium carbonate that must be reacted with excess dilute sulphuric acid to form $329\,cm^3$ of carbon dioxide, measured at room temperature and atmospheric pressure.

   $MgCO_3 + H_2SO_4 = MgSO_4 + H_2O + CO_2$

6 What volume of oxygen, measured at room temperature and atmospheric pressure, is formed when 3.50 g of potassium chlorate(V) is completely decomposed according to the equation

   $2KClO_3 = 2KCl + 3O_2$

Avogadro's law calculations

7 Calculate the volume of carbon dioxide produced when $10\,cm^3$ of propene, C_3H_6, is burned in oxygen to form carbon dioxide and steam only.

   $2C_3H_6 + 9O_2 = 6CO_2 + 6H_2O$

8 Hydrogen and chlorine react to form hydrogen chloride.

   $H_2 + Cl_2 = 2HCl$

   A mixture of $75\,cm^3$ of hydrogen and $50\,cm^3$ of chlorine is ignited.

   Name the gases left after complete reaction and calculate their volumes.

Learning outcomes

After completing the work in this topic you will be able to:

- convert mass-concentration into mol dm^{-3}
- convert mol dm^{-3} into mass-concentration
- use titration results in simple calculations

Chemists carry out many reactions in solution. Therefore the ability to calculate amounts of substances dissolved in solutions is very important.

Chemists need to be able to convert concentrations in g dm^{-3} to concentrations in mol dm^{-3} and vice versa.

The following examples show you how.

Calculation of concentration in mol dm^{-3}

Example
Calculate the concentration in mol dm^{-3} of a solution which contains 1.17 g of sodium chloride, NaCl, in 1 dm^3 of solution.
(relative atomic masses: Na = 23.0, Cl = 35.5)

1 mol sodium chloride formulae has mass $= (23 + 35.5)\,g$
$$= 58.5\,g$$

Concentration of solution $= 1.17\,g\,dm^{-3}$
$$= \frac{1.17}{58.5}\,mol\,dm^{-3}$$
$$= \textbf{0.0200 mol dm}^{-3}$$

An extra stage is involved in this calculation if the original solid is dissolved to make a volume of solution other than 1 dm^3

Example
Calculate the concentration in mol dm^{-3} of a solution which contains 0.234 g of sodium chloride (NaCl) dissolved in 200 cm^3 of solution.
(relative atomic masses: Na = 23.0, Cl = 35.5)

1 mol sodium chloride formulae has mass $= (23 + 35.5)\,g$
$$= 58.5\,g$$

Concentration of solution $= 0.234\,g/200\,cm^3$
$$= \frac{0.234 \times 1000}{200}\,g\,dm^{-3}$$
$$= \frac{1.17}{58.5}\,mol\,dm^{-3}$$
$$= \textbf{0.0200 dm}^{-3}$$

Calculation of concentration in g dm^{-3}

At times we also need to convert concentrations in mol dm^{-3} into concentrations in g dm^{-3}.

The following example shows how this is done.

Example
Calculate the concentration in g dm^{-3} of a solution that contains 10 mol dm^{-3} sulphuric acid (H_2SO_4).
(relative atomic masses: H = 1, O = 16, S = 32)

1 mol sulphuric acid formulae has mass = $(2 \times 1) + 32 + (4 \times 16)$ g
= 98 g

Concentration of solution = 10 mol dm^{-3}
= 10×98 g dm^{-3}
= **980 g dm^{-3}**

This is actually the approximate mass of sulphuric acid in 1 dm^3 of concentrated sulphuric acid!

Titration calculations

Having learnt how to deal with these problems there is one final calculation to consider. Earlier in this module you learnt how to find the volume of an acid solution required to neutralise a given volume of alkali solution or vice versa. The information from this type of experiment can be used to calculate the concentration of one of these solutions, if the concentration of the other solution is known.

Example
In an experiment it is found that 25.00 cm^3 of 0.100 mol dm^{-3} sodium carbonate solution require exactly 24.50 cm^3 of a solution of hydrochloric acid. The concentration of the acid can be calculated as follows.
(relative atomic masses: H = 1, C = 12, O = 16, Na = 23, Cl = 35.5)

$$Na_2CO_3 \ + \ 2HCl \ = \ 2NaCl \ + \ H_2O \ + \ CO_2$$
$$\text{1 mol} \qquad \text{2 mol}$$

24.50 cm^3 x mol dm^{-3} acid react with = 25.00 cm^3 0.100 mol dm^{-3} carbonate solution

1000 cm^3 hydrochloric acid solution contain = x mol

1.00 cm^3 hydrochloric acid solution contains = $\dfrac{x}{1000}$ mol

24.50 cm^3 hydrochloric acid solution contain = $\dfrac{24.50x}{1000}$ mol

1000 cm^3 sodium carbonate solution contain = 0.100 mol

1.00 cm^3 sodium carbonate solution contains = $\dfrac{0.100}{1000}$ mol

25.00 cm^3 sodium carbonate solution contain = $\dfrac{25.00 \times 0.100}{1000}$ mol

$\dfrac{\text{no. moles hydrochloric acid reacting}}{\text{no. moles sodium carbonate reacting}}$ = $\dfrac{24.50x/1000}{25.00 \times 0.100/1000}$ (from experiment)

= $\dfrac{2}{1}$ (from equation)

$$\frac{24.50\ x}{25.00 \times 0.100} = \frac{2}{1}$$

$$x = \frac{2 \times 25.00 \times 0.100}{24.50}$$

$$= 0.2041$$

i.e. **concentration hydrochloric acid = 0.204 mol dm^{-3}**

Note the following points about this answer:
- answers to most calculations in chemistry start from the equation
- under the equation we fill in only the number of moles of the substances whose solution volumes are given
- the 1000's cancel out in the ratio <u>no. moles hydrochloric acid reacting</u>
  no. moles sodium carbonate reacting
- if the concentration of hydrochloric acid was required in g dm^{-3} rather than mol dm^{-3} the conversion can be carried out as in the earlier example using

1 mol hydrochloric acid formulae has mass   = (35.5 + 1.00) g
                                               = 36.5 g
a 1 mol dm^{-3} hydrochloric acid solution contains   = 36.5 g dm^{-3}
a 0.02041 mol dm^{-3} acid solution contains   = 36.5 × 0.2041 g dm^{-3}
i.e. **concentration of hydrochloric acid**   **= 7.45g dm^{-3}**

Key Facts

- Know how to calculate concentrations in mol dm^{-3} from information in g.
- Know how to calculate concentrations in g dm^{-3} from information in mol.
- Know how to use the results of a titration to calculate the concentration for a solution in mol dm^{-3}.

Questions

1   25.0 cm^3 of hydrochloric acid solution neutralise 15.0 cm^3 1.00 mol dm^{-3} sodium hydroxide solution.

$HCl + NaOH = NaCl + H_2O$

Calculate the concentration of the hydrochloric acid in mol dm^{-3}

2   20.0 cm^3 of sulphuric acid solution neutralise 18.0 cm^3 1.00 mol dm^{-3} potassium hydroxide solution.

$2KOH + H_2SO_4 = K_2SO_4 + H_2O$

Calculate the concentration of the sulphuric acid in mol dm^{-3}

3   50.00 cm^3 of potassium hydroxide solution neutralise 34.0 cm^3 0.0500 mol dm^{-3} hydrochloric acid.

$KOH + HCl = KCl + H_2O$

Calculate the concentration of the potassium hydroxide solution in mol dm^{-3} and in g dm^{-3}

4   50.00 cm^3 of sodium carbonate solution react with 14.00 cm^3 0.100 mol dm^{-3} nitric acid.

$Na_2CO_3 + 2HNO_3 = 2NaNO_3 + H_2O + CO_2$

Calculate the concentration of the sodium carbonate solution in mol dm^{-3} and in g dm^{-3}.

Hard water

Science Today

Water is an excellent solvent. In fact it is often called the universal solvent because it dissolves substances so easily, which is great news for everyone from chemists to those who like sugary tea. But it is bad news for many homeowners, their clothes and even their kettles.

People living in areas where the water supply has dissolved lots of magnesium and calcium ions from the surrounding rocks face problems. When water contains these two cations it is known as 'hard' water, and it can most commonly be spotted because of the soap scum that builds up in the bath and shower. The average person spends more than six minutes a month cleaning these tap water spots, streaks and scum.

The magnesium and calcium ions in the water react with soaps to form an insoluble residue that is difficult to remove. And it is often left on hair, skin and clothing too. More seriously, scale can build up over time on the inside of metal pipes, radiators and on boilers, drastically reducing their heating capacity. Electricity and gas bills can shoot up when a boiler has to heat water through a layer of scale. In fact water heaters can typically work up to 30 per cent less efficiently with hard water than soft water.

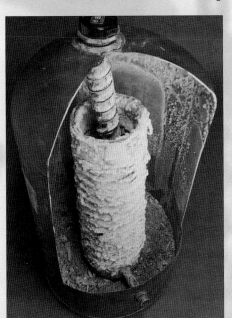

So most people living in areas with hard water want to soften it. The most common and most efficient way to do this is using a technique called ion exchange, where the dissolved calcium and magnesium ions are exchanged for sodium and potassium ions. Sodium and potassium ions do not cause the problems associated with calcium and magnesium ions.

In an ion exchange water softener, the hard water comes into contact with a bed of tiny beads that hold sodium or potassium ions. As the water passes the beads, the magnesium and calcium ions 'stick' to the surface of the beads and dislodge the potassium or sodium ions, which take their place in the water.

In time the potassium or sodium ions run out and the beads – which become covered in magnesium and calcium ions – must be recharged. To do this, a solution containing sodium or potassium ions is washed over the beads to displace the magnesium and calcium ions and place the softening ions on the beads again. The ion exchange units can be made small enough to fit inside jugs to soften small quantities of water, or big enough to build into the central heating system of a house.

There are other ways of softening hard water. In areas where the problem is not so severe, people washing clothes can add chemicals to soften batches of water for example. These work by reacting with magnesium and calcium ions to stop them forming a scum when soap is used. They can be classified as precipitating or non-precipitating depending on whether the compound they form stays dissolved in solution or not.

Others try to use devices based on magnetic and electrical fields to soften water. People have tried to use magnets in this way since the nineteenth century and many companies sell up-to-date versions to wrap around pipes. The companies say the magnetic or electric field changes the way the magnesium and calcium ions behave, to stop scale forming. But some scientists disagree, claiming that they have little or no effect.

Sometimes hard water scale just builds up so badly or quickly that little can be done to stop it. In that case, drastic action is often needed and mechanical scrubbers can be fitted to the inside of pipes to keep them scale free. But despite all these efforts many people and businesses in hard water areas are still often forced to call a plumber to dismantle, clean and even replace their pipes.

1.   Zinc carbonate is added to dilute sulphuric acid in a beaker.

Carbon dioxide is given off in the reaction.

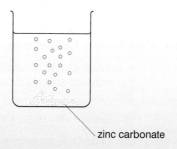

zinc carbonate

(a)   What do you SEE as this reaction takes place?   (1)

(b)   Eventually the reaction stops.

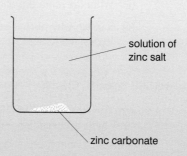

solution of
zinc salt

zinc carbonate

(i)   How can you tell when the reaction has stopped?   (1)

(ii)   How can the solution be separated from the remaining solid?   (1)

(iii)   What is the name of the salt formed by the reaction of zinc carbonate with
sulphuric acid?

A zinc chloride   **B** zinc oxide   **C** zinc sulphate

Write down the correct answer   (1)

(c)   To obtain crystals of the salt, the solution is heated to remove some water.

(i)   What would you use to heat the solution?   (1)

(ii)   What happens to water when it is removed by heating?   (1)

(Total 6 marks)

Edexcel GCSE Science: Chemistry June 2000, paper 2F, no. 2.

2.   A drain cleaner contains sodium hydroxide solution.

In a titration experiment, the sodium hydroxide in a 25.0 cm³ sample of the drain cleaner
was neutralised by 20.0 cm³ of hydrochloric acid.

The concentration of the hydrochloric acid was 0.500 mol dm⁻³.

The equation for the reaction is:

$$NaOH + HCl \rightarrow NaCl + H_2O$$

(a)   Describe, giving the names of the apparatus used, how the titration is carried out.   (4)

(b)   Calculate the concentration in mol dm⁻³ of sodium hydroxide in the drain cleaner.   (3)

Preparing and analysing   149

(c) Calculate the mass of sodium hydroxide in a bottle containing 250 cm³ of this drain cleaner.

(Relative atomic masses: H = 1.0; O = 16; Na = 23)   (3)

(Total 10 marks)

Edexcel GCSE Science: Chemistry June 2001, paper 4H, no. 4. (abridged)

3. (a)   A solution of zinc chloride can be prepared by adding excess zinc carbonate to dilute hydrochloric acid. At the end of the reaction, the remaining zinc carbonate is removed by filtration.

(i)   Explain why excess zinc carbonate is used.   (1)

(ii) State ONE other zinc compound which reacts with dilute hydrochloric acid to form zinc chloride solution.   (1)

(b)   Silver chloride can be made by reacting silver nitrate solution with hydrochloric acid.

(i)   Write the ionic equation, including state symbols, for this reaction.   (2)

(ii) Explain why pure silver chloride could NOT be made by adding silver carbonate to hydrochloric acid.   (2)

(Total 6 marks)

Edexcel GCSE Science: Chemistry June 2000, paper 4H, no. 4.

4.   Iron reacts with hydrochloric acid, HCl, to form a solution of iron(II) chloride, $FeCl_2$, and hydrogen gas. A small sample of this gas was collected in a test tube over water.

(a)   Write a balanced equation for this reaction.   (2)

(b)   (i)   Draw a diagram to show the collection of a sample of hydrogen gas over water.

(Do **not** show how the gas is produced)   (2)

(ii) What is the possible danger when hydrogen is produced in a laboratory?   (1)

(Total 5 marks)

Edexcel GCSE Science: June 2001, paper 2F, no. 7 (abridged).

5. (a)   Write the formulae for:

(i)   a sodium ion;   (1)

(ii) a chloride ion;   (1)

(iii) a copper(II) ion.   (1)

(b)   Copy and complete the following tables which show the tests for some ions.

(i)   Flame tests   (2)

Name of ion	Colour of flame
potassium	lilac
	yellow
calcium	

(ii) Tests for ions in solution

Name of ion	Reagents added	Positive result
copper(II)		light blue precipitate
	dilute nitric acid + silver nitrate solution	white precipitate
sulphate	+	

(5)

(c)   Describe a test to show the presence of ammonium ions in ammonium chloride.   (4)

(Total 14 marks)

Edexcel GCSE Science: Chemistry June 1999, paper 4H, no. 2 (abridged).

6.   A sample of tap water contains the following dissolved salts:

calcium hydrogencarbonate   calcium sulphate   magnesium sulphate

potassium chloride   sodium chloride

(a)   (i)   Hard water can be formed when water is in contact with the rock, gypsum.
              Which salt in the list is present in gypsum?   (1)

(ii)   Name TWO other salts in the list which make water hard.   (2)

(b)   Some methods of treating water are given below.

A adding chlorine   **B** adding a fluoride (fluoridation)

C adding sodium carbonate   **D** boiling the water

Which ONE of the methods (A, B, C and D) removes:

(i)   temporary hardness but NOT permanent hardness: (1)

(ii)   both temporary hardness and permanent hardness?   (1)

(Total 5 marks)

Edexcel GCSE Science: Chemistry June 2000, paper 2F, no. 7 (abridged).

7.   The balanced equation for the fermentation of glucose is

$$C_6H_{12}O_6 \rightarrow 2C_2H_5OH + 2CO_2$$

9.0g of glucose are fermented completely

(i)   Calculate the mass of ethanol formed

      (Relative atomic masses: H = 1.0, C = 12, O = 16)

(ii)   Calculate the volume of carbon dioxide, measured at room temperature and pressure,
      evolved.

      (1 mol of any gas occupies $24\,000\,cm^3$ at room temperature and pressure).

Edexcel GCSE Science: Chemistry June 1999, paper 4H, no. 3 (abridged)

acid	compound that produces hydrogen cations in aqueous solution
anion	negatively charged particle
atom	the smallest particle of an element that can take part in a chemical reaction
base	substance that reacts with an acid to form salt and water only
cation	positively charged particle
hard water	water that does not form a lather with soap.
hard water (chemical definition)	water that contains dissolved calcium and / or magnesium cations
ionic equation	equation that only shows the ions that are undergoing a change in a chemical reaction (ions that do not change are left out of the equation)
molar volume	volume occupied by one mole of molecules of any gas, under the stated conditions of temperature and pressure.
molecule	the smallest particle of an element or compound that naturally exists in the free state
permanent hardness	hardness in water that is not removed by boiling
point of crystallisation	point at which crystals form when a hot solution is allowed to cool
precipitate	insoluble solid formed when solutions are mixed.
reactant	substance which undergoes chemical change in a reaction

relative atomic mass	of an element is the mass of an average atom of the element expressed in terms of the mass of an atom of the most abundant isotope of carbon taken as 12.0000
relative molecular mass (fundamental definition)	of an element or compound is the mass of an average molecule of the substance expressed in terms of the mass of an atom of the most abundant isotope of carbon taken as 12.0000
relative molecular mass	sum of the relative atomic masses of all atoms present in a molecule of an element or compound
salt	substance formed when all or part of the hydrogen in an acid is replaced by a metal or ammonium
scale	solid deposit formed when water containing temporary hardness is boiled
scum	precipitate formed by the reaction of soap with calcium and /or magnesium cations in hard water
softening water	removal of hardness from water.
soft water	water that readily produces a lather with soap
temporary hardness	hardness in water that is removed by boiling the water
water of crystallisation	water that forms an essential part of the structure of some crystals

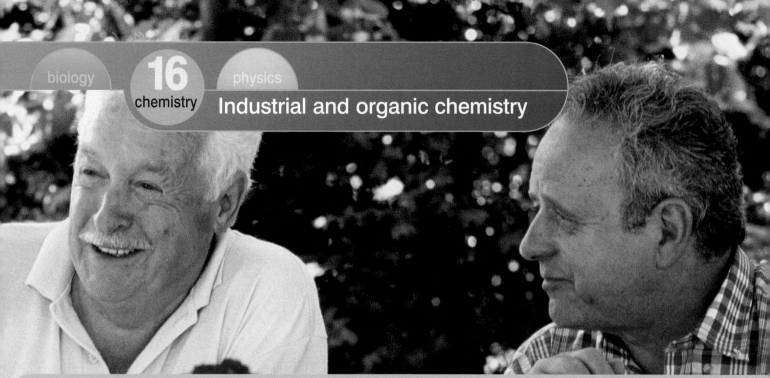

The first part of this section deals with the manufacture of materials which are very important in everyday life. As you examine the uses to which these materials are put and try to imagine life without them, you will readily realise why they are so important. Without them many of your favourite activities and pastimes would be impossible. Therefore large quantities of these and other fundamentally important materials have to be produced and what probably start out as simple laboratory reactions have to be scaled up to operate on a large scale, preferably in a continuous process. One reason why continuous processes are preferred to batch (stop, start) processes is that batch processes tend to waste energy, particularly heat energy. As you study these processes, try to think of the energy implications. You will also see that the properties of pure substances are sometimes not quite what we want for a particular use. Therefore chemists have to find ways to treat the initial products in order to obtain the required properties.

In the second part of this module you will study more organic chemistry. In newspapers and in supermarkets we see much about 'organic' foods. There has even

been a search for an acceptable definition of 'organic'. All chemists know that there has been a definition of organic since the 1800s. Originally it was a wrong definition in that chemists thought a group of chemical substances could only be produced if a living organism was involved at some stage during the process. They quickly learned that all chemicals could be produced by laboratory-type processes and although the name 'organic' was retained, the new definition was that 'organic' referred to compounds containing carbon and hydrogen: other elements might also be present but carbon and hydrogen had to be part of any organic compound. Therefore most of our food is made up of organic compounds and this is nothing to do with the way in which it was grown. Turning to the subject itself, many chemists find organic chemistry very satisfying and, by continuing to study it in this module, you should begin to appreciate that by learning a little more you will be able to discuss and predict very much more; organic chemistry uses patterns and generalisations to reduce the amount that has to be memorised. Hopefully the organic chemistry in this module will whet your appetite for more at Advanced Level!

Learning outcomes

After completing the work in this topic you should be able to:

- explain why aluminium is a less reactive metal than expected
- describe anodising and its effect on aluminium
- describe the uses of aluminium and appreciate the limitations of these
- understand the effect of alloying aluminium and the uses of the alloys

Uses of aluminium

You have already learnt how aluminium is extracted from its naturally occurring ore, bauxite. Knowledge that the process requires large amounts of electricity should enable you to understand why, although it is the most abundant element in the Earth's crust, it is still relatively expensive.

In this section you should come to realise why we must use the metal, even though it is comparatively expensive. We will look at the wide range of uses of aluminium products, aiming to understand the properties of aluminium which make it suitable for these uses. You will also come to appreciate why pure aluminium does not have the ideal properties in all cases and how we can modify these properties to make it more useful.

Figure 16.01 Milk bottle top.

Table 16.01 shows some of the uses of pure aluminium and indicates the properties on which these uses depend.

Use of aluminium	Property on which use depends
milk bottle tops	non-toxic, malleable
tear off seal on drink cartons	non-toxic, malleable, able to be produced as thin foil
cooking foil	non-toxic, malleable
food containers	non-toxic, malleable, low density

Table 16.01 Uses of aluminium.

Figure 16.02 Cooking foil.

Aluminium's reactivity, or lack of it!

Remembering how high aluminium is in the reactivity series, these uses should surprise you. You would expect aluminium to be a very reactive metal and yet it does not react with food (Figures 16.01 and 16.03) and can safely be used in a very hot oven (Figure 16.02)! The explanation for this unexpected lack of reactivity is that, although the surface of aluminium looks shiny, it is in fact covered by a complete but very thin coating of aluminium oxide. This coating is formed very rapidly when any new sample of aluminium comes into contact with air. It prevents the aluminium from reacting as quickly as you would expect with other substances. The effectiveness of this coating can be seen if we remove it from the surface of a sample of aluminium and then compare the reactivity of the resulting piece of aluminium with the reactivity of a piece of untreated aluminium. The oxide film can be removed by **amalgamating** it. This can be done most safely by placing a piece of aluminium foil in a test tube containing mercury(II) chloride solution

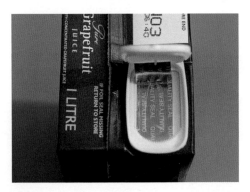

Figure 16.03 Tear off seal.

(CARE) until it begins to effervesce. Your teacher may be able to demonstrate this and then take it out with tongs, wash it under water, dry it on filter paper and leave it on the bench next to a piece of untreated aluminium foil. The result after just a few minutes is shown in Figure 16.04.

Figure 16.04 Untreated and amalgamated pieces of aluminium foil exposed to air.

You will see that the amalgamated piece of aluminium on the right is covered with feathery, white fronds of aluminium oxide and may even have reacted so vigorously that it has holes in it! The amalgamated aluminium is very reactive!

Increasing aluminium's resistance to corrosion

As you would expect, thickening the oxide film increases the resistance of the aluminium to corrosion in the presence of air. The oxide film can be thickened by a process known as **anodising**. As the name implies, this involves making the manufactured aluminium article the **anode** in an electrolytic cell. The electrolyte is dilute sulphuric acid (Figure 16.05).

The reactions at the electrodes are:
At the cathode $\qquad 2H^+ + 2e = H_2$
At the anode $\qquad 2O^{2-} = O_2 + 4e$

The oxygen produced at the anode reacts with the aluminium electrode to form a thicker coating of aluminium oxide on its surface.

Anodised aluminium is suitable for outdoor use (Figures 16.06 – 16.08).

The need for aluminium alloys and their uses

Although, for many purposes, aluminium has the great advantage over other metals of being a low density (light) metal, it lacks strength for most of the uses to which it might be put. Its strength is improved by **alloying** it with other metals to produce the required properties. Alloys are mixtures of metals in a single sample, usually solid. Magnesium, copper and zinc are some of the metals used to increase the strength of aluminium. Uses of the resulting alloys, together with the important properties making those uses possible, are shown in Table 16.02 and Figure 16.09.

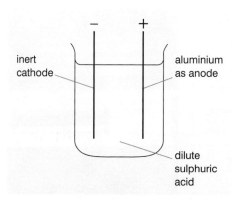

Figure 16.05 Cell used to anodise aluminium articles.

Figure 16.06 Window frames.

Figure 16.07 Greenhouse frame.

Industrial and organic chemistry

Figure 16.08 Door handle.

Use	Important properties for use listed
electrical power lines	low density, good conductor of electricity
kettles and pans	low density, good conductor of heat
drinks cans	low density, non-toxic, corrosion resistant
aeroplane and car bodies	low density, strong, corrosion resistant
car gear boxes	low density, strong, corrosion resistant
tennis racket frames	low density, strong
ladders	low density, strong

Table 16.02 Uses of aluminium alloys.

Figure 16.09 Uses of aluminium alloys.

Did you know?

Electrical power lines are made of aluminium, with a thin steel core to add strength to the wire. Copper is the most commonly used electrical conductor but if power lines were made of copper instead of aluminium, there would be three to four times more pylons scattered over our countryside in order to support the extra mass!

Key Facts

• Aluminium metal samples are protected by a thin but invisible coating of oxide.
• The oxide coating can be thickened by anodising.
• Pure aluminium metal has some uses.
• Alloying aluminium increases its strength and widens its range of uses.

Questions

1 Explain why, although aluminium is the most abundant metal in the Earth's crust, it is expensive by comparison with other less common metals.

2 Aluminium is higher than iron in the reactivity series. If similar-sized samples of each are placed in test tubes with the same volume of dilute hydrochloric acid, initially the iron effervesces more vigorously. However, after a few minutes the aluminium is effervescing much more rapidly.

a) Write balanced equations for the reactions the metals undergo.

b) Explain why the aluminium reacts more slowly initially.

c) Explain why the aluminium eventually reacts more quickly.

3 Aluminium can be (i) anodised and (ii) alloyed. For each process:

a) explain what it is

b) describe how it is carried out

c) explain the advantages of the aluminium that has undergone the process, over pure aluminium.

... more at www.modularscience.co.uk

Iron and steel

Learning outcomes

After completing the work in this topic you should be able to:

- explain the chemical reactions occurring in the blast furnace
- explain the energy changes occurring in the blast furnace
- understand why blast furnace iron and pure iron have few uses
- describe the production of mild steel and understand what happens in the process
- describe uses of mild steel and of some alloy steels

In Book 2 you have seen how iron is extracted from iron ores, such as haematite, in the blast furnace.

What happens in the blast furnace?

The reactions occurring in the blast furnace are described below and shown in Figure 16.10.
The hot air blown into the furnace (Figure 16.11) oxidises coke in the vicinity of the tuyeres to carbon dioxide.

$$C \quad + \quad O_2 \quad = \quad CO_2 \quad \text{at } 1500°C$$

This exothermic reaction provides the heat for the furnace.
The limestone undergoes thermal decomposition.

$$CaCO_3 = \quad CaO \quad + \quad CO_2 \quad \text{at } 1000°C$$

This reaction is endothermic.
The carbon dioxide from both sources rises up the furnace and, on contact with red hot carbon, is reduced to carbon monoxide.

$$CO_2 \quad + \quad C \quad = \quad 2CO \quad \text{at } 800°C$$

The carbon monoxide reduces the iron oxide to iron.

$$Fe_2O_3 + \quad 3CO \quad = \quad 2Fe \quad + \quad 3CO_2 \quad \text{at } 650°C$$

The iron forms as a spongy mass but as it moves down the furnace, it melts and runs to the bottom of the furnace to form a layer of molten iron.
[Red hot carbon also reduces the iron oxide but this is a much slower reaction because it is between two solids. The reaction is therefore much less important because it is responsible for reducing relatively little iron oxide.

$$Fe_2O_3 + \quad 3C \quad = \quad 2Fe \quad + \quad 3CO]$$

In the region where it is produced, the calcium oxide, a base, reacts with silicon(IV) oxide, an acid, to form calcium silicate. (The calcium oxide also reacts with any other acidic impurities.)

$$CaO \quad + \quad SiO_2 \quad = \quad CaSiO_3$$

Calcium silicate is known as slag and forms as a molten layer on top of the molten iron because it is immiscible with and is less dense than molten iron.

The molten iron and molten slag are tapped off separately.

Figure 16.11 Blast furnace.

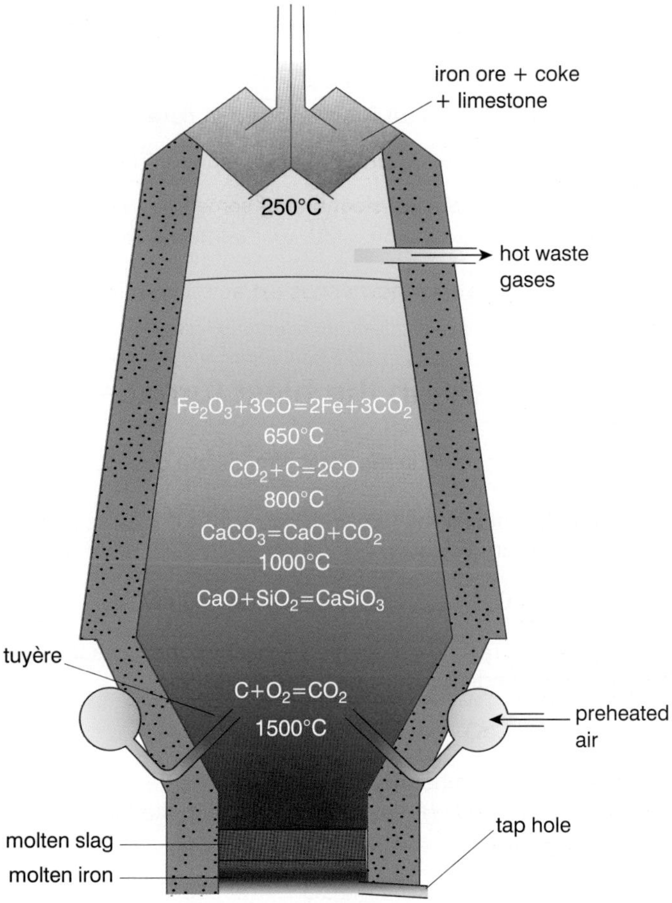

iron ore + coke
+ limestone

250°C

hot waste
gases

$Fe_2O_3+3CO=2Fe+3CO_2$
650°C
$CO_2+C=2CO$
800°C
$CaCO_3=CaO+CO_2$
1000°C
$CaO+SiO_2=CaSiO_3$

tuyère

$C+O_2=CO_2$
1500°C

preheated
air

molten slag

molten iron

tap hole

Figure 16.10 Reactions in the blast furnace.

Making iron useful

Iron direct from the blast furnace has very few uses. It contains a relatively high percentage of carbon (about 4%) and this makes it brittle. It can only be used where it does not have to withstand strong forces. Earlier than about 50 years ago the frames of school desks were thought to provide such a use (Figure 16.12) – until teenagers sat on the desk top and broke the supporting frame!

Removing carbon and other impurities completely to leave pure iron does not improve matters either, because pure iron is very soft and therefore equally useless for construction purposes.

To make iron more useful as a strong and tough material, it is converted to steel. As you would expect, the conversion of iron into steel involves lowering the carbon content and therefore increasing the flexibility of the metal without reducing its strength. To do this molten iron, direct from the blast furnace, is poured into a converter on top of scrap steel. Oxygen under high pressure is then blown onto the mixture through a water-cooled lance (Figures 16.13 and 16.14). This oxidises some of the carbon to carbon monoxide.

Figure 16.12 School desk with cast iron frame.

$$2C + O_2 = 2CO$$

The carbon monoxide combines with more oxygen at the mouth of the furnace, burning to form carbon dioxide.

$$2CO + O_2 = 2CO_2$$

In this way the carbon content is lowered to less than 2%.
One product is **mild steel** which contains between 0.1 and 0.4% carbon.

As with aluminium, the properties of the product may be modified further by alloying it – i.e. adding other metals, such as chromium, nickel, titanium and manganese. The composition and uses of steels are shown in Table 16.03.

Figure 16.13 Steel-making converter.

Figure 16.14 Oxygen lance in converter.

Type of steel	Metals added to produce alloy	Uses of steel
mild steel	none	tin plate, nuts and bolts
stainless steel	chromium, nickel	cutlery, sinks, pans
titanium steel	titanium	replacement hip joints
manganese steel	manganese	safes, armour plate

Note: all these steels contain a small percentage of carbon.

Table 16.03 Composition and uses of steels.

Questions

1 Explain the following:
a) Iron from the blast furnace is not very useful.
b) Pure iron has very few uses.

2 a) Describe how iron from the blast furnace is converted into steel.
b) Describe and explain the change in properties which accompanies the conversion of iron into steel.

3 Write the equation for the reaction in the blast furnace which:
a) is the source of heat
b) forms the reducing agent
c) results in reduction of the iron ore
d) is a thermal decomposition
e) is an acid–base reaction
f) results in formation of slag.

Did you know?

The annual production of iron in the United Kingdom in 2001 was 13.5 million tonnes, compared with 3.9 million tonnes of aluminium.

Key Facts

- Nature and sequence of reactions in the blast furnace.
- Energy changes associated with blast furnace reactions.
- Impure iron is brittle because of its relatively high carbon content.
- Pure iron is soft.
- Steel is made from blast furnace iron by lowering the carbon content.
- Uses of mild steels and alloy steels.

How important is it?

The importance of sulphuric acid can be seen when you realise that it is often said that the wealth of an industrialised nation can be judged by the amount of sulphuric acid it consumes in a year: the more sulphuric acid used, the more prosperous the country. The reason this statement is largely true is that this acid is used for so many industrial processes that are important to our everyday life. Before we look at the uses of the acid we will look at the way it is manufactured.

Manufacture of the acid

Almost all sulphuric acid is made by the Contact Process nowadays. There are three stages to this process (Figure 16.15).

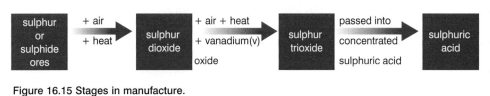

Figure 16.15 Stages in manufacture.

Stage 1 – production of sulphur dioxide from naturally occurring raw materials
Sulphur occurs naturally in some parts of the world and therefore one method of making sulphur dioxide is to simply burn this sulphur in excess air, collecting the gaseous product.

$$S \quad + \quad O_2 \quad = \quad SO_2$$

Alternatively one of the many naturally occurring sulphide ores can be burnt in air.

e.g. $2ZnS \quad + \quad 3O_2 \quad = \quad 2ZnO \quad + \quad 2SO_2$

Usable ores are shown in Table 16.04.

Name of ore	Sulphide present in ore
iron pyrites *	iron sulphide, FeS_2
galena	lead(II) sulphide, PbS
zinc blend	zinc sulphide, ZnS

Table 16.04

* Iron pyrites was known as 'fools' gold' because its gold-like appearance misled some early prospectors into thinking that it was actually gold (Figure 16.16). They rushed along to the assay office only to find that their precious find disappeared, forming a gas smelling of rotten eggs, when reacted with dilute acid!

Figure 16.16 Iron pyrites: 'fools' gold'.

Stage 2 – sulphur dioxide is oxidised to sulphur trioxide
The sulphur dioxide from stage 1 is passed, with excess air, over a vanadium(V) oxide catalyst heated to 420°C.

$$2SO_2 \ + \ O_2 \ \rightleftharpoons \ 2SO_3$$

The reaction is exothermic and after initial heating, not only is it not necessary to heat the catalyst but the system must be cooled to maintain the temperature at 420°C. The heat is a useful by-product and is used as a source of energy elsewhere in the plant.

As you have seen in Book 2, if an equilibrium reaction which is exothermic for the reaction in which reactants give products, is allowed to heat up, the yield of the products at equilibrium will be decreased. Hence it is necessary to cool down the reaction mixture. However, it must not be cooled too much or the reactions will take place too slowly and it will take the system too long to reach equilibrium.
The reaction takes place at a pressure of 1 to 2 atmospheres. You may be surprised by this because the reaction to produce products takes place with a decrease in volume (see equation above) and, again as you saw in Book 2, the equilibrium yield of reactions which take place with a decrease in volume is improved by increasing the pressure. However, in this case the equilibrium yield is good at the chosen pressure and therefore there is no need to spend money on expensive plant that can withstand higher pressures. In addition, if the pressure were to be increased too much, the sulphur dioxide would liquefy, taking it out of the gaseous system.

Stage 3 – conversion of sulphur trioxide to sulphuric acid
If sulphur trioxide is passed into water, a very vigorous, exothermic reaction takes place and small droplets of concentrated sulphuric acid are produced in the air. Obviously this cannot be allowed to happen and the reaction is moderated by passing the sulphur trioxide into concentrated sulphuric acid, which contains only 2% of water.

$$SO_3 \ + \ H_2O \ = \ H_2SO_4$$

As the reaction proceeds, water is also passed into the concentrated sulphuric acid to maintain the concentration of the acid at 98%. Of course the volume of this acid increases during this process as more acid is formed.
[This reaction is often written as a two-stage process.
First the sulphur trioxide reacts with concentrated sulphuric acid to form oleum.

$$SO_3 \ + \ H_2SO_4 = \ H_2S_2O_7$$

Then the oleum reacts with water to form the sulphuric acid

$$H_2S_2O_7 + \ H_2O \ = \ 2H_2SO_4$$

If you add the last two equations together you will obtain the original equation with the extra sulphuric acid formula that was present at the start.]

Uses of sulphuric acid

The following are just some of the main uses of sulphuric acid. Look at the importance in everyday life of the products listed and you will begin to understand why sulphuric acid is so important to the economy of a country.

16.03 Sulphuric acid: a really useful acid

Sulphuric acid is used to make:
- fertilisers –ammonium sulphate and super-phosphate
- paints and pigments
- fibres – rayon
- soaps
- detergents
- plastics
- dyestuffs

The above account for about 84% of the sulphuric acid produced in the United Kingdom.

Key Facts

- Sulphuric acid is widely used in industry.
- Sulphuric acid is manufactured by the Contact Process.
- The three stages in the manufacture.
- The uses of sulphuric acid.

Questions

1   Explain each of the following points about the Contact Process.

   a) Sulphur or a sulphide ore is used as the starting material.

   b) A catalyst is used in the reaction to produce sulphur trioxide.

   c) Sulphur trioxide is dissolved in concentrated sulphuric acid, rather than water, to make sulphuric acid.

2   If a sulphide ore is used as the source of sulphur for the manufacture of sulphuric acid, the oxide of the metal in the ore is also produced.

   a) Write a balanced equation for the change which occurs when lead(II) sulphide is burnt in air.

   b) The lead and zinc oxides produced are used to make lead and zinc.

   Suggest a method for doing this and comment on whether your method would make a suitable industrial process, giving reasons for your answer.

   c) Iron pyrites, FeS_2, is not used to manufacture iron because an impurity would make the iron unsuitable for most purposes.

   Suggest what the impurity is most likely to be and why it makes the iron unsuitable for most purposes.

3   When sulphur dioxide reacts with oxygen an equilibrium is formed.

   $$2SO_2 + O_2 \rightleftharpoons 2SO_3$$

   Explain why

   a) a pressure of 1 to 2 atmospheres is used instead of a pressure of 10 atmospheres, which would improve the equilibrium yield of sulphur trioxide.

   b) a temperature of 420°C is used instead of a temperature of 200°C, which would improve the equilibrium yield of sulphur trioxide.

Learning outcomes

After completing the work in this topic you should be able to:

- define organic chemistry
- define homologous series
- write the names, molecular and structural formulae of the first four members of the alkane and alkene homologous series

Organic chemistry

An organic compound is one that contains carbon and hydrogen in its molecule, possibly alone (in hydrocarbons) or, more frequently, with other elements. In view of this apparent huge restriction, it is amazing that there are far more organic compounds than all the other inorganic (non-organic) compounds put together. What is more, given the right starting materials, we could use comparatively simple laboratory reactions to produce an organic compound that no-one had ever made before! You may find the prospect of studying a branch of chemistry which involves so many compounds, daunting but there is no need to be overwhelmed. The real beauty of organic chemistry is the many patterns it contains, enabling you, for example, to know the reaction of one compound and hence predict the reactions of millions of other similar compounds. Organic chemistry is very satisfying in that a little knowledge goes a long way!

The organic chemistry you encountered in Book 2 did not really provide opportunities for you to see the patterns indicated above. The organic chemistry in this module enables you to begin to appreciate this attractive feature of the subject.

Homologous series

A **homologous series** is a series of compounds that have the same general formula and in which, when placed in order of increasing relative molecular mass, each compound differs in molecular formula from its neighbours by $> CH_2$.

The substances which make up a homologous series are called homologues.

Alkanes...

You have in fact met the first four members of one homologous series. Methane, ethane, propane and butane are the first four members of the alkane series (Figure 16.17). Look at the facts in Table 16.05 to see how these fit the definition above.

methane	ethane	propane	butane	alkane
CH_4	C_2H_6	C_3H_8	C_4H_{10}	C_nH_{2n+2}

Table 16.05 The alkane homologous series.

Note that:
- all have the general formula C_nH_{2n+2}
- each differs in molecular formula from its neighbours by $> CH_2$

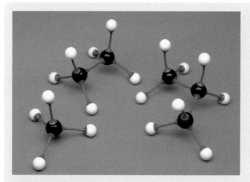

Figure 16.17 Models of methane, ethane and propane molecules.

This is the homologous series of alkanes.

Note that:

• all their names end in -ane
• the prefix (what comes before the -ane) shows the number of carbon atoms per molecule

meth-   1
eth-   2
prop-   3
but-   4

Fortunately for our memories the prefixes become systematic from then on.

Thus
pent-   5
hex-   6
hept-   7
oct-   8

If atomic models are available, make a model of a molecule of methane. Then change this to a model of an ethane molecule. As you do this you will find you remove one hydrogen atom from the carbon atom, attach a $>CH_2$ in its place and then replace the hydrogen atom. The same will happen when you make a model of a propane molecule from the model of the ethane molecule. You are adding $>CH_2$ to make each member of the homologous series into the next.

Alkenes…

You have also met the first two members of another homologous series. Ethene and propene are the first two members of the alkene homologous series. The first four members of this homologous series are shown in Table 16.06.

ethene	propene	butene	pentene	alkene
C_2H_4	C_3H_6	C_4H_8	C_5H_{10}	C_nH_{2n}

Table 16.06 The alkene homologous series.

Note that

• all have the general formula C_nH_{2n}
• each differs in molecular formula from its neighbours by $>CH_2$

This is a homologous series of alkenes.

Note that

• all their names end in -ene
• the prefix (what comes before the -ene) shows the number of carbon atoms per molecule and is the same as listed under the alkanes heading – except, of course, that there is no such thing as 'methene' because all alkenes must have at least two carbon atoms per molecule
• all alkenes have the same **functional group**

$$>C = C<$$

Physical properties of compounds in the same homologous series (homologues)

Another useful generalisation is that successive members of the same homologous series show a gradual variation in their physical properties. Physical properties are properties that do not involve chemical reactions such as boiling points, melting points, solubility in water, and solubility in organic solvents. We will demonstrate this by looking at the boiling points of alkanes and alkenes (Figures 16.18 and 16.19).

Chemical properties of compounds in the same homologous series (homologues)

The final generalisation is that members of a given homologous series show similar chemical properties.
You already know that alkanes burn in air and, on complete combustion, form carbon dioxide and water (Figure 16.20).

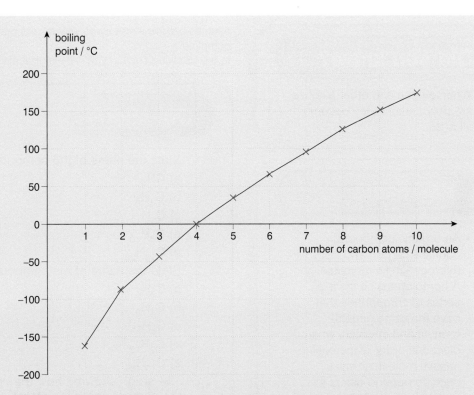

Figure 16.18 Variation in boiling points of alkanes with number of carbon atoms per molecule.

Figure 16.20 Burning methane, propane and butane.

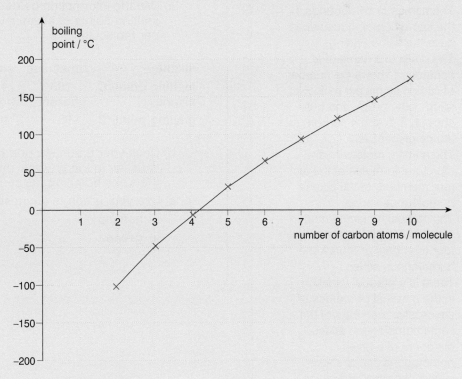

Figure 16.19 Variation in boiling points of alkenes with number of carbon atoms per molecule.

Did you know?

When ethene and other alkenes are polymerised they become alkanes.

Key Facts

- An organic compound contains carbon and hydrogen in its molecule.
- A homologous series is a series of compounds that have the same general formula and in which, when placed in order of increasing relative molecular mass, each compound differs in molecular formula from its neighbours by CH_2.
- The names of compounds in the same homologous series have the same ending.
- The prefix to a name of a compound shows the number of carbon atoms per molecule.
- Meth-, eth-, prop-, and but- show 1, 2, 3 and 4 carbon atoms respectively.
- The names, molecular and structural formulae of the first four members of the alkane homologous series.
- The names, molecular and structural formulae of the first four members of the alkene homologous series.
- There is a gradual variation in the physical properties of successive members of the same homologous series.
- Members of a given homologous series show similar chemical properties.

Alkenes behave in the same way except that it is more difficult to make them burn completely.

In the following section you will see that alcohols too, have similar chemical properties.

Questions

1 State the name of the compound with molecular formula
   a) CH_4
   b) C_3H_8
   c) C_5H_{12}
   d) C_8H_{18}
   e) $C_{10}H_{22}$

2 State the name of the compound with molecular formula
   a) C_2H_4
   b) C_4H_8
   c) C_6H_{12}
   d) C_9H_{18}
   e) $C_{10}H_{20}$

3 The graph showing how the boiling points of alkanes vary with the number of carbon atoms per molecule has been drawn for you in the text.

   a) Use the information below to draw a graph showing how the melting points of alkanes vary with number of carbon atoms per molecule.

alkane	methane	ethane	propane	butane	pentane
melting point/°C	−183	−172	−188	−135	−130
alkane	hexane	heptane	octane		
melting point/°C	−95	−91	−57		

   b) Does your graph support the idea that there is a gradual variation in the physical properties of successive members of the same homologous series? Explain your answer.

   c) Use your graph to suggest the melting point of:
   i) nonane
   ii) decane.

... more at www.modularscience.co.uk

Learning outcomes

After completing the work in this topic you should be able to:

- state the name, molecular and structural formula of ethanol and of methanol, propanol and butanol
- describe how to produce ethanol by fermentation
- describe how to produce ethanol by hydration of ethene
- understand the factors which are relevant to the choice of method to be used to manufacture alcohol
- recall that a concentrated solution of ethanol is produced from a more dilute solution by fractional distillation
- recall the composition of methylated spirit and understand why it is made
- understand the uses of ethanol
- understand that different amounts of alcohol are present in the same volume of different alcoholic drinks
- understand the social issues and possible harmful effects associated with drinking alcoholic drinks

Ethanol

Even the two words in the title of this section require some explanation because the two words 'ethanol' and 'alcohol' are often used interchangeably, especially in connection with 'alcoholic drinks'.

Ethanol has the structural formula

[This is the *full* (sometimes called 'displayed') structural formula of ethanol. It shows all the covalent bonds in the molecule. If you are asked to draw a structural formula in an examination, those like the one above are the safest versions to use.]
In equations, ethanol is often written as C_2H_5OH.
The molecular formula is actually C_2H_6O but this is rarely used.
As you can see the ethanol molecule contains two carbon atoms. The functional group present in it is –OH. There are other compounds, like ethanol, which all contain the –OH group but they have more or fewer carbon atoms in their molecules. Therefore ethanol is *an* alcohol, not the *only* alcohol.

By this stage you should have realised that ethanol has its name because it contains two carbon atoms per molecule and the characteristic ending for the names of members of the homologous series in which it appears is -ol.

It is therefore a member of a homologous series of alcohols shown below.

methanol	ethanol	propanol	butanol	alcohol
CH_3OH	C_2H_5OH	C_3H_7OH	C_4H_9OH	$C_nH_{2n+1}OH$

As members of a homologous series alcohols show a gradual variation in physical properties. Thus, with increasing relative molecular mass:
* their boiling points gradually increase
* their melting points increase
* they are all soluble in/miscible with water but their solubility/miscibility decreases.

Ethanol – a useful organic liquid

Ethanol is important as a solvent, a fuel and as the active ingredient in alcoholic drinks. In the sections to come we will look how it is made and used.

How is ethanol made?

There are two large-scale, industrial methods of making ethanol.
The second of these is only required in the higher tier part of the Edexcel specification.

(i) By fermentation of carbohydrates
The raw material is a carbohydrate – i.e. a sugar or a starch. The sugar or starch, dissolved in water, is mixed with yeast. The yeast contains enzymes (biochemical catalysts) needed for the reaction.
Assume the starting material is sucrose in sugar. The enzyme sucrase in yeast converts sucrose into glucose and the glucose, using another enzyme zymase, is converted to ethanol.

$$C_6H_{12}O_6 = C_2H_5OH + 2CO_2$$

Whatever the starting material in a fermentation process, this is the equation for the last stage of the process.
The final reaction may be the same but the starting material which contains the carbohydrate has a marked effect on the taste of the product, producing a wide range of 'alcoholic drinks' (Table 16.07). All of these contain the one alcohol, ethanol.

Alcoholic drink	Source of carbohydrate
beer	barley
wine	grapes
gin	grain, (flavoured by juniper berries)
rum	cane sugar
whisky (Scotland), whiskey (Ireland)	barley (malted)
vodka	potatoes, rice, grain, molasses

Table 16.07 Alcoholic drinks.

(ii) By hydration of ethene from crude oil.
The ethene for this process is obtained by cracking of some of the fractions produced by the fractional distillation of crude oil (Figures 16.21 and 16.22). Ethene is a by-product of cracking.
The ethene is then mixed with steam and passed, under 60 to 70 atmospheres pressure, over concentrated phosphoric acid on silica at 300°C.

$$C_2H_4 \; + \; H_2O \; = \; C_2H_5OH$$

This is a hydration process because water adds to the ethene in the reaction.

Processes (i) and (ii) are very different in their demands for raw materials, energy and climate. Therefore the process that is the most economical will vary from country to country. In poorer countries with no crude oil deposits but with climates suitable for growing crops (e.g. sugar cane) that contain the necessary carbohydrates, fermentation will be the most favourable process to use. However in richer countries, particularly those that have a plentiful supply of oil, the process using ethene is more economical.

Ethanol in alcoholic drinks is made only by the fermentation process.
But ethanol for other industrial purposes can be made by either process.

Uses of ethanol

Industry usually requires a more concentrated solution of ethanol than is produced in manufacturing processes and therefore the aqueous solution of ethanol formed must be concentrated. Normal distillation will not separate the miscible liquids ethanol and water and therefore **fractional distillation** must be used.

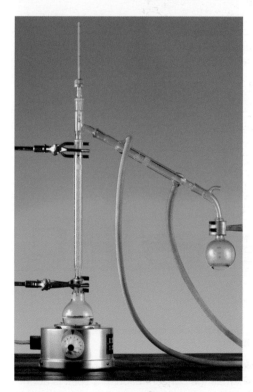

Figure 16.21 Fractional distillation in the laboratory.

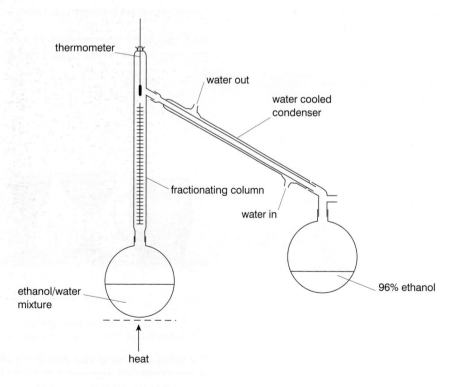

Figure 16.22 Fractional distillation in the laboratory.

This does not produce pure ethanol but the 96% ethanol solution produced from the top of the column and condensed into the receiver is suitable for most purposes. Ethanol is toxic and it would be fatal to drink solutions of this concentration. To make the 96% ethanol solution unfit to drink, 5% methanol is added to it, forming a product called **methylated spirit**. You will often see this as a purple liquid, the purple dye having been added to make it even less attractive as a drink!

Industrial ethanol (or methylated spirit) is used:
• as a fuel in some camping stoves
• as a fuel in cars, being added to some petrols or, for some purposes, used on its own
• as a solvent, for example in some paints and varnishes
• as a solvent in some cosmetics
• to make ethanoic acid
• to make ethyl ethanoate.

Alcoholic drinks

There are many reasons why we should not leave the topic of ethanol and alcohols without talking more about alcoholic drinks. As we have said, the ethanol in these drinks is toxic, particularly in large concentration. In lower concentration it has other harmful effects:
• slows reaction time
• can damage the liver
• can cause people to become aggressive.

On the other hand it also has beneficial effects:
• helps people to relax
• may help to prevent heart problems.

Many people have wrong ideas about the relative amount of ethanol in alcoholic drinks. All the drinks shown in Figure 16.23 contain the same amount of ethanol, known as one unit.

Figure 16.23 Half a pint of beer, glass of red wine, glass of sherry, measure of gin, rum, whisky, vodka (spirits): all contain the same amount of ethanol.

The volumes of the drinks containing one unit of ethanol vary because beer contains a comparatively low concentration of ethanol whereas the concentration in a spirit is about ten times higher (Table 16.08).

Alcoholic drink	Approximate percentage of ethanol by volume
beer	4
wine	10
sherry	20
gin, rum, whisky, vodka (spirits)	40

Table 16.08 Ethanol content in alcoholic drinks.

The most common mistake is to underestimate the strength of beer and think there is **one unit of ethanol** per pint rather than *per half pint*.

The only safe approach to drinking if you intend to drive a car is 'if you are going to drive, don't drink'. Any calculation of how much may be drunk to leave you still below the legal limit to drive a car is affected by size. Bigger people have more blood in their bodies and therefore a given volume of ethanol consumed will produce a lower concentration of ethanol in their bloodstream. In any case, even a comparatively small amount of ethanol in your bloodstream may slow your reaction time sufficiently to cause someone's death in an accident.

Did you know?

Ethanol, coloured by a red dye to make it visible, is used to form the thread in thermometers operating at low temperatures. Mercury cannot be used at temperatures below about $-40\,^{\circ}C$, its melting point.

Key Facts

- Ethanol is an alcohol
- The name, molecular and structural formula of ethanol, methanol, propanol and butanol.
- The fermentation manufacturing process.
- The hydration manufacturing process.
- The advantages and disadvantages of the two manufacturing processes.
- Fractional distillation is used to concentrate dilute solutions of ethanol.
- The uses of ethanol .
- Methanol added to ethanol makes it unfit to drink and forms methylated spirit.
- Different alcoholic drinks contain different amounts of alcohol.
- The disadvantages of, and social issues associated with, alcoholic drinks.

Questions

1. a) Draw out the structural formula of ethanol, showing all covalent bonds, and put a ring around the functional group.

    b) Another alcohol, methanol, has the molecular formula CH_4O.

    Draw out its full structural formula, showing all covalent bonds and put a ring around the functional group.

2. John drinks two pints of beer while Jane drinks three gin and tonics.

    a) Which of them has drunk the most ethanol?

    b) Explain why the one who drank the least amount of ethanol has a higher concentration of ethanol in his/her blood.

3. a) Describe how the glucose in grapes is converted into wine.

    b) In home wine-making, sugar (sucrose) would be added to increase the alcohol in the wine produced. Sucrose is a carbohydrate with molecular formula $C_{12}H_{22}O_{11}$ and in the first stage of the fermentation must be converted, at least in part, to glucose, $C_6H_{12}O_6$.

    Write a balanced equation showing how sucrose produces glucose by reaction with water.

... more at www.modularscience.co.uk

Industrial and organic chemistry 171

Learning outcomes

After completing the work in this topic you should be able to:

- state the name, molecular and structural formula of ethanoic acid and of methanoic, propanoic and butanoic acids

- recall that ethanol can be oxidised to ethanoic acid

- understand why wine exposed to the air deteriorates

- recall that vinegar is a dilute solution of ethanoic acid

- recall that vinegar is used as a flavouring and a preservative

- understand that ethanoic acid has the properties you would expect of an acid

A pattern in organic chemistry

If we think of compounds containing two carbon atoms per molecule, we have considered three in our organic chemistry so far.

2 carbon atom compound	Structural formula	Homologous series	Functional group
ethane		alkane	none
ethene		alkene	C = C
ethanol		alcohol	O – H

In this section we are going to look at another compound with two carbon atoms in its molecule, ethanoic acid. It has the structural formula

In equations, ethanoic acid is often written as CH_3COOH.
The molecular formula is actually $C_2H_4O_2$ but this is rarely used.

Note that
* ethanoic acid has two carbon atoms per molecule
* its functional group is –COOH
* there are other compounds like ethanoic acid, which all contain the –COOH group but they have more or fewer carbon atoms in their molecules.

Ethanoic acid is a member of a homologous series of carboxylic acids shown in Table 16.09.

methanoic acid	ethanoic acid	propanoic acid	butanoic acid	carboxylic acid
HCOOH	CH_3COOH	C_2H_5COOH	C_3H_7COOH	$C_nH_{2n+1}COOH$
(structure)	(structure)	(structure)	eg. (structure)	

Table 16.09 A homologous series of carboxylic acids.

The rest of this section will be concerned with ethanoic acid only.

Figure 16.24 Stopper for wine bottle and its air-extraction pump.

Figure 16.25 Heating under reflux with an electric heating mantle.

Figure 16.26 Heating under reflux with a water bath.

Making ethanoic acid…

It is made by the oxidation of ethanol.

This reaction occurs in an open wine bottle and is why a wine bottle should be stoppered after use if only part of the wine in the bottle has been used and the remainder is to be kept for later. Even better for preservation of the wine in good condition, is to use a stopper with a facility to extract air from inside the bottle once the stopper has been inserted (Figure 16.24).

All these precautions are to prevent the ethanol in the wine from coming into contact with air and being oxidised to ethanoic acid. Wine that has a taste of vinegar is not very pleasant!

The oxidation can also be carried out in the laboratory using an oxidising agent. Potassium

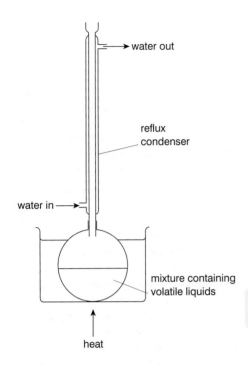

water out

reflux
condenser

water in

mixture containing
volatile liquids

heat

Figure 16.27 Heating under reflux with a water bath.

Did you know?

These organic acids are weaker than the inorganic acids (hydrochloric, sulphuric and nitric) you have studied. This is why they do not readily cause damage when used in contact with metals (e.g. removing scum from elements in electric kettles).

dichromate(VI) or potassium manganate(VII), each used in the presence of dilute sulphuric acid, are suitable oxidising agents. However both reactions require heating for an hour or more and this presents a practical problem that arises frequently in organic chemistry. As you have learnt, ethanol is both volatile and flammable and heating it in an open container with a naked flame from a Bunsen burner would be unwise and hazardous. Using an electric mantle or water bath to heat the test tube, flask or beaker containing the ethanol would reduce the risk of a fire caused by the flammable vapour catching fire. However it would not overcome the problem that the ethanol would boil and escape as a vapour, probably before it had time to react! Laboratory chemists have a simple and clever way of overcoming this problem. They put a vertical condenser into the mouth of the flask containing ethanol or any other volatile liquid. When the contents of the flask are heated, volatile substances boil and vaporise but the vapour condenses as it passes up the condenser, turns back to a liquid and runs back into the flask. This process is called **heating under reflux** and the condenser in this vertical position is said to be a **reflux condenser**. In this way volatile liquids can be heated for long periods of time without being lost from the reaction mixture (Figures 16.25–16.27).

The reaction taking place is
C_2H_5OH oxidised to CH_3COOH

C_2H_5OH + H_2O = CH_3COOH + $4H^+$ + $4e$
Note this involves loss of electrons and is therefore oxidation of the ethanol.

Uses of vinegar…

Ethanoic acid is a colourless liquid with a smell of vinegar. Vinegar is, in fact, a dilute solution of ethanoic acid and is used to flavour foods (e.g. your chips!) and also to act as a preservative (e.g. in pickled onions, pickled cabbage, etc.).

Ethanoic acid as an acid…

Even though ethanoic acid is an organic substance, as its name implies it is also an acid and has all the properties that you would expect of an acid:

- it turns acid–base indicators the usual colours in acid solutions
  e.g.   litmus   red
          methyl orange   pink
          phenolphthalein   colourless
          universal indicator   orange/pink

- it reacts with metals above hydrogen in the reactivity series to produce salts and hydrogen

  e.g. Mg + $2CH_3COOH$ = $(CH_3COO)_2Mg$ + H_2

- it reacts with bases to form ethanoate salts and water

  e.g. $NaOH$ + CH_3COOH = CH_3COONa + H_2O

- it reacts with carbonates to form salts, water and carbon dioxide

  e.g. Na_2CO_3 + $2CH_3COOH$ = $2CH_3COONa$ + H_2O + CO_2

This last reaction is often used to remove calcium carbonate scale deposits from utensils in hard water areas. When temporary hard water is boiled, e.g. in filter coffee makers, deposits of calcium carbonate form by thermal decomposition of calcium hydrogencarbonate in the water. These deposits slow the operation of the coffee maker and the makers often recommend that this problem can be solved by putting vinegar through the coffee maker instead of water (and without any coffee!) for a couple of times. The deposit dissolves as soluble calcium ethanoate in the reaction:

$$CaCO_3 \text{ (s)} + 2CH_3COOH \text{ (aq)} = (CH_3COO)_2Ca \text{ (aq)} + H_2O \text{ (l)} + CO_2 \text{ (g)}$$

Glacial ethanoic acid…

Concentrated ethanoic acid has quite a high melting point and can therefore be frozen quite easily. Your teacher might be able to put a corked tube of concentrated ethanoic acid in a refrigerator. After some time you will find it has frozen to an ice-like solid. This is why concentrated ethanoic acid is frequently called **glacial** ethanoic acid.

Questions

1 a) Draw out the structural formula of ethanoic acid, showing all covalent bonds, and put a ring around the functional group.

b) Another acid in the same homologous series, methanoic acid, has the molecular formula CH_2O_2. Draw out its full structural formula, showing all covalent bonds.

2 A waiter uncorks a bottle of red wine. Before pouring the wine, he smells the cork and detects a peculiar smell. A taste of the wine confirms that it is undrinkable, even though the wine was very good when it was bottled.

a) Explain how and why the wine had deteriorated after it had been bottled.

b) Suggest why some wine producers prefer to use plastic plugs to seal bottles of even top quality wine.

3 a) What action would you expect propanoic acid, C_2H_5COOH, to have on universal indicator?

b) Describe two other different types of reaction that show that propanoic acid is an acid. Include equations for the reactions.

… more at www.modularscience.co.uk

Key Facts

- The name, molecular and structural formula of ethanoic acid and of methanoic, propanoic and butanoic acid.
- Ethanoic acid is formed by the oxidation of ethanol.
- Ethanol is oxidised to ethanoic acid in an open wine bottle.
- Vinegar is a dilute solution of ethanoic acid.
- Vinegar is used as a flavouring and a preservative.
- Ethanoic acid has the usual reactions of an acid:
  - with indicators it produces the usual acid colours
  - with metals above hydrogen in the reactivity series, it forms salt + hydrogen
  - with bases, it forms salt + water
  - with carbonates, it forms salt + water + carbon dioxide.

Flavours and fragrances

Learning outcomes

After completing the work in this topic you should be able to:

- recall that ethyl ethanoate is an ester
- describe how ethanol reacts with ethanoic acid to form ethyl ethanoate
- recall that esters are sweet-smelling substances
- recall that esters are responsible for many flavours and perfumes

Making ethyl ethanoate

Your teacher may be able to show you an experiment in which five drops of ethanol are mixed with five drops of glacial ethanoic acid and one drop of concentrated sulphuric acid (**CARE**). If the mixture is gently warmed and then poured onto sodium carbonate solution in an evaporating dish, you will detect a very pleasant odour which you may recognise as that of nail varnish remover. The product you can smell is ethyl ethanoate. [Pouring the mixture produced onto sodium carbonate solution in this way neutralises any strong-smelling unreacted ethanoic acid (to give odourless sodium ethanoate) and spreads the product, which is immiscible with water and less dense than water, over a large surface area. This makes it easier to smell.]

Ethyl ethanoate has the structural formula:

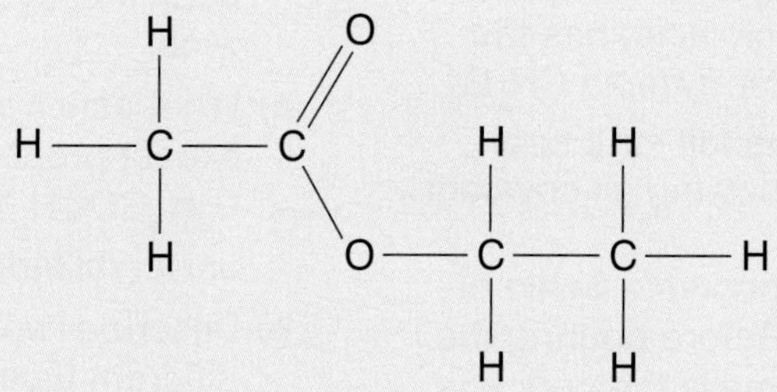

Figure 16.28

In equations, it is often written as $CH_3COOC_2H_5$

[Its molecular formula is $C_4H_8O_2$ and is never used]

The preparation reaction…
It can be produced by the reaction

$$CH_3COOH + C_2H_5OH \rightleftharpoons CH_3COOC_2H_5 + H_2O$$

You will notice that the concentrated sulphuric acid does not appear in the equation. It is present for two purposes: (i) to remove water and so improve the equilibrium yield of the reaction, and (ii) to act as a catalyst.

The homologous series of esters

Like all the other organic substances you have met, ethyl ethanoate is just one of a homologous series of compounds. These compounds are called **esters**.

In this case it is not as simple to write the formulae of its homologues. The four simple carboxylic acids and the four simple alcohols you have met give rise to not four but sixteen different esters! This is because each of the four carboxylic acids can combine with each of the four alcohols to give a different ester!

Fortunately it is quite easy to learn how to work out the structures and names of the possible esters.

Any carboxylic acid, RCOOH, can be reacted with any alcohol, R'OH, to give an ester RCOOR'

The structural formula of the ester is

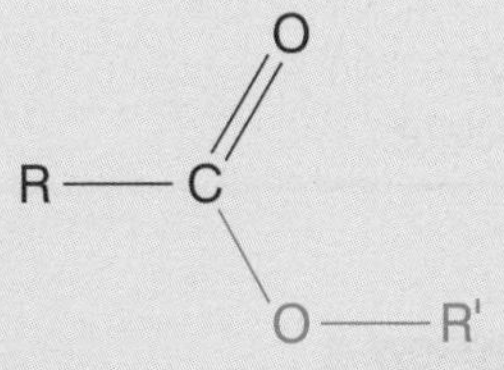

Figure 16.29

Consider it to be made up of the RCO group (shown in red) from the acid, RCOOH, and the R'O (shown in blue) group from the alcohol, R'OH

A reaction to produce the ester RCOOR' is therefore

i.e.   RCOOH   +   R'OH $\rightleftharpoons$ RCOOR'   + H_2O

Any reaction in which an ester is produced is known as an **esterification reaction**.

Table 16.10 shows how this works for ethyl ethanoate and two other esters.

Ethyl ethanoate is just one of a group of organic compounds called esters. They are all sweet smelling substances and it is these compounds that are responsible for most of the flavours of fruits and the fragrances of flowers. As you might guess blends of different esters are used to make perfumes. You may have tasted the sweets, pear drops; the flavouring in these sweets is pentyl ethanoate, an ester (Figures 16.30–16.34).

carboxylic acid	alcohol	ester
ethanoic acid	ethanol	ethyl ethanoate
methanoic acid	ethanol	ethyl methanoate
ethanoic acid	methanol	methyl ethanoate

Table 16.10

Figure 16.30

Figure 16.31

Figure 16.32

Figure 16.33

Figure 16.34

Pentyl ethanoate...

The structural formula of pentyl ethanoate is shown in Figure 16.35.

and it is usually written as $CH_3COOC_5H_{11}$

You should be able to predict that it is made by reacting ethanoic acid, CH_3COOH, with pentanol, $C_5H_{11}OH$.

Figure 16.35 Pentyl ethanoate.

Test for all alcohols

Indeed the formation of a sweet smell when a substance is mixed with glacial ethanoic acid and a little concentrated sulphuric acid and warmed can be used to show that the substance is an alcohol because all members of the alcohol homologous series will give an ester in this reaction. Once again this shows that members of the same homologous series have similar chemical properties.

Tests for all carboxylic acids

Conversely the formation of a sweet smell when a substance is mixed with ethanol and a little concentrated sulphuric acid and warmed can be used to show that the substance is a carboxylic acid because all members of the carboxylic acid homologous series will give an ester in this reaction

Did you know?

Oils and fats are naturally occurring esters. There is no chemical difference between them, just the physical difference that oils are liquids and fats solids at room temperature. This can cause confusion when an oil leaves a hot country to arrive in a colder country as a fat, with an apparently inappropriate label!

Key Facts

- Ethyl ethanoate is made by reacting ethanoic acid with ethanol.
- Ethyl ethanoate is an ester.
- The formulae and structures of esters made from the first four members of the carboxylic acid homologous series reacting with the first four members of the alcohol homologous series.
- Esters are sweet smelling substances.
- Esters provide flavourings and perfumes.
- Esterification is a reaction which shows that all alcohols have similar chemical properties and can be used as a test for alcohols.
- Esterification is a reaction which shows that all carboxylic acids have similar chemical properties and can be used as a test for carboxylic acids.

Questions

1. Draw the structure of the following esters, showing all covalent bonds.

   a) ethyl ethanoate

   b) methyl ethanoate

   c) propyl ethanoate

2. Draw the structure of the carboxylic acid and the alcohol that would react to form each of the following esters. Show all covalent bonds.

   a) ethyl propanoate

   b) propyl butanoate

   c) butyl methanoate.

3. A perfume manufacturer wants to investigate the odour of an ester with the molecular formula $C_5H_{11}COOC_6H_{13}$.

   Describe an experiment to produce a small sample of this ester to test its odour from a carboxylic acid and an alcohol. Your answer must include the names and structural formulae of the starting materials, the conditions for the reaction, the name of the product and the equation for the reaction.

... more at www.modularscience.co.uk

The bridge over the river Tay

Science Today

On the evening of December 28th 1878 one of the most famous accidents in the world took place. The mighty railway bridge over the River Tay in Scotland collapsed under the weight of a train, plunging the train, passengers and crew into the icy waters below and killing 75 people.

The bridge had only opened six months earlier to great acclaim because it was by far the longest bridge in the world at that time, over two miles long. Heralded as a supreme piece of Victorian engineering, it cost £300 000 (an incredible sum in those days) used over 10 million bricks and some 4 000 tons of cast iron. The resulting enquiry found problems with most aspects of the bridge's engineering, and more recent analysis has also pointed the finger at the cast iron girders used to build it.

To Victorian engineers, cast iron was an ideal material with which to work. It was cheap, made from easily available materials and could be moulded into just about any shape. And it was hard, very hard.

But that hardness comes with a price. Cast iron is so hard that it is also extremely brittle. For example, apply a force in an attempt to twist the metal and it will retain its shape until the very last second before snapping.

This was tragically demonstrated again much more recently in 2001 when the failure of cast iron girders was blamed for another railway accident, this time in India. More than 250 people were badly injured and 52 killed when a bridge over the Kadalundi river collapsed under the weight of a train. This time the bridge was very old, in fact it was built by the British before the ill-fated Tay Bridge.

The Indian disaster demonstrates why engineers have developed replacements for cast iron. Cheaper manufacturing techniques and better designs mean that materials like steel and aluminium are now the favourite choice of bridge builders. Elsewhere, other engineers are replacing heavy, cast iron underground gas pipes laid decades ago with plastic. At the time, cast iron was virtually the only material available to make pipes hard enough to install underground.

But cast iron pipes can only handle low pressures, and because they are so brittle they break easily when disturbed during construction work or when it gets very cold. Furthermore, because pipes made of cast iron are so heavy, they could only be made in very short lengths and so have joints every few metres. Many of these joints are now starting to leak and have to be repaired.

But that does not mean that cast iron is now redundant. In fact it is still one of the most widely used materials for some specialised purposes. It is still cheaper and harder than many other materials, and because it melts at a relatively low temperature it can be poured into intricate shapes. As a result, cast iron is used to make specialised engine parts, valves and engine blocks for locomotives, printing presses and machine tool frames. It is also becoming popular again with cooks and chefs in the kitchen, being increasingly used to make cooking pots and frying pans.

1.   Aluminium is often used in the form of an alloy.

   (a)   What is an alloy?   (1)

   (b)   Why is an aluminium alloy more useful than pure aluminium?   (1)

   (c)   Aluminium alloys can be used to make stepladders and parts of aeroplanes. Give two
         reasons why aluminium alloys are better than steel for these uses.   (2)

                                                                            (Total 4 marks)

Edexcel GCSE Science: Chemistry June 2001, paper 2F, no. 2. (abridged)

2. (a) Use words from the box to copy and complete the paragraph.

   | carbon   coke   iron   limestone   oxygen   slag   steel   titanium |

   Production of steel

   The metal produced in the blast furnace is ....

   It contains about 4% carbon. Some of this carbon must be removed to produce
   .... This is done by blowing .... through the molten
   metal. To produce alloys, other metals such as .... may be added.   (4)

   (b) Copy and complete each of the following sentences.   (1)
        (i)   Steel is better than cast iron for making car bodies because steel...

        (ii) Stainless steel is better than mild steel for making saucepans because stainless
              steel...   (1)

        (iii) Aluminium alloy is better than stainless steel for making aeroplanes because
              aluminium alloy...   (1)

                                                                            (Total 7 marks)

Edexcel GCSE Science: Chemistry Chemistry June 1999, paper 2F, no. 1

3.   Molten, impure iron is made from iron ore in the blast furnace.

   (a) In the blast furnace, reducing agents change iron ore into iron.
        Give the name of ONE substance which can act as a reducing agent in the blast furnace.
                                                                                            (1)

   (b) The main impurity in iron ore is silicon dioxide (SiO_2)
        Describe how this is removed.
        Give the name of the raw material which must be present to remove this impurity and
        describe the reactions involved, naming the waste product formed.
        You should include equations for the chemical reactions taking place.   (5)

                                                                            (Total 6 marks)

Edexcel GCSE Science: June 2000, paper 4H, no. 5.

4.   Some industrial processes involve passing gases over heated solid catalysts. This
        happens in the manufacture of sulphuric acid in the Contact Process.

   (a) For the catalysed reaction for the manufacture of sulphuric acid in the Contact Process,
        give the names of:

Industrial and organic chemistry

the TWO reacting gases (2)

the product (1)

the solid catalyst (1)

(b) Sulphuric acid is used to make fertilisers.

Explain what fertilisers are used for and the problems that they cause when they are washed into rivers. (3)

(Total 7 marks)

Edexcel GCSE Science: Chemistry June 2000, paper 2F, no. 5.

5. The alcohols are an example of a homologous series.

(a) (i) The structures of the first two alcohols in the series are shown.
Copy and complete the table to show the names and the structures of all the alcohols.

Name	Structure
	$H-\overset{\overset{H}{|}}{\underset{\underset{H}{|}}{C}}-O-H$
ethanol	$H-\overset{\overset{H}{|}}{\underset{\underset{H}{|}}{C}}-\overset{\overset{H}{|}}{\underset{\underset{H}{|}}{C}}-O-H$
propanol	
butanol	

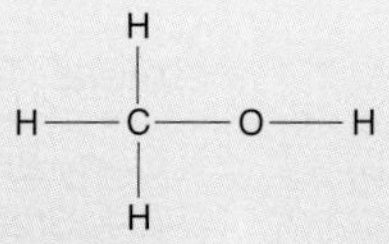

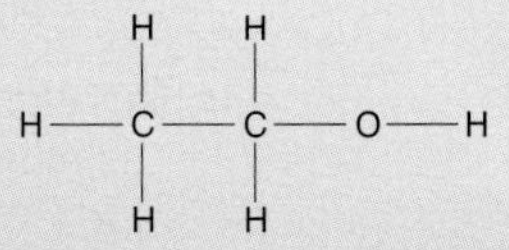

(3)

(ii) Why are these alcohols members of the same homologous series? (1)

(iii) Describe a trend in a physical property of these alcohols. (2)

(b) Compounds in the same homologous series undergo similar chemical reactions.
Describe one such reaction of the alcohols.
Write a balanced equation to show this reaction for one of the alcohols. (4)

(Total 10 marks)

Edexcel GCSE Science: paper 6C, Chem B specimen no. 4.

6.   Ethanol is present in alcoholic drinks.
      Its formula is C_2H_5OH.

(a)   (i) The structures of four molecules are shown.

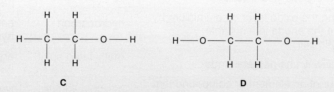

      Which structure represents ethanol? Write down the correct answer.   (1)

      (ii) Give the names of the three elements in ethanol.   (3)

(b)   (i) A copy of the label from a bottle of beer, an alcoholic drink, is shown.

+---+
| |
| Beer |
| |
| 200 cm³ |
| |
| Alcohol content 5% |
| |
+---+

      Calculate the volume of alcohol in the bottle.   (2)

      (ii) Whisky, another alcoholic drink, contains up to 50% alcohol.
            Explain why it is more dangerous to drink 500 cm³ of whisky than to drink the same
            volume of beer.   (1)

      (iii) Why should a person who is going to drive a car not have an alcoholic drink?   (2)

                                                              (Total 9 marks)

Edexcel GCSE Science: Chemistry June 2001, paper 2F, no. 4.

Glossary 16

alkane	saturated hydrocarbon
alkene	unsaturated hydrocarbon which contains one carbon to carbon double bond
alloy	a homogeneous mixture of metals in a single sample
alloying	converting a pure metal to an alloy
amalgamating aluminium	treating aluminium with mercury to remove its oxide layer
anode	the positively charged electrode
anodising aluminium	thickening the oxide layer on aluminium by making it the anode in a suitable electrolytic cell
cathode	the negatively charged electrode
chemical property	behaviour of an element or compound that involves a chemical reaction (to produce new product)
ester	compound formed by the reaction of an alcohol with a carboxylic acid
endothermic reaction	reaction which takes in heat from its surroundings
exothermic reaction	reaction which gives up heat to its surroundings
fractional distillation	separation of a mixture of miscible liquids by distillation using a fractionating column

functional group	the atom or group of atoms in a molecule of an organic compound that is responsible for the compound's characteristic chemical reactions
heating under reflux	heating volatile liquids in a flask fitted with a vertical condenser.
homologous series	a series of compounds that have the same general formula and in which, when placed in order of increasing relative molecular mass, each compound differs from its neighbours by $>CH_2$.
hydrocarbon	compound that contains carbon and hydrogen only in its molecule
methylated spirit	aqueous ethanol to which methanol has been added
miscible liquids	liquids which mix together in all proportions
oxidation	the addition of oxygen or a non-metallic element: it may involve the removal of electrons
physical property	behaviour of an element or compound that does not involve a chemical reaction
reduction	the removal of oxygen or a non-metallic element: it may involve the addition of electrons
reflux condenser	condenser fitted to a flask in a vertical position to allow volatile liquids to be heated without loss of vapour

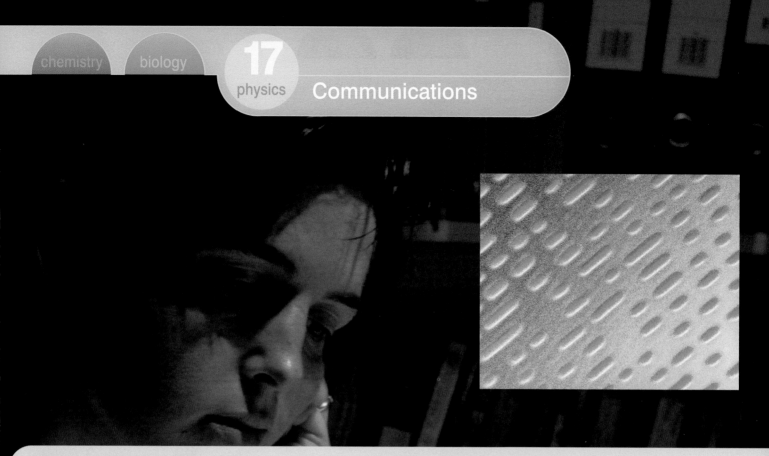

Sending a text message is part of normal life but only a couple of years ago it couldn't happen. We use encoders, modulators, transmitters, receivers, amplifiers and transducers without thinking, every time we send a message. In this module you will find out exactly what goes on when you text or phone someone – and how science has made it possible.

Everything is going digital. The previous generation technology is no longer good enough. Find out why optical fibres and digital signals make such a difference to all our communications systems. Find out also why images and sound sometimes arrive at your receiver out of sequence or badly distorted. Digital transmission of messages should be better – but is it really?

To some people digital storage of music is supposed to be better than the old analogue systems. Others claim you only get the real depth of sound from vinyl.

Here you will find out how CDs, vinyl and tape store sound and how loudspeakers and microphones work so we can hear sound clearly.

We've been communicating by code since the first smoke signals were sent. Getting wireless messages across the Atlantic a hundred years ago was a major advance. Now we can simply bounce radio waves off the ionosphere or off a passing satellite. News reports from anywhere in the world can be beamed into your home within fractions of a second of the event happening, thanks to satellites. How do engineers launch, control and talk to the thousands of satellites now orbiting the earth? And how much can they see when they are looking at you? This module finally looks at the different types of communication systems and how satellites are becoming essential for leisure and business use.

Learning outcomes

After completing the work in this topic you will be able to:

- recall that communication systems can be broken down into a number of blocks, each having specific functions

- recall the terms for the various building blocks and their associated functions
  - encoder
  - modulator
  - decoder
  - storage
  - transmitter
  - receiver
  - transducer
  - amplifier

Making contact

Oh so simple…

You want to text message a friend. You press the buttons on your mobile the required number of times to generate each letter, press send and… That's it. Simple! But there's so much going on in the background it's almost frightening (Figure 17.01)!

Figure 17.01 Sending a text message may only cost a few pence BUT there's a huge amount of technology behind it.

Did you know?

You are covered in transducers. Each of your five senses: touch, taste, smell, sight and hearing work because a sensor converts the input into an electrical signal which your brain interprets. For example the retina in your eye is a transducer. It converts light (the input signal) into an electrical signal that is transmitted along your optic nerve to your brain where it generates an image. Your skin can sense touch or temperature (the input signals). Transducers (sensors) in your skin convert the input signals to electrical signals for your brain. Your brain interprets the information and you react with a feeling of pain or pleasure.

Person	Part of the system	What the technology does
you press buttons on the phone to write message	**transducer**	transducer (sensor) senses pressure on button and converts it to electrical signals (voltages)
or speak into phone	**encoder**	electronics in phone converts your voice into binary code i.e. converts **analogue signal** (continuously varying voltages) to **digital signal** (pulses or sequence of on/off voltages)
press send	**modulator**	electronics in phone modulates digital signal (adds it to a carrier wave)
	transmitter	modulated carrier wave (carrying your message) transmitted from phone to nearest antenna (mobile phone aerial)
	amplifier	message has to be sent through optical fibres to an antenna near to your friend's phone. It may need boosting on the way by an amplifier if the signals lose energy
	storage	message remains stored on the system until your friend accesses it

Table 2.2 Comparison of cell division in mitosis and meiosis.

friend accesses messages	**receiver**	friend's phone instructs central hub to send any messages it holds. It then picks up the carrier wave from the nearest mobile phone mast (antenna) with your message on it
	demodulator	electronics in friend's phone subtracts carrier wave leaving your message in binary code
friend reads your message	**decoder**	electronics in friend's phone decodes binary code into electronic signals (voltages) which a transducer converts to the voltages which put letters on their phone display – your message has arrived!

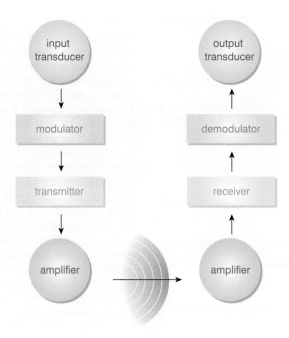

Figure 17.02 Each part of a communications system has an important function. If one part doesn't work the whole system fails.

Questions

1   Start your own dictionary of communications words to be built up as you go through this module. Explain what each word in the middle column of the table above means in your own words.

2   For each of your five senses explain what the input signal to the transducer in your body is and, therefore, what 'signal' the transducer is converting to an electrical signal.

3   For a live television programme make a block diagram of the parts of the system (as in Figure 17.02) but add labels to say exactly what each block does in this case.

... more at www.modularscience.co.uk

This shrinking world

'Telecomms' and 'the telecomms industry'. We've been communicating for generations but it's only recently that the 'tele' word got put in. *Tele* comes from the Greek word for distance. Now we are even sending and looking for messages from outer space.

Making light work...

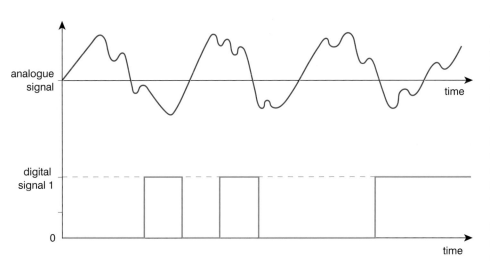

Figure 17.03 Analogue signals are continuous waves. Digital signals are pulses in binary code.

Most signals start off as mechanical inputs, for example: the sound as you speak into a microphone; the pressure as you touch a button; the temperature of an object or the light in an area.

A transducer converts this input into an electrical signal but it doesn't have to be transmitted as an electrical signal. More and more information is now transmitted as light signals through optical fibres. Once the encoder has converted the analogue electrical signal into a digital signal (Figure 17.03), the system can use the digital signal to switch on and off (pulse) light. LEDs (light emitting diodes), lasers and, now, laser diodes are switched on and off by the digital signal. Each flash of light goes along an **optical fibre** to the decoder ready for the receiver to receive the information.

What's good about light...

One big advantage of using light pulses in optical fibres instead of electrical pulses (or even analogue signals) in electrical wires is that the light pulses travel much further before they need boosting. All signals are **attenuated** (their energy is reduced) as they travel. Light signals are attenuated less than electrical signals. This means that when the cables are installed underground fewer boosters are needed.

Another advantage of using light pulses along optical fibres compared with electrical signals is that you can send several messages at the same time. For example, it is possible to send 12 000 channels of communication down a single optical fibre which is only 125 nm (0.125 mm) diameter.

One way to do this is to use different wavelengths of light for each message. This is limited by the number of separate wavelengths of light we have available. At present we can use 160 different wavelengths.

Another way is called 'time **multiplexing**'. This means sending bits of each person's message in sequence (a chunk of the first message, then a chunk of the second, etc.) (Figure 17.04).

Did you know?

In the future we will be able to send enough information along optical fibres to have 60 million television channels or more phone calls than there are people on Earth. We need to be able to do this to allow all the computers to talk to each other.

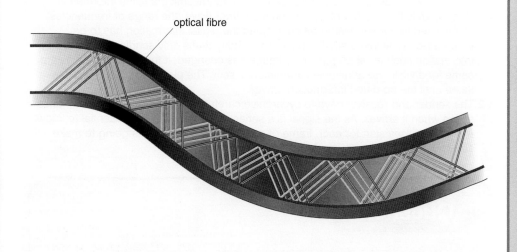

optical fibre

Figure 17.04 By using different wavelengths of light for each message we can send several messages down the same fibre. This is multiplexing.

Upgrading to digital

Optical fibres cannot transmit analogue signals. They only work with digital. Everyone is talking about how good digital is. Digital signalling has certainly given us the ability to transmit hundreds of television channels. There are some very good reasons why we prefer it.

The advantages of digital signals are:
1 The electronic circuits for digital devices are relatively cheap.
2 It's easy to encrypt (scramble) signals so users can be sure their messages are secure. This is important for internet shopping, for example.
3 It is easy to combine several types of information on one channel by multiplexing – for example sound and video on one channel for a video phone.
4 Digital signals can be compressed so that more channels can be transmitted on a smaller bandwidth than is needed for analogue signals (but see 'disadvantages').
5 There's less of a problem with 'noise' so the signal you receive is usually clear and correct. Noise is where the information is corrupted usually by extra bits being added on by mistake. Analogue systems often have problems with noise such a hissing on a radio or white speckles on a TV picture.
6 The electronics used for digital systems can be programmed to look for errors in the message or picture and to make corrections. So even if something does go wrong because of the signal being reflected off something or part of the information getting lost, the system can usually put it right before the receiver sees or hears it.

Did you know?

Even when you are phoning or e-mailing someone at the end of your street the information may end up going round the world before it arrives at the receiver. This is because all the information goes first to a centralised node before it is sent through the network. So the route it takes may not be the best or fastest one it could take. Even more surprising is that each piece of information may go by different routes between you and the receiver. This is how some information gets lost or arrives out of sequence.

Key Facts

- Flashes of light can be used to transmit signals via an optical fibre. The on/off flashes correspond to the 1s and 0s of a digital signal.
- Using digital signals has several advantages over analogue signals:
  - the electronic circuits for digital devices are relatively cheap
  - it's easy to encrypt (scramble) signals so users can be sure their messages are secure
  - it is easy to combine several types of information on one channel
  - there's less of a problem with 'noise' so the signal you receive is usually clear and correct
  - the electronics used for digital systems can be programmed to look for errors in the message or picture signal and to make corrections.

There are some disadvantages with digital systems:

1 Digital systems usually need more 'bandwidth' to transmit the same information. Bandwidth is the amount of 'space' on the carrier wave (the range of frequencies) that is used to carry the information. Instead the digital information has to be compressed to fit into a smaller bandwidth. This means only sending new bits of information such as when part of an image has changed. If the picture remains the same for a while, no additional information is sent. The picture you see stays the same until the up-dated information arrives.

2 The sender and receiver have to sychronise carefully so that the information makes sense when it arrives. As the signal is a series of short pulses it is essential to know when the pulses start for each frame of a picture if the decoder is going to make sense of them.

Questions

1 Write an 'infomercial' which explains to potential customers for optical fibre communication systems how light can be encoded to transmit information and show how the information is transmitted along an optical fibre. Use labelled diagrams to help your explanation. Finally describe how the optical fibre can transmit more than one message at a time and list all the benefits of optical fibre technology to impress your potential customer. (An infomercial is really a commercial or advertisement but looks like it is simply giving information. The trick is to persuade your potential customer that you are only being helpful when you are really trying to show how good your product is – in a very subtle way.)

2 Your parents and teachers will only have had analogue television and phone systems when they were your age. Interview them about how different television and phones were in 1960s/1970s compared with today. Write a brief overview of what they remember and then write an explanation for them of how digital communication systems are an improvement on what they were used to. Beware! not all of the changes they will talk about are due to digital technology.

Learning outcome

After completing the work in this topic you will be able to:

* recall the different methods of storage and retrieval of information including:
  - digital storage as used with CD players
  - analogue storage as used in record players
  - use of magnetic tape, photo diode and diode-laser

The end of a civilisation

Historians talk about the invention of writing as a major step in civilisation. The invention of the printing press suddenly allowed thousands more people to read the thoughts and ideas of others (Figure 17.05). So much of our past has been recorded in writing – or 'hard copy' as we now call it. But now we are entering an era where all information can be stored electronically. CDs, DVDs, web pages, electronic journals and books are all examples of how we can store information. Scientists are now developing electronic paper which can be taken away to be read but reprogrammed with a different text when you are ready. Maybe this will allow people to change history AFTER it has happened!

Figure 17.05 The printing press allowed everyone to read what they wanted when they wanted. Electronic paper is the same BUT the text can be changed simply by reprogramming.

Reading with light…

The shiny side of a compact disc (**CD**) is covered with information but it is invisible to the naked eye. Only a laser can probe the information that it holds. When you write to a CD on your computer you 'burn' information onto it. You are making tiny holes or pits in its surface. To read the CD a laser beam from a tiny diode laser is made to scan the pits (Figure 17.06).

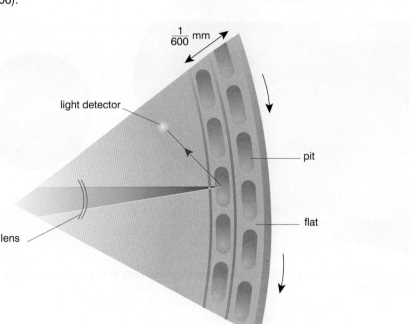

$\frac{1}{600}$ mm

light detector

pit

flat

lens

Figure 17.06 A CD or DVD is read by a laser beam and the electronics of your system decodes the digital signal and puts the information onto your screen. If the laser light is reflected the system receives a 1. If the laser hits a pit in the disc surface the system receives a 0.

If there is no pit the laser light is reflected. The light sensor (photo diode) picks up the reflected laser light and registers a 1. If the laser beam hits a pit the light sensor receives no light and registers a 0. This happens over and over again and the series of 1s and 0s are noted by the decoder and the information is understood as you see it on the screen or hear it from the speakers.

It wasn't always like this...

Parents will still talk about 'record players' and may even have a collection of albums gathering dust somewhere. For a long time records were the most popular way to store music. The record has one long groove running round and round from the outside edge to the centre. Deep inside this groove is a series of 'lumps'. The record is made to go round and round at a particular speed (33 r.p.m. – revolutions per minute – for long playing records or albums, 45 r.p.m. for singles). As the needle on the 'pick up' of the record player hits each 'lump' on the groove in turn, a tiny magnet inside the pick up arm moves inside a coil and generates a varying analogue current that goes up and down with the lumps on the record. This current is sent to the amplifier and 'decoded' to give you the music you hear from the speakers. The series of lumps in the groove are a real copy of the sound wave you eventually hear (Figure 17.07).

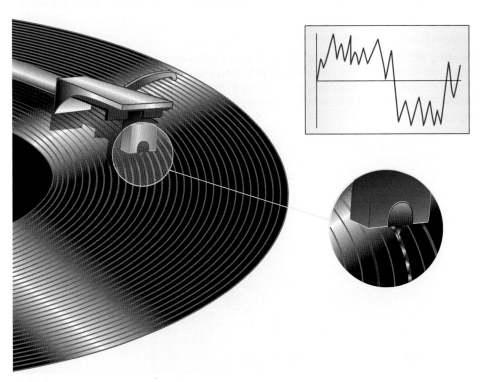

Figure 17.07 The lumps in the record groove are a real copy of the sound wave it generates in the hifi system.

DAT – son of magnetic tape...

Very early music recording on large reel-to-reel machines relied on magnetism to work. VHS video recorders and cassette players use the same idea. They all have long lengths of plastic tape. The plastic tape has magnetic particles embedded in it. The particles are magnetised in different directions along the tape. As the tape is played the magnetised particles go past the play-back head. The varying magnetism induces a varying current in the play-back head and this is an analogue signal. This analogue signal is sent to the amplifier and then to the speakers to be output as the music or TV programme you want to enjoy (Figure 17.08).

Modern Digital Audio Tape (DAT) uses the same idea but the information is encoded into a digital signal when the tape is recorded and decoded by the tape player when it is played.

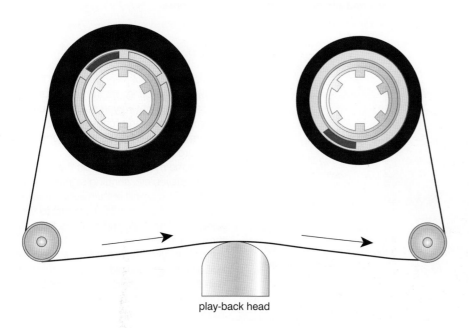

play-back head

Figure 17.08 The magnetic particles in the tape are magnetized in different directions. The tape head senses this and decodes the information to produce sound.

Key Facts

- Information is stored on a CD as digital code. A diode laser is reflected off the surface of the CD. A photo diode senses the reflected light and so the digital code is read, decoded and the output played.
- Analogue information can be stored on a record as a series of lumps. These generate an analogue electrical signal which matches the analogue sound wave.
- Magnetic tape can be used to store analogue or digital information. Magnetised particles in the tape store the encoded information.

Questions

1 What is the difference between digital information and analogue information?

2 Explain why people say that vinyl records store analogue information and CDs store digital information.

3 What do the diode laser and the photo diode do in a CD player?

4 Magnetic tape can store analogue or digital information. How does it do this?

5 Do you think there is a danger that we will lose information as the technology for CDs is over taken by the next generation of communications technology? Might it be possible to re-write history if so much of our written record is in electronic form only, such as on the internet?

... more at www.modularscience.co.uk

Learning outcome

After completing the work in this topic you will be able to:

- understand the physical principles of a variety of transducers, including
  - moving coil loud speaker
  - moving coil microphone
  - erase, record and playback heads of a tape recorder

Hear the music

Loudspeakers look very dull; inside there is simply a large cone. Yet they can vibrate in precisely the right way to sound exactly like a complete concert orchestra, a live performance by a band, the sea lapping on the shore or a baby crying.

To hear the music you rely on the CD player or tape player, etc. sending signals to the amplifier. The amplifier then sends analogue signals (varying electrical currents) to the speakers. These varying currents flow through the wires of a coil and, therefore, create a varying magnetic field around the coil. The magnetic field of the coil interacts with the magnetic field of a magnet that surrounds the coil. This makes the coil move. As the coil moves, so the loudspeaker cone (diaphragm) attached to it moves (Figure 17.09). This is how the vibrating cone sends out sound waves across the room where your ear can distinguish between each instrument and all the notes they are playing.

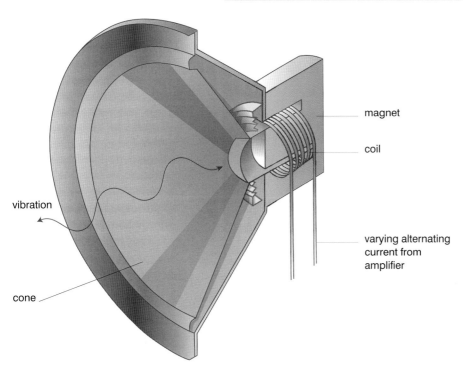

magnet

coil

vibration

varying alternating current from amplifier

cone

Figure 17.09 In the loadspeaker, the coil receives an analogue signal (varying current) from the amplifier. The coil's magnetic field interacts with the magnet's field so the coil moves. This makes the cone of the speaker vibrate.

Karaoke night

Put a microphone into someone's hand and they instantly think they are the next great celebrity. Sometimes you might wish microphones had never been invented. A microphone is exactly the same as a loudspeaker working in reverse. The sound waves as you sing hit the diaphragm which is delicate enough to move with every sound that hits it (like your ear drum does). As the diaphragm moves it makes a coil move back and forth around a magnet. Each time the coil moves it induces a current in itself. This varying current (analogue signal) is then fed to the sound system where it might be recorded on tape or CD or output directly through an amplifier and speakers for everyone to hear (Figure 17.10).

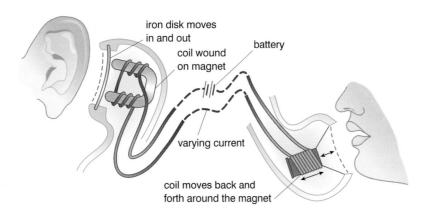

iron disk moves in and out

coil wound on magnet

battery

varying current

coil moves back and forth around the magnet

Figure 17.10 The diaphragm of the microphone is pushed by the air as you sing. This makes the coil move and induces a current in the coil. This feeds to the hifi, is amplified and is output through the speakers.

Play it again Sam

Recording onto magnetic audio tape is a very simple process. Analogue signals (varying current) from the microphone are fed to the recording head in the tape machine. These signals change the direction and strength of the magnetic field of the recording head. The recording head magnetises the magnetic particles in the plastic tape as the tape runs past (Figure 17.11). Obviously the magnetic particles are magnetised in the same direction as the recording head at the time it goes past. The magnetised particles carry the information needed to reproduce the sounds when you play the tape. They stay magnetised in the same pattern so you can replay the tape as often as you want – until you re-record the tape.

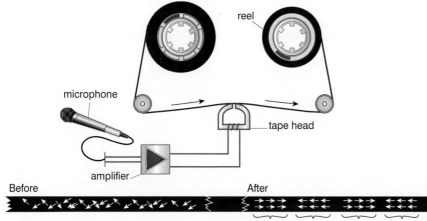

Figure 17.11 The tape is magnetised as it runs past the recording head and stores the information ready for playback.

To play back the tape passes the playback head which senses the direction that the magnetised particles are magnetised. The changing magnetic field from the magnetised particles generates a changing current which is fed to the amplifier to be output as sound (and images if it's a video tape).
Erasing simply means putting a random signal into the recording head so that the magnetised particles in the tape are not aligned in any particular pattern

Questions

1   Explain why it is reasonable to say that a microphone and a loudspeaker are the reverse of each other.

2   Describe the difference between a record head and a playback head of a tape recorder.

3   Describe clearly how magnetism is involved in each stage of making a tape recording and playing it back (include the microphone and loudspeaker stages).

Did you know?

Inside high-quality loudspeaker cabinets there are usually two speakers. The small one will work best for higher sounds. It is called the tweeter. The large one will work best for lower pitched sounds. It is called the woofer.

Key Facts

*   A moving coil loud speaker relies on a changing current to induce a changing magnetic field which causes a coil to move. The coil makes the cone vibrate to generate sound.
*   A moving coil microphone is the reverse of a loudspeaker. The sound makes the diaphragm vibrate which induces a changing current in the coil. This analogue signal (varying current) is sent to the amplifier to be output as sound through the speakers.
*   A tape recorder has a record head which magnetises particles in the tape into a particular pattern to represent the sound (and images). The playback head senses the direction that the particles are magnetised and generates a matching varying current. The analogue signal is decoded by the electronics in the amplifier and output as sound (and images).

Noise: what's that all about then?

If there were no noise on communications signals we could communicate messages to the outer limits of the universe without the messages ever becoming corrupted. Unfortunately noise gets in everywhere. **Noise** is random signals that get in and spoil the real signal.

Did you know?

The first optical amplifier was recently invented at Southampton University. In all the underground optical fibre cables presently in use, the optical signal has to be converted to an electrical signal before it can be amplified. The repeater uses a photo diode to convert the optical signal to an electrical signal. An electrical amplifier then amplifies it before it is converted back to an optical signal. The repeater is adding energy to the signal so it has to be powered. Typically the repeaters work on 12 kV DC. Getting this supply to repeaters under the sea and providing effective insulation to keep water out of the joints is still causing engineers considerable problems and much research is being done to solve these problems.

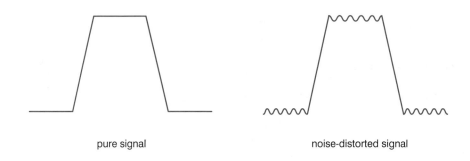

pure signal   noise-distorted signal

Figure 17.12 A pure signal and one corrupted by noise. The noisy signal is corrupted by additional information added. This makes it unclear and difficult to understand.

When you receive the noisy signal you get more than you bargained for. You get the main message plus some extra which usually spoils the quality of what you wanted to hear or see (Figure 17.12). On a radio, noise might cause a continuous hissing or buzzing on the sound or a 'crack' when someone switches on the light. On television you might get a snowy effect on the images (Figure 17.13).

The regeneration…

If a signal has started to deteriorate it makes sense to try to repair it before it becomes unrecognisable. That's where

Figure 17.13 A noisy signal makes watching TV very frustrating.

regenerators come in. A digital signal's pulses can become corrupted by noise. A **regenerator** will regenerate the original signal by working out whether the signal is a 0 or a 1 and 'clean it up', giving the original perfect signal.

Attenuating - not such a good thing either...

Attenuation means loss of energy or loss of intensity. If you are a long way from a radio or television transmitter the signal may be very low strength by the time it gets to you (in the same way that sound dies away as you move further from the source). Mobile phone users often notice that their signal strength is sometimes not strong enough if they are too far from a mobile phone mast or they go into a train tunnel. This might cause the call to 'break up' or simply go dead.

Repeaters...repeaters...repeaters...

Attenuation was always a problem for electrical signals in cables such as in the old telephone systems. The resistance of the wire caused the energy of the signal to decrease gradually the further it went. Boosters (repeaters) had to be put in every few kilometres to amplify the signal (to add energy to it and so increase its amplitude) so it could reach the receiver with enough energy to be understood. Optical fibres don't have resistance so you might think there shouldn't be a problem with attenuation. However, attenuation can still be a problem with light signals travelling down an optical fibre. Typically an optical signal can travel 300 km along a fibre without suffering serious attenuation. However some signals need to travel several hundred or even thousand kilometres, under the sea perhaps. Attenuation of the light pulses can then mean that the signal gets too weak to be received successfully. To overcome this engineers install a **repeater**, usually every 100 km for long-distance installations, to amplify the signal.

Figure 17.14 Light signals travel 300 km along optical fibres without suffering attenuation. To travel further than that they need amplifying from time to time. Repeaters add energy to the signal so that it can arrive with enough power to be decoded successfully.

Key Facts

- Noise is the additional unwanted information that sometimes get added to a signal and corrupts it making it difficult to understand.
- Attenuation is when a signal strength is reduced. Electrical signals are attenuated by the electrical resistance of the wires. Light signals are attenuated by being dispersed by impurities in the glass. This makes the signal too weak to be decoded by the receiver.
- Regenerators will take a corrupted digital signal and return it to its original form so that it can be understood.
- Repeaters in electrical cables and optical fibre communications add energy to the signal so that it arrives with enough power to be understood when it is decoded.

Questions

1 Why is noise a nuisance for telecommunications? What effect does it have and how does it happen?

2 What does the word 'attenuation' mean? How is this problem overcome?

3 Add words like attenuation, noise, digital, analogue, etc. to your Telecoms Dictionary.

... more at www.modularscience.co.uk

Transmitting radio waves

Learning outcome

After completing the work in this topic you will be able to:

- Recall a brief history of the development of sending and receiving information including
  - communication by telegraph
  - wireless transmissions leading to radio and television
  - satellite communications

How it all started

Timeline

1834	Carl Gauss and Ernst Weber build the first electromagnetic telegraph
1838	William Cooke and Charles Wheatstone build telegraph
1844	Samuel Morse demonstrates telegraph line
1858	First trans-Atlantic cable is laid – fails after 26 days!
1876	Alexander Bell patents first telephone
1894	Oliver Lodge demonstrates wireless (radio) communication over 150 metres
1901	Guglielmo Marconi transmits first trans-Atlantic wireless signal
1905	Reginald Fessenden transmits speech and music by radio
1915	Bell System completes a telephone line across America
1920	First scheduled radio programme broadcast
1926	John Logie Baird demonstrates television
1933	Edwin Armstrong invents frequency modulation
1936	BBC begin first television broadcasts
1937	Alex Reeves invents pulse code modulation (digital modulation)
1941	John Atanasoff invents the computer
1947	The transistor (component of every silicon chip) is invented
1950s	Microwave communication links are developed
1953	Colour television developed in USA
1953	First trans-Atlantic telephone cable laid – can carry 36 voice channels
1957	First Earth space craft launched by Russia – Sputnik 1

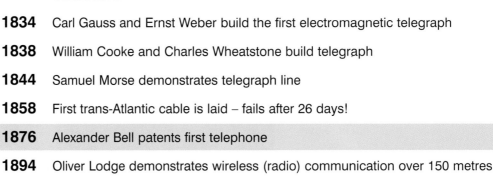

1958 Laser invented by A. Schawlow and C. Townes

1958 First silicon chip produced by Robert Noyce

1961 First stereo radio broadcasts

1962 First satellite television link between USA and Europe – Telstar 1

1963 First touch-tone phone

1965 First commercial communications satellite put into orbit – Early Bird

1968 Cable television systems first developed

1971 Intel develops first single chip microprocessor

1972 First cellular phone developed by Motorola

1976 Personal computers developed

1980 Bell Systems develop optical fibre communication

1980 Compact disc first developed by Philips and Sony

1981 First IBM PC introduced

1985 Fax machines become popular

1989 'Pocket' mobile phone introduced by Motorola

1990 World Wide Web began

1993 Two million web sites in existence

1996 Thirteen million web sites in existence

1997 Intel Pentium processor produced with 7.5 million transistors on it

1998 Satellite and cable digital television becomes popular in UK

1999 Interactive television becomes popular

Figure 17.15

Questions

1 When was it first possible to send telecommunications across the Atlantic?

2 What is the difference between telegraph and radio?

3 When was speech and music first transmitted by radio?

4 When was the first satellite launched?

5 When did the BBC first transmit television programmes?

6 Stereo radio is an example of multiplexing. When did this first happen?

7 When did the first communications satellite go into orbit?

... more at www.modularscience.co.uk

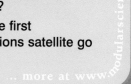

Getting there

Electromagnetic waves travel in straight lines. This should mean that you can only send radio information between a transmitter and receiver that are in line with each other. This would be very limiting as the Earth is curved. Fortunately we have worked out ways of sending radio waves to receivers over the horizon. By choosing the frequency carefully we can send radio waves successfully as ground waves, sky waves or space waves.

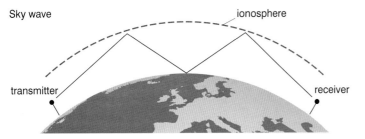

2–30 MHz – high frequency – sky waves – waves reflect off the ionosphere – used for amateur radio, international broadcasting, long-distance aircraft and ship communication, telephone, fax

below 2 MHz – waves travel as ground waves – used for long-range navigation; submarine communication

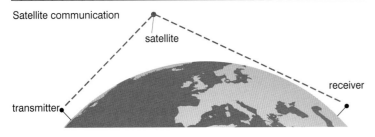

3–30 GHz – space waves – used for satellite communication and radar microwave links

Figure 17.16

Space waves – line of sight

30–300 MHz – very high frequency – line of sight propagation – used for VHF, FM two-way radio

0.3–3 GHz – used for cell phones, radar, microwave communication – line of sight

Figure 17.17

Ionosphere – transparent to light, but reflects radio waves

The **ionosphere** is a layer of the atmosphere high above the Earth where cosmic rays and UV radiation from the sun cause ionization of the atoms and create lots of free electrons. Although light from the sun can get through this layer perfectly well, the ionisation in the rarefied air at high altitudes affects medium- and high-frequency radio waves. This means we can use the ionosphere to reflect radio waves and bounce them back to Earth.

The ionosphere at different heights affects different parts of the spectrum in different ways.

* The layer at about 45–55 miles height will absorb lower frequency radio waves and refract higher frequency radio waves.
* The layer about 65 miles up will reflect high frequency waves during the day (but disappears at night)
* The layer above at about 90–250 miles altitude will reflect high frequency waves at night.

Unfortunately the amount of ionisation varies at different times of the day as well as with different seasons of the year and sun spot activity. This means it is not always certain that a high-quality signal will get to the receiver if we have to rely on the ionosphere to reflect the signals.

Diffraction

Radio waves, like all waves, can be diffracted (Figure 17.18). The size of the gap or obstacle must be about the same size as the wavelength of the wave for diffraction to happen. For radio waves the gap or obstacle has to be anything from a few metres to a few kilometres in size. This means only buildings or mountains can diffract radio waves. Diffraction of radio waves makes the signal sometimes end up in regions you don't expect it to. Radio waves can also be diffracted so that they follow the curvature of the Earth.

radio waves

Figure 17.18 Radio waves can be diffracted around obstacles that are similar in size to their wavelength.

Interference

Interference in telecommunications is a form of 'noise'. Noise occurs when additional signals are added to the main signal and degrade it and make it difficult to decode. This gives a very low quality image or sound. On a radio signal it might sound like hissing or

Key Facts

- Transmitted radio waves can reach the receiver as ground, sky or space waves depending on the frequency.
- The ionosphere between 45 and 250 miles above the earth can reflect radio waves.
- Radio waves can be diffracted by buildings, mountains, curvature of the Earth and transmission dishes.
- The amount of diffraction depends upon wavelength and physical dimensions involved.
- Radio waves are long wavelength electromagnetic waves.
- Interference affects the quality of the received signal.

humming. On a television picture it might appear as a 'snowy' effect or white spots flashing on the screen or might cause extra, faint, images to appear (ghosts) (Figure 17.19). Interference can happen in any of three places:

- the signal source: the transmitter may generate extra signals which are added to the signal it is transmitting
- the receiver may cause the interference: especially if it is suffering overload
- there may be interference on the transmission channel itself. This means extra signals get mixed into the main signal during transmission.

Figure 17.19 The image has ghosting where additional images appear behind the main image. These extra signals are due to additional signals added on during transmission perhaps because the main signal was reflected off a building. This is an example of interference.

Questions

1 What is the difference between ground waves, sky waves and space waves?

2 Make a chart to show the difference in wavelength (and frequency) of waves that are typically ground waves, sky waves and space waves.

3 Explain the word diffraction. Why are radio waves only diffracted by particularly large obstacles?

4 How does interference affect the quality of a signal? Where might interference get into the system?

... more at www.modularscience.co.uk

Working it out

All radio waves travel at the same speed, 300 000 000 m/s, through a vacuum. They are long wavelength electromagnetic waves. Their speed is less if they are travelling through air (but not much less). The equation that works out precisely what speed waves travel at, whatever the conditions is:

$v = f \lambda$

v = wave speed in metres per second
f = wave frequency in hertz
λ = wavelength in metres

So an ultra high frequency (UHF) radio wave may have a frequency of 3 GHz. As it travels through space from a satellite its wavelength will be:

$v = f \lambda$
$\lambda = v/f$

3 GHz is 3 gigahertz or 3 000 000 000 Hz

$\lambda = 300\,000\,000/3\,000\,000\,000$
$\lambda = 0.1\,m$

Basic radio waves are ground waves and are Amplitude Modulated (**AM**). This means the carrier wave has the signal wave added to it which changes its amplitude (Figure 17.20).

carrier wave   signal wave   amplitude modulated

Figure 17.20 Ground radio waves are amplitude modulated. The carrier wave has its amplitude changed (modulated) by the added sound information.

When the receiver receives the combined wave it has to demodulate it by subtracting the carrier wave from it and then it can use the signal to create the sound you hear on the radio.

Key Facts

- Relationships between wave speed, frequency and wavelength are:

  $v = f\lambda$, $f = v/\lambda$, $\lambda = v/f$

- The triangle to remember this is

- Amplitude modulation (AM) and frequency modulation (FM) are used in radio communications.
- AM alters the amplitude of the carrier wave by adding the signal wave to it.
- FM uses the frequency of the signal to alter the frequency of the carrier wave.
- AM signals have a greater range and are more susceptible to noise than FM signals.
- FM signals are often preferred as they are more likely to produce a clean signal without noise.

An AM wave could have a frequency of 6 MHz. It would still travel at close to 300 000 000 m/s through the atmosphere so its wavelength would be

$v = f\lambda$
$\lambda = v/f$

6 MHz means 6 megahertz or 6 000 000 Hz

$\lambda = 300\,000\,000/6\,000\,000$
$\lambda = 50\,m$

Amplitude modulated radio waves can be transmitted long distances as they follow the curvature of the ground due to diffraction. But AM radio waves tend to pick up interference from the atmosphere during transmission so the sound from the radio can often have a lot of hissing and other problems on it. Customers prefer to hear a clean sound so many radio stations now use Frequency Modulated (**FM**) waves to transmit their programmes. Higher frequency radio waves can be frequency modulated. This means the frequency of the carrier waves is altered by adding on the signal wave.

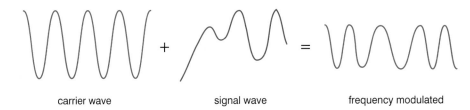

carrier wave   signal wave   frequency modulated

Figure 17.21 The frequency of the carrier wave is modulated by the signal it carries. This is frequency modulation.

To work out the wavelength of an FM wave at 150 MHz

$v = f\lambda$
$\lambda = v/f$

150 MHz means 150 megahertz or 150 000 000 Hz

$\lambda = 300\,000\,000/150\,000\,000$
$\lambda = 2\,m$

Questions

1. Calculate the wavelength of the following radio waves as they travel through the atmosphere at 300 000 000 m/s:

   a) Amateur radio waves at 12 MHz

   b) FM radio at 210 MHz

   c) VHF television at 300 MHz

   d) Mobile phone communications at 0.3 GHz

2. Add the words 'amplitude modulation' and 'frequency modulation' to your Telecoms dictionary.

3. Why do listeners prefer radio stations that use frequency modulated signals rather than amplitude modulated signals?

Interview with Dr Abdul-Hamid Sadka

Science Today

Abdul-Hamid Sadka works at The University of Surrey in the Electronics and Computer Science Department. He is working on ways to make video networking better. **Here he explains what he is doing and how it will make the next generation of video phones much better than what we have today.**

'For a long time we could have had video phones but no one was prepared to pay the cost of sending images and sound using analogue technology. It needed such a wide bandwidth that it cost too much. Now we have digital technology it is possible to send video and sound much more cheaply.'

'For a start, with analogue signals you can't send different channels on the same frequency carrier wave, for example BBC and ITV have very different frequencies from each other. The gap between the frequencies is needed to fit in all the information for each image (25 per second) and for the sound. This is called the bandwidth.'

'Digital is much better as you can send lots of different things – video, speech, internet data etc on the same carrier wave by multiplexing. For example you can send chunks of information about each one in sequence. Of course this means the sender and receiver have to be very well synchronised so that the receiver can make sense of what it's receiving.'

'The other big advantage about digital is that you can connect several users to the same link – this is how the internet and video conferencing work.'

'Of course the problem with video phones and video conferencing is that the image is often jittery and of low visual quality. When two people are communicating by video phone the first one has to send an image then the second one has to reply with an image. These images travel through a complicated network of phone lines and often the images can get corrupted. Sometimes the images arrive at the user out of sequence or one might get lost altogether. What you see is not very accurate and that's why it appears jittery. This is what I'm working on at the moment.'

'The idea is called "compression". Instead of sending every part of every image every time, we only send the areas that have changed. For the areas that are the same we just send a type of "ditto" mark. The decoder will receive all this and simply change the parts of the image that are different and leave the rest as it is. It's as if some parts of the image are frozen. You only notice the sections that change.'

Questions

1. Why does Abdul say that digital technology is going to make video phones cheaper?

2. What other advantages does he mention about digital technology?

3. Why are video phones not very good at the moment?

4. Abdul plans to use 'compression' to make video phone images better. How does this work?

5. How is it possible for a series of images to arrive out of sequence when you send them over a digital network?

... more at www.modularscience.co.uk

Satellites

Learning outcomes

After completing the work in this topic you will be able to:

* recall the difference between passive and active satellites

* describe the different uses for satellite communication systems including:
  - telephone and television communications
  - surveillance and monitoring
  - navigation

* understand the features of a geostationary orbit and explain the importance to telecommunications of geostationary satellites

* understand the connection between the Earth's spin and the use of monitoring satellites place in low polar orbits

Going higher

The future is in space...

Satellite television, satellite navigation systems, weather satellites, spy satellites.... There are tens of thousands of man-made items orbiting the Earth – and the majority of them are just waste (Figure 17.22).

There has always been a satellite orbiting the Earth. The Moon is the Earth's natural satellite. However since 1962 we have been launching artificial satellites into space for everything from communications to surveillance and navigation.

Here's looking at you...

Telstar 1 was the first active satellite to be launched. It relayed television pictures between America and Europe (Figure 17.23). For the first time we were able to watch news reports direct from America. Unfortunately the satellite was in polar orbit so broadcasters had to time their transmissions to coincide with when Telstar was overhead. **Active satellites** receive and send out information (Figure 17.24). They are controlled from a control station on Earth and transmit their information to the control station when interrogated.

Figure 17.22 There are over 10 000 artificial objects orbiting the Earth but not many are still in working order.

Did you know?

The astronauts in the space shuttle often have to change course as they orbit the Earth to avoid crashing into space debris.

Figure 17.23 Telstar 1 was the first ever artificial satellite. It was so famous that it even had a song in the charts of the time named after it.

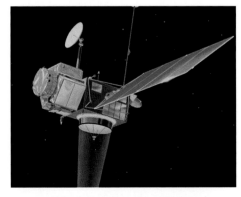

Figure 17.24 Signals have to travel up to the satellite and reflect off to the receiver on Earth. This distance causes the signals to be delayed slightly.

Early Bird, launched in 1965 was the first commercial communications satellite. Like all the modern communications satellites since, it was put in **geostationary orbit** (Figure 17.25). This means it was about 36,000 km above the surface of the Earth (about six times further from the Earth than the Earth's radius) and travelled at the right speed to orbit once in 24 hours. To do this a satellite has to be in an equatorial orbit. This way it stays above the same point on the Earth's surface as viewed from the Earth. The satellite dishes always point at the satellite and always receive the television pictures.

Figure 17.25 Geostationary communications satellites are in equatorial orbit so cannot be used by people working in Antarctica. They have to use Polar orbiting satellites which only come overhead every 2 hours or so.

Watching you, watching me...

Governments and companies around the world can buy ready-made satellites from a company in Surrey. Surrey Satellite Technology Limited is the only UK company building and launching satellites and it has customers from all over the world such as Portugal, Taiwan and Malaysia. These countries need surveillance or monitoring satellites. They use them to monitor land use and deforestation, weather patterns and storms, sea temperatures, land movement during or after earthquakes and the military activity of their neighbours. These satellites are only about 900 km above the Earth's surface so they orbit much faster than the communications satellites. Typically they orbit once in 100 minutes.

Figure 17.26 PoSAT–1, Portugal's first satellite achieved through a technology transfer programme with SSTL Carries Store and Forward DSP communications, GPS and Earth observation payloads.

As these low earth orbit satellites are sent up to orbit over the poles, they will see the Earth segment by segment as it spins beneath them (Figure 17.27). This is how the surveillance satellites can see so much in a day. Of course their Mission Control stations can only transmit and receive information when the satellite is overhead. Each pass last only 10–20 minutes so the engineers have to track them carefully and be ready to send and receive.

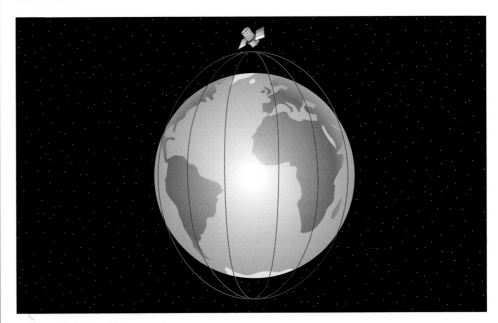

Figure 17.27 Polar orbiting satellites orbit over the poles and see the whole earth, segment by segment, as it spins beneath the satellite.

The GPS constellation…

There are even satellites that orbit the Earth as a group. There is a constellation of 24 satellites that orbit the Earth twice a day and work together to aid navigation. The Global Positioning System satellites broadcast location coordinates to receivers on Earth. Planes, ships and even individual people and cars can receive information from these satellites and work out where they are to within 5–10 m.

Even satellites carry GPS receivers. PoSAT-1 receives data from the GPS satellites and works out its own position and velocity. Using an accurate on-board time reference PoSAT-1 can generate its own schedule and synchronise itself with other computers. For reference look at: www.ph.surrey.ac.uk/satellite or www.sstl.co.uk

Key Facts

- Passive satellites simply reflect signals. Active satellites will receive information and respond to it, perhaps by making measurements and sending back the information.
- the different uses for satellite communication systems include:
  - telephone and television communications
  - surveillance and monitoring
  - navigation.
- A geostationary satellite takes 24 hours for one orbit. This keeps the satellite over the same spot as seen from the Earth.
- Telecommunications satellites have to be in geostationary orbit so that we can send and receive information at any time.
- Monitoring satellites in low polar orbits take only 100 minutes to orbit the Earth so they see the whole Earth, segment by segment as it spins beneath them.

Questions

1 Make a chart to indicate all the uses of satellites. Separate geostationary satellites from low earth orbit (polar) satellites in your chart.

2 Why should a communication satellite be in geostationary orbit?

3 Why is it impossible for people in Antarctica to use satellites in geostationary orbit to communicate? How do they get round this problem?

4 Why are polar orbiting satellites better for surveillance operations?

Learning outcomes

After completing the work in this topic you will be able to:

- use the quantitative relationship between orbital speed, orbital radius and time period:

$v = 2 \pi r/T$

- understand the role of gravitational force of the Earth as the centripetal force on the satellite

- use the quantitative relationship between the force acting on a satellite, mass, orbital speed and radius: $F = m v^2/r$

Keeping up with your satellite

Controllers in mission control have to know when each satellite is due to pass overhead so that they can be ready to download the information it is carrying. By knowing the orbital speed and radius they can work out the time period. If it doesn't arrive at the right time they know its orbit might be decaying so it is falling closer to the Earth. They can use thrusters to change its speed and orbit radius and return it to its correct orbit.

$$\text{Orbital speed} = \frac{2 \pi \times \text{orbit radius}}{\text{Time period}}$$

$$v = \frac{2 \pi r}{T}$$

For example a monitoring satellite in LEO might be at an orbital height of 900 km above the Earth.
The Earth's radius is 6400 km (you have to include this in the satellites orbit radius)
The satellite's time period is 100 minutes

$$v = \frac{2 \pi r}{T}$$

$$v = \frac{2 \pi \times (900 + 6400) \times 1000}{100 \times 60}$$

$$v = \frac{2 \pi \times 7\,300\,000}{6000}$$

$$= 7644.5 \text{ m/s} \quad \text{Quite fast!!!!}$$

Keeping your satellite in orbit

All satellites need the gravitational pull of a planet to make them orbit. Without this they would simply carry on in a straight line forever (as Newton's First Law predicts). The gravitational pull is always pulling the satellite towards the Earth, changing its direction from a straight line into a curve. The gravitational force is the centripetal force on the satellite that keeps it going in a circle.

Did you know?

All satellites are slowly spiralling into the Earth. Controllers at Mission Control can boost satellites into higher orbits if they fall too far. However when a satellite is old it is usually allowed to fall towards the Earth where it burns up as it falls through the atmosphere because of friction with the air. Or it is boosted to a higher 'graveyard orbit' to keep it out of working satellites.

Key Facts

- The quantitative relationship between orbital speed, orbital radius and time period is: $v = 2\pi r/T$.
- The gravitational force of the Earth provides the centripetal force on the satellite to keep it in orbit.
- The quantitative relationship between the force acting on a satellite, mass, orbital speed and radius: $F = m v^2/r$.

Working out the force...

Some satellites are only the size of a football and do not require a very strong centripetal force.

SNAP only weighs 10 kg and it is in LEO at 7910 km. It travels at 7650 m/s

To work out the centripetal force on SNAP:

$$\text{Force} = \frac{\text{mass} \times (\text{orbital speed})^2}{\text{radius}}$$

$$F = \frac{m \times v^2}{r}$$

$$F = \frac{10 \times 7650^2}{(6400 + 900) \times 1000}$$

$$F = \frac{585\,225\,000}{7300 \times 1000}$$

$$F = 80\,N$$

Gravity provides this force to keep the satellite in orbit. When the satellite is on Earth the force of gravity on it is 100 N. This is what keeps it on the Earth's surface. You can see from this calculation that the force of gravity is less as you move away from the Earth.

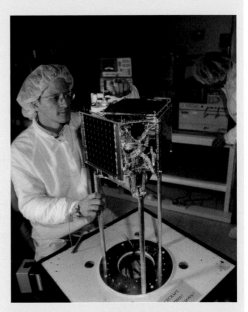

Figure 17.28 SNAP-1 Jerome: SNAP-1, a 6.5 g satellite, undergoes final checks at the Surrey Space Centre in preparation for launch.

Questions

1. If a geostationary satellite is 36 000 km above the Earth and the Earth's radius is 6,400 km at what speed is the satellite travelling?

2. If such a satellite was 2 tonnes in mass, what force is needed to keep it in orbit? Where does this force come from?

3. Satellites tend to fall towards the Earth. How do scientists at mission control overcome this problem?

4. If a satellite is allowed to fall to Earth why is it unlikely to cause any damage?

1. (a)   Satellites in geostationary orbits are used for transmitting television pictures to all parts of the world.

(i)   What is the orbital time period of a geostationary satellite?   (1)

(ii)   State two differences between a polar orbit and a geostationary orbit.   (2)

(b)   Sky waves can be used to send radio signals round the Earth by making use of the ionosphere.

(i)   Copy and complete the diagram to show how a receiver at B receives a signal from a transmitter at A.

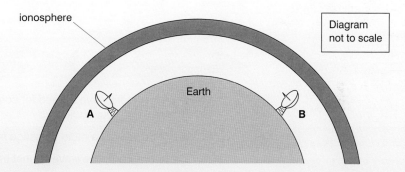

(2)

(ii)   What does the ionosphere do to the sky waves?   (1)

(iii) Name another type of radio wave which could travel from A to B without using or passing through the ionosphere.   (1)

(Total 7 marks)

Edexcel GCSE Science: June 2001, paper 4H, no. 1.

2.   Television programmes are broadcast using both analogue and digital signals.

(a)   Use diagrams to show the difference between an analogue and a digital signal.   (2)

(b)   Describe one advantage of using a digital signal.   (2)

(c)   Most television sets are designed to receive analogue signals.
The diagram shows a television set used with a decoder to receive a digital signal.

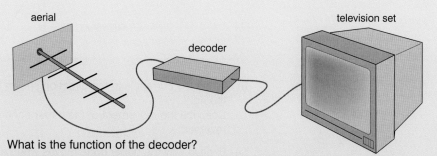

What is the function of the decoder?   (2)

(d)   Both analogue and digital signals are broadcast with a wavelength of 0.060 m.
Calculate the frequency of these waves.
The speed of the waves is 3.0×10^8 m/s (300 000 000 m/s).   (3)

(Total 9 marks)

Edexcel GCSE Science, June 2001, paper 4H, no. 3.

3. Radio waves can travel from the transmitter to a receiver in three different ways.
Space waves can only be received if the receiver is within sight of the transmitter.
Sky waves are reflected by the ionosphere.
Ground waves follow the Earth's curvature.

The diagrams show these waves.

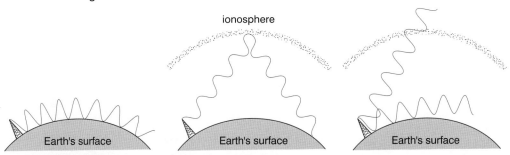

(a) Which type of radio wave is used for communications with satellites?
Give a reason for your choice. (2)

(b) In 1901, Marconi sent a radio message from Canada to Cornwall.

  (i) Explain why a space wave cannot travel from Canada to Cornwall. (1)

  (ii) Suggest why the first radio transmissions were called 'wireless'. (1)

(Total 4 marks)

Edexcel GCSE Science: June 2000, paper 4H, no. 1.

4. The diagram shows a moving coil loudspeaker.

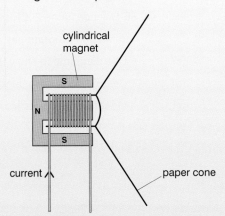

(a) (i) When the current is in the direction shown in the diagram, the paper cone moves to the right.
Describe the movement of the paper cone when the direction of the current is reversed. (1)

  (ii) Explain why the paper cone moves when a current passes in the coil. (2)

(b) An alternating current passes in the coil.
Describe the movement of the paper cone. (1)

(c) The loudspeaker is used to produce a sound that has a frequency of 800 Hz.
The wavelength of the sound as it leaves the loudspeaker is 0.40 m.
Calculate the speed of the sound in air. (3)

(Total 7 marks)

5. (a)   Telecommunications satellites are generally placed in geostationary orbit round the Earth.

(i)   Explain what is meant by geostationary orbit.   (2)

(ii) Where does the centripetal force come from that keeps the satellite in orbit round the Earth?   (1)

(b)   A satellite is in geostationary orbit with a radius of 42 400 km (4.24×10^7 m).

(i)   Show that the orbital speed of the satellite is about 3100 m/s.   (3)

(ii) Use this orbital speed to show that the centripetal acceleration of the satellite is 0.23 m/s^2.   (2)

(iii) The mass of the satellite is 1000 kg. Calculate its weight in this orbit.   (2)

(Total 10 marks)

Edexcel GCSE Science: June 2000, paper 4H, no. 5.

6. (a)   Sound and video recordings can be stored in analogue or digital form.

Which method is used by:

(i)   a vinyl disc (record);   (1)

(ii) a compact disc (CD)?   (1)

(b)   Magnetic tape can be used to store information in either analogue or digital form.
The tape passes over an erase head before a recording is made. This removes any previous recordings.
The diagram shows an erase head.

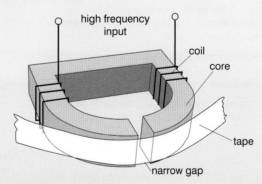

(i)   name a suitable material for the core.   (1)

(ii) Explain why this material is suitable.   (2)

(iii) The diagram shows the magnetic regions in a tape after it has passed over the erase head.

Complete the diagram below to show how the magnetic regions are arranged when the tape stores a signal of constant frequency.   (2)

(c)   Magnetic tape can stretch.
Explain how this can affect the sound heard during playback.   (2)

(Total 9 marks)

Edexcel GCSE Science: June 1999, paper 4H, no. 4.

Active satellite This is a satellite that receives and sends out signals. It is controlled from a control station on Earth.

AM Amplitude modulated. This is a radio wave that has had the signal added to it in a way that changes the amplitude of the wave carrying the signal.

Amplifier This adds energy to the wave to make it 'louder' if it loses too much energy and gets too faint.

Analogue signal A signal that varies continuously. An analogue electrical signal is a continuously changing voltage.

Attenuated A signal is attenuated when its amplitude gets smaller and smaller because energy is lost from the signal. Boosters or repeaters along the electrical wire or optical fibre amplify the attenuated signal.

CD Compact disc. The shiny side stores information as a series of tiny holes burned into the surface. These are detected by the laser beam used to 'read' the disc.

Decoder This changes the message in binary code into a signal as a continuously varying voltage (analogue signal).

Demodulator This subtracts the carrier wave from the received wave, leaving just the message in binary code.

Digital signal A signal made from a series of on/off pulses. The 'message' stays clearer when it is carried as a digital signal.

Encoder Changes an analogue signal, such as continuously varying voltages, to a digital signal, such as pulses or a sequence of on/off voltages.

FM Frequency modulated. This is a radio wave that has had the signal added to it in a way that changes the frequency of the wave carrying the signal.

Geostationary orbit A satellite that takes 24 hours to orbit the Earth. This means it always stays above the same place on Earth.

Input signal The signal that is received by a system. Your input signals are the sights, sounds, smells and so on that your senses detect.

Interference Extra signals added onto the main signal, usually due to a problem with the system. A form of noise

Ionosphere A layer of the atmosphere high above Earth, that is used to reflect radio waves back down towards the surface of Earth.

Magnetic tape Plastic tape containing magnetic particles. An audio or video signal is changed to a changing magnetic signal that makes the magnetic particles line up in a pattern that stores the information.

Modulator This adds the digital signal of on/off voltages to the carrier wave that transmits the signal from phone to phone.

Multiplexing Sending more than one message at a time either by using different wavelengths of light or by splitting each message into chunks and sending bits of each message in sequence.

Noise Unwanted, random signals that get mixed up with the signal being carried, to make hissing on sound or white flecks on picture. Digital signals are much less affected by noise than analogue signals.

Optical fibre Cables that carry messages as light signals. Electrical wires (carrying electrical signals) are often replaced by optical fibres because the light signals do not need boosting as often as electrical signals.

Passive satellite This type of satellite just reflects signals sent to it. It acts like a mirror for radio signals.

Receiver This collects carrier waves from the nearest mobile phone mast (antenna).

Regenerator Regenerators 'repair' digital signals by working out whether a voltage is supposed to be high (an 'on' pulse) or low (an 'off' pulse) and changing it to what it is supposed to be.

Repeater Repeaters add energy to an electrical or optical signal to make up for the attenuation (loss of signal strength) because of resistance in wires or impurities in glass fibres. Also called boosters.

Transducer A device that changes one type of signal into another type, for example pressure on your phone buttons into electrical voltages.

Transmitter This sends the carrier wave and its message from your phone to the nearest antenna (mobile phone aerial).

The majority of the universe is very, very cold. It's about –269 °C. The question of whether there is a lowest possible temperature has fascinated scientists for years and now researchers in the UK are less than seven-thousandths of a degree away from what they believe is the lowest temperature possible. But exactly what is temperature? Is it a fundamental thing in nature or simply a scale we have invented? This module looks at the link between how fast molecules move and our idea of temperature.

When the word atom was first used, everyone thought that atoms could not be divided into anything smaller. A hundred years ago experiments in the UK changed all that. Since then we have been finding smaller and smaller particles and trying to make sense of how they fit together to make up the matter – and the antimatter – that surrounds us.

Some isotopes disintegrate naturally: they are radioactive. Some emit an antimatter particle or a high energy electromagnetic wave (gamma ray). Others are made to split in two by firing a neutron at them: fission reactions. Why do atoms disintegrate in so many different ways? Can we predict which ones will decay and when? Certainly fission processes have provided us with a valuable source of energy in nuclear reactors for many years. Here you will consider whether people are right to be concerned about the radioactive waste they produce or perhaps there are ways of managing the problem.

Electron guns have been around for a long time and there's probably one in almost every house in the country. Televisions and computer monitors rely on electron guns. But how can such tiny particles as electrons create such amazing images on TV and computer screens? This is the subject of the final part of this module.

Learning outcomes

After completing the work in this topic you will be able to:

- understand there is an absolute zero of temperature which is –273°C

- describe the Kelvin scale of temperature and be able to convert between Kelvin and Celsius scales

The right temperature scale for the job

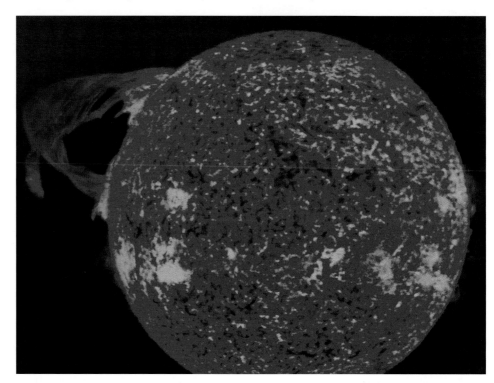

Figure 18.01 These flares reach 100 000 km into space and over 1 million°C in temperature.

How hot can you get?…

Some scientists believe that the sun is getting hotter and that this might be a cause of global warming. The SOHO spacecraft is watching the sun very carefully. In 1998 it captured an image of ionised iron streaming out of the sun's thin atmosphere at an amazing temperature of 1 million degrees Celsius (Figure 18.01). More recently they have found evidence of temperatures of 2 million degrees Celsius – and they are still looking. This is even more surprising when you realise the surface of the sun is only 6000°C.

Out in the cold…

The majority of the universe is much, much colder than the sun – about –269° C. The Kelvin temperature scale is much more useful to astronomers and scientists who specialise in cryogenics (the study of the very cold). They spend a lot of their time working with negative temperatures on the Celsius scale. The **Kelvin scale** of temperature starts with the lowest possible temperature – thought to be –273° C. This is called '**absolute zero**'. On the Kelvin scale the majority of the universe is at 4 K.

Did you know?

Below 80 K ice will expand as you cool it further. Most solids contract as you cool them. Scientists have still to work out why ice behaves like this.

In laboratories around the world, scientists are racing to be the first to get down to 0 K (zero Kelvin). So far Lancaster University in the UK has got down to 7 microKelvin (0.000 007 K) but at Helsinki University they have got to 100 picoKelvin (0.000 000 000 1 K)!

The conversion…

To convert from the Celsius scale to the Kelvin scale you simply add 273

	Celsius scale	Kelvin scale
Freezing point of water	0° C	273 K
Room temperature	20° C	293 K
Boiling point of water	100° C	373 K
Liquid nitrogen temperature	−196° C	77 K
Absolute zero	−273° C	0 K

Heat death…

To understand why there is an 'absolute zero' of temperature we have to imagine what happens when objects are cooled. What we see as a lower temperature, molecules experience as reduced vibration. As we get to lower and lower temperatures, molecules vibrate less and less. Eventually, we must get to a point where they stop altogether. This is absolute zero. Lord Kelvin called this point 'heat death'.

Not so cool…

The human body is not well adapted to the cold. Our first response is to form 'goose bumps' as muscles in our skin cause our body hair to lift and create a thicker layer to trap air and insulate us from the cold. Soon shivering starts as our bodies try to generate warmth by muscular movement. Blood flow to our toes and fingertips is reduced and they turn white. In extreme conditions the tissue will die due to frostbite. Finally, gangrene (tissue decay) may set in. Arctic explorers often lost toes and fingers from frost bite.

Key Facts

- The lowest temperature is 'absolute zero' or zero Kelvin (0 K) which is equal to −273°C.
- To convert from a Celsius temperature to Kelvin, add 273.
  temperature in Kelvin = (temperature in Celsius + 273).

Did you know?

James Joule spent his honeymoon taking the temperature of the water at the top and bottom of Niagara Falls. He discovered that the water is slightly warmer at the bottom of the waterfall. This is because its kinetic energy (as it falls) is converted to heat energy on impact. His new bride was not impressed.

Figure 18.02 James Joule discovered the temperature was higher at the bottom of a waterfall.

Questions

1   Write a brief outline recommending to scientists who work in cryogenics why they should use the Kelvin scale of temperature and how to make the conversion from the Celsius scale.

2   Copy and complete this table by converting the temperatures from one scale to the other.

	Celsius	Kelvin
Body temperature	35	
Hot day	28	
Icy night	−6	
Where metals superconduct (lose their electrical resistance)		4
Surface of the sun		6500

… more at www.modularscience.co.uk

Pressurised

Learning outcomes

After completing the work in this module you will be able to:

- understand that an increase in temperature results in an increase in speed of gas particles and that the Kelvin temperature of the gas is proportional to their average kinetic energy

- explain the pressure exerted by a gas in terms of the motion of its particles

- describe the qualitative relationship between pressure and Kelvin temperature for a gas in a sealed container

- use the quantitative relation between pressure and the Kelvin temperature $P_1/T_1 = P_2/T_2$

Hot wheels…

We may talk about the **temperature** of a substance increasing but, for the atoms it is simply a matter of speeding up. The central heating system in your house causes the air molecules in the room to speed up so their average kinetic energy is higher. You simply notice the air temperature has gone up (Figure 18.03). Put scientifically: 'the Kelvin temperature of a gas is proportional to the average **kinetic energy** of the molecules'.

The pressure is on

Every time a gas molecule hits a surface it exerts a tiny force. Add these tiny forces up for millions and millions of gas molecules and its obvious why a gas exerts a pressure on any surface it is in contact with. For example a balloon stays inflated because the gas molecules inside it continually hit the inside surface and exert a force outwards. Of course the air molecules on the outside are also bombarding the outer surface and exerting pressure on it. The pressure outwards is balanced by the pressure inwards (exerted by the atmospheric air molecules and the stretched skin of the balloon) which is why the balloon remains the same size (Figure 18.04).

As soon as you heat the gas its molecules speed up and hit the surfaces harder and more often. The obvious result is higher pressure. The balloon would begin to expand as the pressure outwards

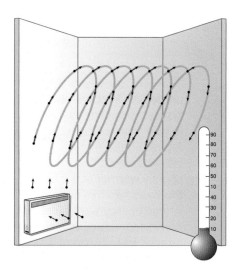

Figure 18.03 Higher air temperature is caused by the air molecules having a higher average kinetic energy (moving faster).

Figure 18.04 The gas molecules hit the inside of the balloon and the overall effect is enough pressure to keep the balloon inflated.

Figure 18.05 The gas pressure in an aerosol can gets even higher when you heat it and that's what makes it explode violently if it is put on a fire.

exceeded the pressure inwards. Eventually the pressures would equalise again and the balloon would stop expanding.

This explains why an aerosol can is so dangerous if it is heated (Figure 18.05). The gas is already at high pressure so that the molecules are able to rush out at high speed as soon as you press the button. Make them speed up by heating the can and you risk them splitting the can apart – violently! Each molecule hits the surface harder AND they all hit the surface more often because they are travelling faster. Once the pressure inside gets too high for the can to contain it will explode – often with dangerous results!

Put an inflated balloon in the fridge and it will deflate. Again this is because the lower temperature air molecules cannot exert such a high pressure on the inside of the balloon.

Working it out

To see just how much the pressure increases when gases are heated you can use

$$\frac{\text{Pressure before heating (Pa)}}{\text{Temperature before heating(K)}} = \frac{\text{Pressure after heating (Pa)}}{\text{Temperature after heating(K)}}$$

$$\frac{P_1}{T_1} = \frac{P_2}{T_2}$$

For example: air in a car tyre may be at 200 000 Pa and at a temperature of 7°C. What happens after a journey when it has warmed up to 37°C.

$7°C = 280 \text{ K}$ and $37°C = 310 \text{ K}$

so $\dfrac{200\,000 \text{ Pa}}{280 \text{ K}} = \dfrac{P_2}{310 \text{ K}}$

$P_2 = \dfrac{200\,000 \text{ Pa} \times 310 \text{ K}}{280 \text{ K}} = 221\,428 \text{ Pa}$

Did you know?

The air pressure inside an aircraft is lower than on the ground even though the cabin is pressurised. If you take a plastic water bottle and open it while in flight, some of the gas inside will rush out because it is at higher pressure than the air in the cabin. Close the bottle and wait until you land. When you look at the bottle again it will be crushed and crumpled because the gas inside is now at a much lower pressure than normal air pressure. The gas molecules inside the bottle cannot hit the inside of the bottle enough to keep it in shape.

Key Facts

- Gas molecules increase in speed when the temperature of the gas increases.
- The average kinetic energy of gas molecules is proportional to the gas temperature in Kelvin.
- When gas molecules of a gas hit a surface the combined effect is a pressure exerted on that surface.
- Increasing the temperature of a gas will increase the pressure it exerts on a surface as the molecules hit the surface harder and more often.
- The relation between temperature and pressure is $P_1/T_1 = P_2/T_2$.

Questions

1 Explain, by describing what happens to the molecules:

   a) why a balloon deflates if you put it in the fridge

   b) why an aerosol explodes if you leave it in bright sunlight for too long.

2 The temperature of the gas in a balloon is reduced from 20°C to the freezing point of water. The pressure inside the balloon starts at 200 000 Pa. What is its pressure when it is at 0°C?

3 Copy out the table below, calculate and fill in the missing values.

Pressure before (Pa)	Pressure after heating (Pa)	Temperature before heating (K)	Temperature after heating (K)
100 000	400 000	300	
300 000		300	1000
	750 000		1500
	100 000	50	400
400 000	1 200 000	250	

more at www.modularscience.co.uk

Particles 219

Learning outcomes

After completing the work in this module you will be able to:

- describe the results of Geiger and Marsden's experiments with gold foil and alpha particles

- describe Rutherford's nuclear model of the atom and how it accounts for the results of Geiger and Marsden's experiment and understand the factors (charge and speed) which affect the deflection of the alpha particles by a nucleus

Hitting the target

The world's biggest…

It's odd that it needs the world's biggest experiment to look at the world's smallest particles. One hundred metres below the soil in Switzerland is a circular tube 27 km long (Figure 18.06). It would take you 7 hours to walk all the way round but tiny electrons and **positrons** (antimatter electrons) can get round 11 000 times per second as they travel close to the speed of light.

Did you know?

The kinetic energy of each particle travelling round the accelerator at CERN is only about 10 times the kinetic energy of a flying mosquito. However these particles are so small they end up travelling at almost the speed of light (300 000 000 m/s).

Figure 18.06 The world's biggest experiment is taking place 100 m underground at CERN in Switzerland.

The world's smallest…

At CERN, the European Laboratory for Particle Physics, some of the world's smallest particles are being used to try to find out exactly what everything is made of – and how it got that way. By making them crash into other particles they can create mini Big Bangs. This is as close as we can get to the beginning of the universe but it all helps us to work out what happened at the real Big Bang at the beginning of the Universe 15 billion years ago.

Figure 18.07 By firing alpha particles at gold these scientists worked out the exact structure of an atom.

Rutherford Appleton Labs…

At the Rutherford Appleton Labs (RAL) in Oxfordshire they also have an **accelerator**, but it's much smaller than the one in Switzerland. At RAL they fire neutrons at a whole range of materials to find out exactly where the atoms are and what they are doing. This helps them to understand how drugs work to cure disease or how to make designer materials. It's no coincidence that the first person to think of firing particles at targets to work out their structure was called Rutherford.

The importance of Ernest…

Ernest Rutherford worked in Manchester University. In 1909 he got two new students who were working for their Ph.D. degrees (Doctor of Philosophy qualification after which they earn the title Doctor). Rutherford had an idea for an experiment. He asked his students, Hans Geiger and Ernest Marsden, to work in a darkened room and fire **alpha particles** (from a radioactive material) at a thin piece of gold foil (Figure 18.07). He told them to count the flashes of light as the alpha particles went through the foil and hit a detector material on the other side of the target. He also wanted to know exactly where the alpha particles landed. Geiger and Marsden did exactly what they were asked. But they didn't get exactly the results they expected. Instead of going through the gold foil, some of the alpha particles came straight back at them. 'It was as if you fired a gun at a piece of paper and the bullet came back and hit you in the face!' said Rutherford, later (Figure 18.08).

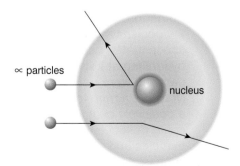

Figure 18.08 Rutherford worked out that the nucleus of an atom was very dense. This is why some of the alpha particles rebounded instead of going straight through the gold foil.

Key Facts

- Rutherford's students, Geiger and Marsden, fired alpha particles at gold foil and discovered that some rebounded while others were deflected as they went through.
- Rutherford worked out a model for the atom. It had positively charged protons in the centre and a cloud of negatively charged electrons around the outside. Most of the atom was empty space.
- Some of the alpha particles in Geiger and Marsden's experiment were deflected as they went through the empty space in the atom. This is because of the positive charge on the nucleus repelling the positive alpha particles.
- Alpha particles that passed closest to the nucleus were deflected the most BUT faster moving alpha particles were deflected less than expected as they were repelled for a shorter time.

Confusing…

In 1909 scientists thought that atoms had positive charges and negative charges spread evenly throughout – they called it the 'plum pudding model'. Geiger and Marsden's results made it clear that this was not true. Rutherford had to come up with a new idea. Finally he worked out that all the mass of the atom *and* all the positive charge of the atom, were concentrated in an extremely tiny volume right in the centre of the atom (Figure 18.09). This way the mass and charge could be concentrated enough to make the alpha particles rebound when they hit it straight on.

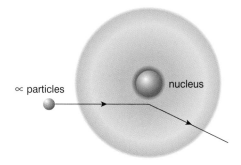

Figure 18.09 Rutherford also worked out that the nucleus was positively charged. This is what deflected the positively charged alpha particles as they went through. Alpha particles passing close to the nucleus were repelled and deflected the most.

Positive ideas…

Rutherford also realised that the particles that made up the nucleus were positively charged. This meant that the tiny negatively charged electrons must be forming a sort of cloud far away from the nucleus. The rest of the atom was empty space. He named the tiny positive particles in the nucleus, protons. His idea of positive protons was perfect because it explained why some of the alpha particles went through the gold but were deflected: the positively charged alpha particles had been repelled by the positive charge on the nuclei as they went past.

The speed of the alpha particles also made a difference. Faster moving alpha particles are not so affected by the repulsion from the nucleus as they are affected by it for a much shorter time.

Questions

1 Write a newspaper article which announces the results of Geiger and Marsden's experiment.

2 Rutherford worked out that the nucleus must have a concentrated positive charge by looking at how the alpha particles were deflected. Draw a diagram to show how a positively charged nucleus could deflect the alpha particles and why it is impossible for the alpha particles to be deflected in the same way by a negatively charged nucleus.

3 Rutherford's theory was very quickly accepted because he was able to make predictions about how different target nuclei would deflect alpha particles. What would you predict would be the effect of using a target material with a more massive nucleus and a target material with fewer protons in the nucleus?

… more at www.modularscience.co.uk

Neutrons – flavour of the month

Scientists are rather fond of firing neutrons at things. Ever since Chadwick managed to find a neutron for the first time in 1932, scientists have been using them as battering rams. Some scientists look at how neutrons are deflected when they go through a material. Others look at the particles that come out of the target when the neutrons hit them. Others fire neutrons at the target material so that they hit the nucleus and become part of it. They are hoping to make the heaviest material in the world. Unfortunately the new heavy atom doesn't last long as the extra neutron makes the whole nucleus unstable. After a fraction of a second the new element will decay and make new, smaller atoms.

Breaking up is easy

Give an atom an equal number of protons and neutrons and it will be stable – it won't decay (fall apart) (Figure 18.10). As soon as the number of neutrons is noticeably different from the number of protons, things begin to go wrong. The 'unbalanced' atom becomes unstable and will decay and become an atom of a different element. It will continue to decay, changing, from element to element, until it finally becomes a **stable isotope**.

Did you know?

Scientists have only recently worked out how water molecules are arranged alongside their neighbours in liquid water. They had to use neutron scattering to do this.

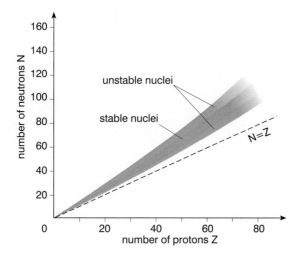

Figure 18.10 Stable atoms have the right ratio of neutrons to protons. Stray too far from this line and the whole thing will begin to fall apart.

Change of identity

Having too many neutrons is a problem. The ideal arrangement for atoms is almost equal numbers of protons and neutrons. To solve this problem, nature has provided **beta decay**. Quite simply one of the neutrons in the nucleus turns into a proton. Obviously the proton is positive while the neutron was neutral. The left over negative charge is emitted from the nucleus as a fast-moving electron – called a beta particle (β^-) (Figure 18.11).

$$\ce{^{A}_{Z}X} \longrightarrow \ce{^{A}_{Z+1}X} + \ce{^{0}_{-1}e}$$

Figure 18.11 The neutron changes into a proton and the excess negative charge is carried away by a fast-moving electron – called a beta particle.

Key Facts

- A graph of the number of protons against the number of neutrons for all the elements will be a straight line except for the heaviest elements.
- If an element has unbalanced numbers of protons and neutrons it will not fit on the line of the graph and this shows it is unstable and very likely to decay by emitting radioactivity.
- A nucleus with too many neutrons will change a neutron into a proton and emit the excess negative change as a beta particle. This makes it more stable.

Questions

1 Create a dictionary to explain these words: proton; neutron; electron; isotope; stable; radioactive; decay; beta minus particle; (leave space to add more words as you meet them).

2 Explain why some types of unstable isotope undergo beta minus decay.

3 Why is it unlikely that the most abundant isotopes of oxygen – oxygen-16 (as found in air) is unlikely to emit beta minus particles?

... more at www.modularscience.co.uk

PETs

PET scanners are the latest way hospitals have of monitoring your brain activity (Figure 18.12). PET stands for Positron Emission Tomography. Positrons are positively charged electrons. Positrons are defined as antimatter particles because they have the same mass as an electron but the opposite charge.

Antimatter is much more common than you might think. Some beta particles are positively charged (β^+). This means they are positively charged electrons – or positrons. If a radioactive isotope has too few neutrons compared with the number of protons it is unstable. It will lie below the line on the graph on page 223.

This is exactly the opposite situation from beta minus decay (β^-). The extra proton will turn into a neutron. The extra positive charge now has to be emitted as a positively charged positron (Figure 18.13).

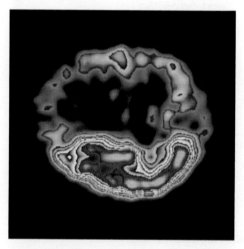

Figure 18.12 This image shows a baby's brain using a PET scanner. The yellow areas may indicate epilepsy.

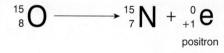

$$^{15}_{8}\text{O} \longrightarrow {}^{15}_{7}\text{N} + {}^{0}_{+1}\text{e}$$

positron

Figure 18.13 Atom changes a proton into a neutron and emits a positively charged beta particle (positron).

All change

Carbon-14 is a well-known radioactive material. It is often used in radioactive carbon dating to find the age of organic materials. The radioactive isotope of carbon has too many neutrons (6 protons and 8 neutrons). By changing a neutron into a proton and emitting a beta minus (β^-) it solves the problem and becomes more stable. It now has 7 protons and 7 neutrons – the ideally balanced arrangement! But it is no longer carbon. The element with 7 protons is nitrogen.

Did you know?

At the Big Bang it is thought that equal amounts of matter and antimatter should have been created. Scientists are still not sure why our universe has so much more matter than antimatter now.

$$^{14}_{6}\text{C} \longrightarrow {}^{14}_{7}\text{N} + \beta^{-}$$

The same things happens to a radioactive isotope of oxygen. Oxygen-15 has too few neutrons. It has 7 compared with the 8 in the more common form of oxygen. It converts one of its protons into a neutron – and becomes nitrogen in the process!

$$^{15}_{8}\text{O} \longrightarrow {}^{15}_{7}\text{N} + \beta^{+}$$

In both these cases the mass number of the element doesn't change.
A β^{+} particle isn't the only type of antimatter particle. In fact every particle has an antimatter equivalent. For example there are muons and antimuons, pions and antipions, neutrinos and antineutrinos, etc. When a matter particle meets its antimatter equivalent the two particles will completely annihilate each other and disappear as a flash of energy. The amount of energy you get is worked out by Einstein's famous equation $E = mc^2$, where c is the speed of light $300\,000\,000$ m/s and m is the total mass of the two particles.

Key Facts

- The positron is a fundamental positively charged particle with the same mass as the electron.
- Elements with too few neutrons will lie below the stable line on the neutron : proton curve and will, therefore be unstable and radioactive.
- These isotopes convert a proton into a neutron and emit a beta plus (positron) to become stable.
- Emitting a beta minus will increase the proton number of the element while the mass number stays the same.
- Emitting a beta plus will decrease the proton number while the mass number stays the same.

Questions

1   Add these words to your dictionary: beta plus decay; antimatter; positron; proton number; mass number.

2   Invent five unstable isotopes (and give them names) then show how they decay into daughter products by either beta plus decay or beta minus decay:

for example

Antimatterium → Stablellium

$$^{190}_{44}\text{A} \rightarrow {}^{190}_{43}\text{Sm} + \beta^{+}$$

... more at www.modularscience.co.uk

Learning outcomes

After completing the work in this module you will be able to:

- recall that nuclei with greater than 82 protons usually undergoes alpha decay

- recall that as a result of β^- or β^+ decay nuclei often undergo rearrangement with a loss of energy and gamma radiation

Losing weight – the alpha plan

Television advertisements frequently try to persuade us to have alpha particles in our homes. Life-saving smoke detectors have a small piece of radioactive material that emits alpha particles. Alpha particles contain 2 protons and 2 neutrons bound together. They have a positive charge and a mass of 4 times a single proton. They cannot travel very far in air before they are stopped by colliding with air molecules. In a smoke detector the smoke gets between the alpha source and the detector. The alpha particles can no longer reach to detector as they keep colliding with smoke particles. As soon as the detector senses too few alpha particles, the alarm will go off.

Your alpha source has to be a **massive element**. (Massive in this sense means having a large mass – not simply being very big as in informal use). Unstable isotopes with more than 82 protons are likely to be able to emit alpha particles (Figure 18.14). These elements typically have well over 82 neutrons too. By emitting an alpha particle the atom immediately loses mass. This helps it become more stable. It may keep on emitting alpha particles until it reaches the magic 82 protons. In other words it slowly turns into lead.

> ### Did you know?
>
> Radioactive materials often emit a whole stream of different particles (they turn into a series of 'daughter' elements) as they try to become more stable – and often don't stop until they turn into lead.

$$^{208}_{84}\text{Po} \longrightarrow {}^{208}_{82}\text{Pb} + {}^{4}_{2}\text{He}$$

∝–particle

Figure 18.14 Atoms with more than 82 protons often emit an alpha particle to become more stable.

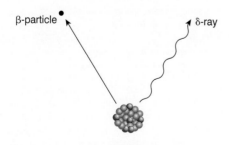

β-particle   δ-ray

> ### Did you know?
>
> It's very difficult to break up an alpha particle. The combination of 2 protons and 2 neutrons is a very close package which holds together very strongly. All atoms with 2p + 2n in their nucleus (Helium) or 4p + 4n (Berylium) or 6p + 6n (Carbon) etc. are particularly stable.

Figure 18.15 Emitting an alpha particle or a beta particle may leave the atom with too much energy. It gets rid of its extra energy as a gamma ray.

Key Facts

- Unstable nuclei with more than 82 protons often decay by emitting an alpha particle.
- Gamma radiation is a by-product of beta decay. The unstable isotope emits its excess energy as a gamma ray.

Lose energy – the gamma plan

While emitting alpha or beta particle makes an atom more stable, gamma radiation cannot offer such a benefit. **Gamma radiation** is electromagnetic radiation, not particles. There is no change to the radioisotope's mass or proton number. Instead gamma emission is a by-product of alpha or beta decay. When an atom emits a particle of either sort, it is left with too much energy (the word used is 'excited'). It has to get rid of the excess energy somehow. So it emits the energy as a high-energy gamma ray (Figure 18.15).

Questions

1   Add these words to your dictionary: alpha particle; gamma radiation.

2   Write an instruction sheet entitled 'How to be Radioactive'. Explain what is required of an isotope if it is going to be radioactive and what types of radiation it might emit. In particular emphasise the properties of isotopes that typically emit each form of radiation.

Or for radioactive isotopes write an instruction sheet entitled 'How to become Stable'. This should explain what requirements there are to enable an isotope to emit radiation of any type.

3   Make a chart to explain how alpha, beta plus, beta minus and gamma emission are different from each other.

4   Devise a board game for younger pupils where players are aiming to make an unstable isotope into a stable isotope. As they land on squares they may have the right to emit an alpha or beta particle. The one with a proton number closest to 82 at the end wins.

... more at www.modularscience.co.uk

Splitting the atom

After completing the work in this module you will be able to:

- understand that a nucleus of uranium-235 can be split (fission) by collision with a neutron and that this process releases energy in the form of kinetic energy of the fission products

- recall that fission of uranium-235 produces two daughter nuclei and a small number of neutrons

- understand that a chain reaction can be set up if the neutrons produced by one fission strike other uranium-235 nuclei

- describe in outline how the fission process can be used as an energy source to generate electricity

- understand that the products of nuclear fission are radioactive and the implications this has for their safe storage over prolonged periods

Getting it wrong

Atoms are badly named. The word 'atoma' comes from the Greek meaning 'indivisible'. For a long time scientists thought that atoms were the smallest thing possible and that they could not be split into anything smaller. Now we know better.

Neutrons again

Every day thousands of people around the world rely on neutrons hitting uranium atoms and splitting them apart. Splitting the uranium atoms is called **fission** and it's the basis of nuclear power for generating electricity.

Figure 18.16 Uranium is mined in very high-tech mines across the world. This uranium is not naturally radioactive so it is completely safe to work in the mine.

Start with uranium...

Uranium is mined in places like Canada, Africa and Australia. Most uranium is not naturally radioactive so it's completely safe to handle (Figure 18.16). It is made into fuel rods ready to be used in nuclear power stations around the world.

Split apart...

Inside the power station neutrons are fired at the uranium fuel rods. When a neutron hits a uranium nucleus it embeds in it (described as being 'captured' in the trade). This makes the nucleus too big to be stable. Almost immediately the atom splits into two unequal pieces. These two pieces are the uranium atom's two daughter atoms (Figure 18.17). There are also a few neutrons left over which are emitted at high speed and go on to hit other uranium nuclei and split them apart (Figure 18.18).

Dangerous daughters...

The two daughter nuclei can be more or less anything from the middle of the Periodic Table for example krypton and barium. The only requirement is that the

Did you know?

Some nuclear bombs are made of uranium. Power stations cannot explode like a nuclear bomb because the uranium is too spread out with lots of graphite between the fuel rods. This means it is too dilute to explode. The graphite is there to slow the neutrons down so that they can hit uranium nuclei properly. However some accidents have happened when the reactor had overheated and melted the core (meltdown), usually because of human error. Radioactive materials have escaped into the atmosphere and caused health problems in animals and people. Even so, fewer people have died as a result of nuclear power than as a result of coal power.

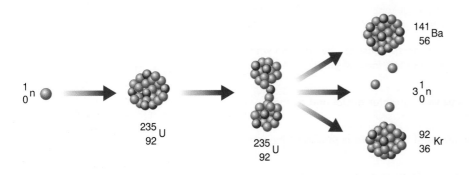

Figure 18.17 The neutron impacts on the uranium nucleus and causes it to split into two daughter products with a few extra neutrons left over.

total number of protons in the two daughter nuclei is equal to the 192 protons in the parent uranium atom. Unfortunately the daughter nuclei usually each have far too many neutrons to be stable. They are radioactive isotopes. These isotopes are what people refer to as radioactive waste.

Chain reaction...

The left over neutrons are emitted at very high speed. If they are slowed down they have a good chance of hitting another uranium nucleus so the whole thing can keep itself going until there are very few uranium atoms left in the fuel rod. This is when the rod is 'spent fuel' and has to be replaced with a new fuel rod.

Did you know?

Scientists are working on nuclear fusion as the next step in generating electricity. This is how the sun generates its power – and you need very high temperature to get it to work properly. On Earth we use two isotopes of hydrogen – deuterium and tritium. These are fired at each other to make them stick together (fuse). This is not as easy as it sounds. Firstly the materials are so hot they have to be keep away from the walls of their container otherwise they will melt their way out. Scientists do this by using strong magnetic fields to confine the plasma to the centre of the container. Secondly we still have to use more energy getting the nuclei to fuse together than we get out so it is not an efficient process. When it works the waste product is completely safe helium gas.

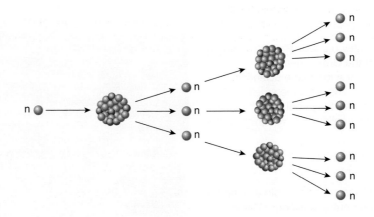

Figure 18.18 Neutrons from one reaction go on to cause another nucleus to split.

The spent fuel rod is now almost entirely made of radioactive 'daughter' products with hardly any uranium atoms left intact. These fuel rods have to be processed. The radioactive isotopes have very long half lives and have to be stored for a long time before they become safe

Energy generation...

All of the fission products (the daughter isotopes and the extra neutrons) have very high kinetic energy. This means the whole core of the nuclear rector (filled with fuel rods) gets very hot. This is what makes it useful. In most UK power stations carbon dioxide gas is circulated round the hot fuel rods until it gets hot. The hot gas it sent through pipes to heat water to turn it

Figure 18.19 The reactor core creates steam to drive the turbines and generate electricity.

steam. The hot steam turns a turbine (as in any power station) and the rotating turbine causes a generator to generate electricity (Figure 18.19).

The nuclear waste solution...

Scientists are now working on ways of dealing with the radioactive waste from power stations. The latest idea is to transmute the radioactive daughter products into other radioactive materials which have much shorter half lives. This means they will become safer much sooner. In the meantime the waste products are stored carefully to make sure they cannot contaminate water supplies or enter the food chain. The materials can be vitrified (turned into unreactive glassy materials), put into steel drums and encased in concrete. The whole thing can be buried in geologically stable sites where they are monitored and can easily be retrieved if necessary (Figure 18.20). Evidence from America has shown that dealing with radioactive waste is not as difficult as was predicted.

Figure 18.20 The waste is treated and kept safe by careful storage.

Key Facts

- The nucleus of uranium-235 can be split by hitting it with a neutron. The fission products have kinetic energy.
- Fission of uranium-235 produces two daughter products and a few neutrons.
- Neutrons from one fission can go on to cause another fission. This is a chain reaction.
- Fission of uranium-235 can generate heat which is used to create steam in a power station. The steam drives a turbine which turns a generator to generate electricity.

Questions

1   Add these words to you dictionary: chain reaction; fission; fusion.

2   Explain why the nuclear waste (daughter) products of uranium fission reactions are radioactive

3   Draw a series of blocks to show the sequence of events from uranium being mined to electricity being fed into the national grid. It has been started for you.

| Mined Uranium formed into fuel rods | → | Rods inserted into reactor core, with graphite rods between | → |

... more at www.modularscience.co.uk

Particles everywhere

JJ's legacy…

When JJ Thomson first discovered the electron in 1897 he could not have predicted where it would lead. It was a bit of a shock to scientists at the time who still believed that the atom was indivisible. We still have no evidence that an electron can be split into anything smaller so it is confidently called a '**fundamental particle**'.

Particle explosion…

Since JJ's time scientists have discovered more and more particles. The best known are protons and neutrons in the nucleus of the atom. For a long time scientists believed these were fundamental particles because they were indivisible. However since 1963 we have had other ideas. We are now convinced that protons and neutrons are made of even smaller fundamental particles called **quarks**. It took until the mid-1990s for scientists to find all of the six types of quark. In the meantime they have found many more particles and the search is not over yet.

Making a proton…

Scientists now believe that protons are made of two 'up' quarks and one 'down' quark while neutrons are made of two 'down' quarks and one 'up' quark.

By changing an up quark into a down quark a proton can become a neutron – which is exactly what is needed for positron decay (β⁺) decay. The opposite process turns a neutron into a proton which gives beta minus (β⁻) decay.

Key Facts

* Electrons are fundamental negatively charged particles.
* Protons and neutrons are not fundamental particles but are made of three quarks.
* Protons and neutrons are made of two types of quark – up and down. When an up changes into a down (or vice versa), the proton will change into a neutron (or vice versa) and the result is beta radiation.

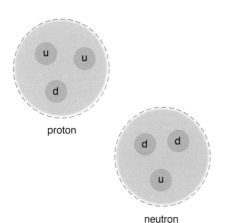

Figure 18.21 Protons are made of two 'u' and one 'd' quark and a neutron made of two 'd' quarks and one 'u' quark.

Questions

1 Add the work 'quark' to your dictionary

2 An electron is called a 'fundamental particle' but a proton and a neutron are not. Why do scientists use the word 'fundamental' for electrons?

3 What are the fundamental particles that make up protons and neutrons?

4 Draw a series of diagrams to show how a proton can turn into a neutron during beta decay – but including the quarks this time.

5 Make a 'mind map' of how all the items listed in your dictionary are linked together.

… more at www.modularscience.co.uk

Working electrons

Learning outcomes

After completing the work in this module you will be able to:

* recall that a beam of electrons is equivalent to an electric current

* understand that electrons are 'boiled off' hot filaments and this is called thermionic emission

* understand the principles of a simple electron gun with a heated cathode and accelerating anode

* understand the principle uses of electron beams including
  - TV picture tubes
  - computer monitors

Beaming electrons

When JJ Thomson did his experiments he started with what he called 'cathode rays'. He was trying to see whether electric currents could pass through gases. He simply heated up a metal wire and connected it to the negative terminal of a battery and got a stream of 'something invisible' coming off the hot wire. The name cathode rays came from the hot metal wire which was called the cathode. What he had produced was a stream of electrons flowing through the vacuum in the tube. We now know that a stream of electrons is equivalent to an electric current.

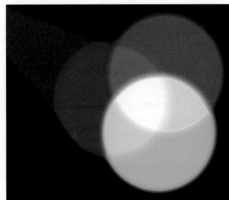

Electron guns in every home...

Now almost all of us have cathode rays in our homes as part of the electron gun in our television sets. The electron gun is at the back of the set. The cathode in the electron gun is heated by an electric current and electrons conveniently emerge from its surface. This is called **'thermionic emission'**. It's then simply a matter of getting them to the front of the TV where they can hit the screen and make the chemicals (phosphors) glow in each of the three primary colours of light (red, green or blue).

A positively charged electrode attracts the electrons towards the screen. This is called the accelerating anode. Then high-speed electronics change a strong magnetic field around the television to guide the electron beam so that it can hit the right coloured spot on the screen. The electron beam will scan the 500 dots on the 625 different lines on the screen 25 times per second to make the complete moving picture (Figure 18.22). That's over 300 000 dots hit 25 times per second!

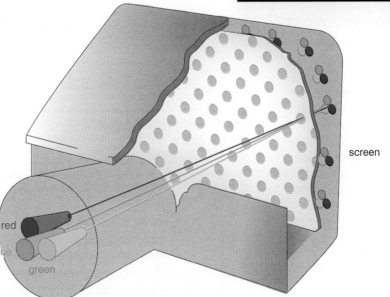

Figure 18.22 The electrons are fired from the cathode in the electron gun and hit the television screen to make the picture.

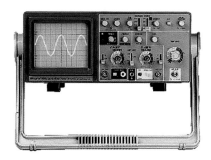

Figure 18.23 The electrons are aimed at the screen using charged metal plates to attract and repel them.

Electron guns in every computer…

Televisions are not the only place to use an electron gun. A computer monitor works on the same basis

…and in every cathode ray oscilloscope

A cathode ray oscilloscope (CRO) is like a very low-tech television. The electrons are generated by thermionic emission and accelerated to the screen by an accelerating anode. However there are no large magnetic fields to direct the beam as it travels towards the screen. Simple electrostatic attraction and repulsion is used instead.

The metal plates are connected to the voltage you want to measure. A higher voltage will charge the plates more so the electron beam is deflected to hit the screen higher up. By choosing a suitable scale you can read off exactly what the voltage is.

The oscilloscope has another use. The beam can be made to scan across the screen by changing the voltage on two metal plates on each side of the screen. This is called the timebase. If the voltage on the top and bottom plates is changing at a certain frequency you will see the level go up and down as the beam scans across the screen.

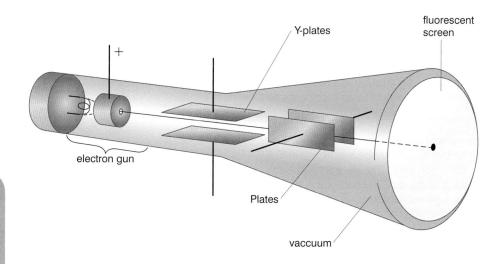

Figure 18.24 Inside a cathode ray oscilloscope.

Key Facts

- A beam of electrons is equivalent to an electric current.
- Electrons can be 'boiled off' hot filaments. This is called thermionic emission.
- A simple electron gun has a heated cathode to produce electrons and accelerating anode to attract them to the screen.
- Electron beams are used in:
  - TV picture tubes
  - computer monitors.

Questions

1 Define the term 'thermionic emission'.

2 Where does the term 'cathode rays' come from? What are cathode rays made of?

3 How can cathode rays be made to accelerate away from the cathode and towards the television screen?

4 How are the electrons aimed at the right point on the screen?

5 When the electrons hit the screen, what happens to form the picture?

Electrons at work

Bend that beam

Electrons are negatively charged particles which means they are attracted to positively charged objects. Electronic engineers use this fact to aim electron beams (or any beam of charged particle) in any direction they like.

Ink-drop printers work because the ink drops are given an electric charge (Figure 18.25). They are fired between metal plates which carry an electric charge. By changing the electric charge on the plates the beam can be aimed in any direction to create the letters on the paper.

Bonus...

If electrons hit a metal target hard enough you can get X-rays emitted as the electrons around the atoms are rearranged. X-ray guns in hospitals work on this principle (Figure 18.25).

Keeping control...

We now understand how electron guns work enough to be able to control everything about them.

In a television you may want to alter the brightness of the picture. By making the electrons travel faster and hit the screen harder you get a brighter picture. To do this you have to attract them towards the screen with a higher voltage on the anode. This is called the accelerating voltage.

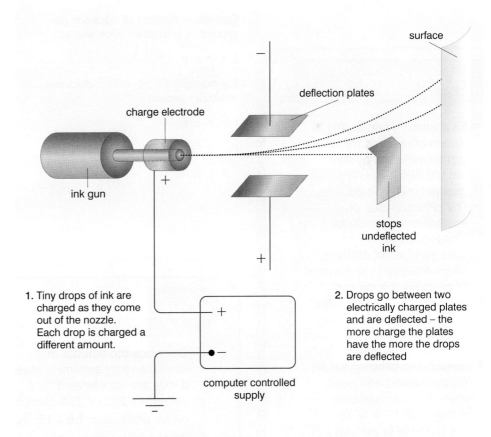

1. Tiny drops of ink are charged as they come out of the nozzle. Each drop is charged a different amount.

2. Drops go between two electrically charged plates and are deflected – the more charge the plates have the more the drops are deflected

Figure 18.25 The ink drops are charged so they can be attracted or repelled by charges on the metal plates. This is how they can be aimed at exactly the right spot on the paper.

Kinetic energy (KE) of electrons = electron charge × accelerating voltage

$$KE = e \times V$$

For example:
If electrons are accelerated through a voltage of 400 kV and the electron charge is 1.6×10^{-19} C.

$$KE = e \times V$$

$$KE = 1.6 \times 10^{-19} \times 400\,000$$

$$KE = 6.4 \times 10^{-14}\,J$$

It is also possible to work out how many electrons are arriving at the screen per second if you know that charge on each electron and the total current.

Current = number of electrons per second × charge on each electron

$$I = n \times e$$

For example if 6.25×10^{18} electrons arrive per second

$$I = n \times e$$

$$I = 6.25 \times 10^{18} \times 1.6 \times 10^{-19}$$

$$I = 1\,A$$

Figure 18.26 The voltage is varying at a certain frequency as the beam scans across the screen. As the time base is 0.02 s per cm we can see that the voltage changes direction once in 0.02 s. This means its frequency is 50 Hz.

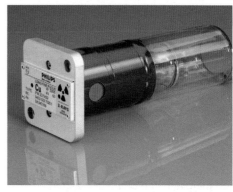

Figure 18.27 When electrons hit a metal hard enough they make the metal emit X-rays. This is how X-rays are produced in a hospital.

Key Facts

- An electron beam or a stream of charged ink drops can be deflected by the electric field between parallel charged metal plates.
- The principle uses of electron beams include:
  - oscilloscopes
  - the production of X-rays.
- An oscilloscope can be used to measure voltage and frequency by deflecting the beam as it approaches the screen.
- There is a quantitative relationship between kinetic energy gained, electronic charge and accelerating voltage: $KE = e \times V$.
- It is possible to perform simple calculations involving the rate of flow of electrons and the current given the electronic charge.

Questions

1 Calculate the amount of kinetic energy electrons have if they are accelerated by a voltage of 250 kV. The charge on an electron is 1.6×10^{-19} C.

2 What accelerating voltage is needed to give electrons 4.8×10^{-18} J of kinetic energy?

3 How many electrons are needed per second to give a beam current of 0.5 A?

4 If 6.5×10^{17} electrons are aimed at the screen per second, what is the current?

5 Make up two calculation questions about electrons and work out the correct answer to each one.

... more at www.modularscience.co.uk

Hot and Cold

As climates go, Britain's is very reasonable. It may feel freezing cold in the winter and scorching hot on occasional days during the summer but we rarely suffer severe or extremes of temperatures.

Not so in a place called El Azizia in Libya, on the fringes of the Sahara Desert in north Africa. On September 13 1922 the temperature reached a blistering 58 degrees centigrade, about twice as hot as even the warmest British summer day. And running El Azizia a close second is Death Valley in America, which had the mercury almost bursting out of the thermometers when the temperature soared to 57 degrees C on July 10 1913.

No prizes for guessing where temperatures reach the other extreme. The frozen continent of Antarctica, shielded from the sun during almost the whole day during its winter. The lowest temperature ever recorded in Antarctica was –89 degrees C

Away from Earth things get much, much more extreme. In fact, things can get so cold that scientists use a different temperature scale to measure them. As things get colder, their atoms and molecules vibrate more slowly. This allows scientists to predict the coldest that it is ever possible to be. They call this point absolute zero.

Absolute zero is –273 degrees centigrade, but 0 on a different scale called Kelvin, after William Thomson, later made Lord Kelvin, the British physicist who devised it. Scientists think it is impossible to ever achieve absolute zero, though some places are chilly enough to come close.

The coldest place in the Solar System is probably Triton, a frozen moon of the distant planet Neptune, which is nearly 3000 million miles away. At the temperature of Triton — –235 degrees C or 38 K – nitrogen can freeze like ice. Away from our Solar System in deep space the temperature drops even lower. Outer space is filled with a type of radiation left over from the Big Bang with a steady temperature of 2.73 K, or about –270 degrees C.

Nearer to home, the star that we call our Sun is the hottest place around. The core of the sun, which is where its heat-producing chemical reactions occur, easily reaches nearly 6000 degrees. But then something puzzling happens. Above the surface of the sun the temperature begins to rise to as high as 20 000 degrees.

Even more strange, the temperature in the very outer region of the sun, which is called the corona, rockets to over a million degrees. Scientists do not yet understand how this happens, in fact they often argue about it. But still the Sun is far from the hottest thing in the Universe. Younger and more massive stars called 'O' stars have surface temperatures some 5 to 10 times hotter than the Sun.

Despite the extreme hot and cold of the Universe, the hottest and coldest temperatures ever achieved have probably been here on Earth. The record temperature ever recorded in a laboratory is an incredible 510 million degrees, during a nuclear fusion experiment at a university in America. Scientists hope that by creating these blistering conditions, they will be able to harness the fusion reactions at the centre of the Sun for a future source of clean energy.

The coldest temperatures recorded have also been made in scientific laboratories. By cooling gas atoms to very, very low temperatures, scientists can create a weird new form of matter called a Bose–Einstein condensate. Atoms in the super-chilled cloud bunch together to form a 'superatom' at a temperature just a few billionths of a degree above absolute zero. This is a million times colder than the chill of outer space and perhaps as cold as it is ever possible to be.

1. (a) The grid shows the neutron and proton numbers of the isotopes formed during part of a radioactive sequence.

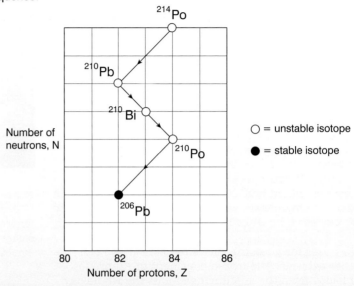

(i) Describe what happens to the proton number and the mass (nucleon) number when an alpha particle is emitted by a nucleus. (2)

(ii) Use the grid to find the number of neutrons in a ^{210}Bi nucleus. (1)

(iii) What type of decay occurs when ^{210}Pb decays to ^{210}Bi? (1)

(iv) What is meant by the term stable isotope? (1)

(b) When a gamma ray is emitted from a nucleus the mass (nucleon) number and the proton number do not change. Explain this. (2)

(c) Explain why, when nuclei undergo decay by alpha particle emission, gamma radiation is often produced. (3)

(Total 10 marks)

Edexcel GCSE Science: June 2001, paper 4H, no. 5.

2. (a) The atoms $^{14}_{7}$N and $^{15}_{7}$N are isotopes of nitrogen.

Write down one similarity and one difference between the nuclei of these isotopes. (2)

(b) The graph shows the relationship between the number of neutrons and the number of protons in a nucleus.

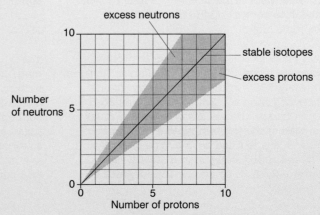

(i) What is the relationship between the number of protons and the number of neutrons in a stable nucleus? (1)

(ii) Use an X to mark the position of $^{15}_{7}N$ on a copy of the graph. (1)

(iii) Give the reason why $^{15}_{7}N$ is unstable. (1)

(iv) The diagram shows the decay of $^{15}_{7}N$.

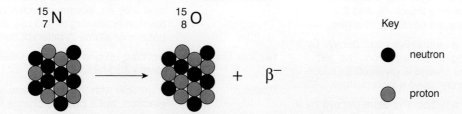

What changes take place when the nucleus of $^{15}_{7}N$ decays? (3)

(Total 8 marks)

Edexcel GCSE Science: June 2002, paper 4H, no. 3.

3.   Uranium-235 is used as a fuel in nuclear reactors.
            The diagram illustrates the process that takes place in a reactor.

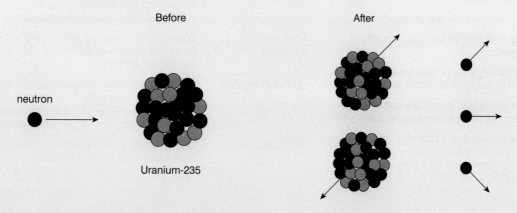

(a)   Name the process shown in the diagram. (1)

(b)   During this process, energy is released. In what form is this energy? (1)

(c)   Explain how this process could lead to a chain reaction. (3)

(Total 5 marks)

Edexcel GCSE Science: June 2002, paper 4H, no. 4.

Glossary 18

Absolute zero
A temperature of O K or –273°C. It is the lowest temperature it is possible to have.

Accelerator
Sometimes called a particle accelerator. Apparatus used to make tiny particles, like electrons or neutrons, travel at speeds close to the speed of light.

Alpha particles
Particles given off by some radioactive materials. An alpha particle is a helium nucleus containing 2 protons and 2 neutrons. They are positively charged.

Beta decay
This is when a radioactive atom decays by a neutron changing into a proton. The 'left over' negative charge is given off as a fast-moving electron called a beta particle.

Beta minus decay
This is when a radioactive atom decays by a proton changing into a neutron. The 'left over' positive charge is given off as a fast-moving positron.

Chain reaction
When the neutrons given off by the radioactive decay of one atom hit another atom and make that atom decay as well, giving off more neutrons.

Daughter element
The element that a radioactive atom turns into after it decays.

Fission
Another name for nuclear fission.

Fundamental particle
A particle that cannot be split into any smaller particles.

Gamma radiation
Very high energy electromagnetic radiation given off by some radioactive elements.

Gas pressure
The pressure a gas exerts on something because of all the gas molecules hitting it.

Kelvin scale
The temperature scale used by scientists studying low temperatures. 1 degree Kelvin (1 K) is the same size as 1 degree Celsius (1°C) but 0 °C = –273 K.

Kinetic energy
The energy something has because it is moving. Increasing the speed increases the kinetic energy.

Massive elements
Elements where each atom has a large mass. Scientists usually call elements with more than 82 protons and 82 neutrons 'massive'.

Neutron scattering
Firing neutrons at a target and looking to see how they are scattered. Scientists use neutron scattering to find out about the pattern of atoms in different materials.

Nuclear fission
Splitting up one atom into smaller 'daughter' atoms and radioactivity.

Positron
A particle with the same mass as an electron, but a positive charge instead of the electron's negative charge.

Quarks
The fundamental particles that make up protons and neutrons. There are six different types of quarks.

Stable isotope
An atom with approximately equal numbers of protons and neutrons. Stable isotopes are not radioactive.

Temperature
A measure of how fast the particles in something are moving. If the temperature increases the particles move faster.

Thermionic emission
When metal wires are made very hot, they give off a stream of electrons. This is thermionic emission.

Unstable isotope
An atom with very unequal numbers of protons and neutrons. The atom gives off radioactive particles, or splits into smaller atoms, or both, until it becomes stable.

Vitrification
Changing radioactive waste into safe, unreactive glass-like materials.

Index

Periodic Table

Period	Group 1	2											3	4	5	6	7	0
1	1 **H** hydrogen 1																	4 **He** helium 2
2	7 **Li** lithium 3	9 **Be** beryllium 4											11 **B** boron 5	12 **C** carbon 6	14 **N** nitrogen 7	16 **O** oxygen 8	19 **F** fluorine 9	20 **Ne** neon 10
3	23 **Na** sodium 11	24 **Mg** magnesium 12											27 **Al** aluminium 13	28 **Si** silicon 14	31 **P** phosphorus 15	32 **S** sulphur 16	35.5 **Cl** chlorine 17	40 **Ar** argon 18
4	39 **K** potassium 19	40 **Ca** calcium 20	45 **Sc** scandium 21	48 **Ti** titanium 22	51 **V** vanadium 23	52 **Cr** chromium 24	55 **Mn** manganese 25	56 **Fe** iron 26	59 **Co** cobalt 27	59 **Ni** nickel 28	63.5 **Cu** copper 29	65 **Zn** zinc 30	70 **Ga** gallium 31	73 **Ge** germanium 32	75 **As** arsenic 33	79 **Se** selenium 34	80 **Br** bromine 35	84 **Kr** krypton 36
5	85 **Rb** rubidium 37	88 **Sr** strontium 38	89 **Y** yttrium 39	91 **Zr** zirconium 40	93 **Nb** niobium 41	96 **Mo** molybdenum 42	99 **Tc** technetium 43	101 **Ru** ruthenium 44	103 **Rh** rhodium 45	106 **Pd** palladium 46	108 **Ag** silver 47	112 **Cd** cadmium 48	115 **In** indium 49	119 **Sn** tin 50	122 **Sb** antimony 51	128 **Te** tellurium 52	127 **I** iodine 53	131 **Xe** xenon 54
6	133 **Cs** caesium 55	137 **Ba** barium 56	139 **La** lanthanum 57	178 **Hf** hafnium 72	181 **Ta** tantalum 73	184 **W** tungsten 74	186 **Re** rhenium 75	190 **Os** osmium 76	192 **Ir** iridium 77	195 **Pt** platinum 78	197 **Au** gold 79	201 **Hg** mercury 80	204 **Tl** thallium 81	207 **Pb** lead 82	209 **Bi** bismuth 83	210 **Po** polonium 84	210 **At** astatine 85	222 **Rn** radon 86
7	223 **Fr** francium 87	226 **Ra** radium 88	227 **Ac** actinium 89															

Key

Relative atomic mass
Symbol
Name
Atomic number